VIRUS GROWTH AND VARIATION

Other Publications of the
Society for General Microbiology

THE JOURNAL OF GENERAL MICROBIOLOGY
(*Cambridge University Press*)

THE STRATEGY OF CHEMOTHERAPY
EIGHTH SYMPOSIUM OF THE SOCIETY
(*Cambridge University Press*)

MICROBIAL ECOLOGY
SEVENTH SYMPOSIUM OF THE SOCIETY
(*Cambridge University Press*)

BACTERIAL ANATOMY
SIXTH SYMPOSIUM OF THE SOCIETY
(*Cambridge University Press*)

MECHANISMS OF MICROBIAL PATHOGENICITY
FIFTH SYMPOSIUM OF THE SOCIETY
(*Cambridge University Press*)

AUTOTROPHIC MICRO-ORGANISMS
FOURTH SYMPOSIUM OF THE SOCIETY
(*Cambridge University Press*)

ADAPTATION IN MICRO-ORGANISMS
THIRD SYMPOSIUM OF THE SOCIETY
(*Cambridge University Press*)

THE NATURE OF VIRUS MULTIPLICATION
SECOND SYMPOSIUM OF THE SOCIETY
(*Cambridge University Press*)

THE NATURE OF THE BACTERIAL SURFACE
FIRST SYMPOSIUM OF THE SOCIETY
(*Blackwell's Scientific Publications Limited*)

VIRUS GROWTH AND VARIATION

NINTH SYMPOSIUM OF THE
SOCIETY FOR GENERAL MICROBIOLOGY
HELD AT THE
SENATE HOUSE, UNIVERSITY OF LONDON
APRIL 1959

CAMBRIDGE

Published for the Society for General Microbiology

AT THE UNIVERSITY PRESS

1959

PUBLISHED BY
THE SYNDICS OF THE CAMBRIDGE UNIVERSITY PRESS
Bentley House, 200 Euston Road, London, N.W. 1
American Branch: 32 East 57th Street, New York 22, N.Y.

Printed in Great Britain at the University Press, Cambridge
(Brooke Crutchley, University Printer)

CONTRIBUTORS

ANDERSON, E. S., Central Enteric Reference Laboratory and Bureau, Public Health Laboratory Service, Colindale, London.

ARMSTRONG, J. A., National Institute for Medical Research, Mill Hill, London, N.W.7.

COOPER, P. D., Virus Culture Laboratory, Medical Research Council Laboratories, Carshalton, Surrey.

HARRISON, B. D., Rothamsted Experimental Station, Harpenden, Herts.

HIRST, G. K., Division of Infectious Diseases of The Public Health Research Institute of the City of New York, Inc.

HOSKINS, J. M., Department of Bacteriology, University of Manchester.

ISAACS, A., National Institute for Medical Research, Mill Hill, London, N.W.7.

KELLENBERGER, E., Laboratoire de Biophysique, Université de Genève, Switzerland.

LURIA, S. E., Department of Bacteriology, University of Illinois, Urbana.

MAITLAND, H. B., Department of Bacteriology, University of Manchester.

MORGAN, C., Department of Microbiology, College of Physicians and Surgeons, Columbia University, New York.

NIVEN, JANET S. F., National Institute for Medical Research, Mill Hill, London, N.W.7.

POSTLETHWAITE, R., Department of Bacteriology, University of Manchester.

ROSE, H. M., Department of Microbiology, College of Physicians and Surgeons, Columbia University, New York.

RUBIN, H., Department of Virology, University of California, Berkeley, California.

SCHÄFER, W., Max-Planck-Institut für Virusforschung, Tübingen, Germany.

STOKER, M. G. P., Department of Pathology, University of Cambridge.

CONTENTS

Editors' Preface . . . . *page* viii

S. E. LURIA:
Viruses: a Survey of some Current Problems . . . 1

E. KELLENBERGER:
Growth of Bacteriophage 11

B. D. HARRISON:
The Multiplication of Viruses in Plants 34

W. SCHÄFER:
Some Observations concerning the Reproduction of RNA-containing Animal Viruses 61

G. K. HIRST:
Studies of Mixed Infections with NDV, Poliovirus and Influenza 82

A. ISAACS:
Viral Interference 102

J. M. HOSKINS:
Host-Controlled Variation in Animal Viruses . . . 122

M. G. P. STOKER:
Growth studies with Herpes Virus 142

H. RUBIN:
Special Interactions between Virus and Cell in the Rous Sarcoma 171

H. B. MAITLAND & R. POSTLETHWAITE:
Studies on Vaccinia Virus in HeLa Cells . . . 185

P. D. COOPER:
The Chemical Approach to the Study of Animal Virus Growth 200

E. S. ANDERSON, J. A. ARMSTRONG & JANET S. F. NIVEN
Fluorescence Microscopy: Observation of Virus Growth with Aminoacridines 224

C. MORGAN & H. M. ROSE:
Electron-Microscopic Observations on Adenoviruses and Viruses of the Influenza Group 256

ERRATA

age 220...line 15 : for 'age' read 'size'.

age 226...line 5 : for 'necessary' read 'unnecessary'.

EDITORS' PREFACE

Although this symposium covers similar ground to that of the second symposium of the Society, held in 1952, the lapse of seven years is reflected in big changes both in the subjects discussed and in the approach of those discussing them. Many important advances in basic knowledge have been made in the interval and much that was then heresy is now orthodox (and vice versa). The papers included in this volume also emphasize the narrowness of the gap which now separates the strictly biological and strictly biochemical approaches to virus research. Indeed, throughout the symposium the overriding importance of viral nucleic acids emerges as a dominant theme and the focus at which biologist, geneticist, biochemist and microbiologist can exchange ideas with mutual understanding and profit. But from this point the interest spreads outwards in many directions—to the ways and places in which virus nucleic acids impress their stamp on the cells and induce the production of more or less perfect copies of more or less complete viruses, to the effects of viruses on cellular structure and function, to virus genetics, the nature of proviruses and tumour viruses and to many other problems. Some of these problems are here at least partially resolved, but the elucidation of others may well have to await the sixteenth symposium of this Society.

A. ISAACS

National Institute for Medical Research
Mill Hill, London, N.W. 7

B. W. LACEY

Westminster Medical School
London, S.W. 1

VIRUSES: A SURVEY OF SOME CURRENT PROBLEMS

S. E. LURIA

Department of Bacteriology, University of Illinois, Urbana

An outline of current perspectives in a field evolving as rapidly as virology could easily become an extensive survey of our science in all its complexity and multidirectional developments. To limit the size and scope of this introductory paper, I shall discuss only a few outstanding recent advances, mainly in the bacteriophage field, which have led to some unifying concepts in virology. In the light of these concepts I shall try to indicate the directions in which progress may be expected and the areas where more concentrated efforts are desirable. The immediate test of the ideas that I am presenting will be whether they provide a useful framework for the other papers in this symposium and whether they can at least stand confrontation with the facts presented in those papers. To use the jargon of our trade, my speculations, if defective, can be prevented from establishing a persistent defective infection of our minds by interference from the almost immediate challenge of healthy, effective data.

Of the two aspects of virology, a branch of cellular biology and a branch of pathology and medicine, the major theoretical advances since 1952, the date of our Society's last symposium on viruses, have occurred in the former. This reflects the general progress in the genetic, biochemical, and cytochemical analysis of cellular organization; in fact, virology has made a distinguished contribution to this progress. Major recent advances in applied virology—such as the effective vaccination against poliomyelitis and the controlled epidemiology of myxomatosis—do not represent an introduction of new concepts, but rather an exploitation of advances at the fundamental level. It seems likely that future practical advances, as in chemotherapy, may be based directly on advances in the study of viruses at the level of cellular phenomena.

VIRUSES AND NUCLEIC ACIDS

The first and major advance has been in the establishment of the primacy of nucleic acids in viral infection. The basic landmarks were, for phage, the injection experiments of Hershey & Chase (1952); for tobacco mosaic virus, the reconstitution experiments of Fraenkel-Conrat (1956) and the RNA infectivity tests by Gierer & Schramm (1956); for animal viruses, the extraction of infective, RNase-sensitive materials from several viruses (Colter, Bird, Moyer & Brown, 1957).

The identification of phage DNA with the major and possibly the only essential initiator of phage infection; the discovery of the structure of DNA (Watson & Crick, 1953); the advances in bacterial genetics, especially the unravelling of the mating process (Wollman, Jacob & Hayes, 1956) and of the role of DNA in this process (as well as in transformation phenomena; see Hotchkiss, 1955); and the analysis of lysogeny and of its chromosomal determinants or *prophages* (Jacob & Wollman, 1957; Bertani, 1958) have led to a unified view of bacterial genetics having DNA as its protagonist. DNA has emerged as the essential genetic constituent of the bacterial chromosome, of the prophage, of the vegetative form of the phage, and of the infectious phage particle. The concept of phage infection as cellular parasitism at the genetic level (Luria, 1950) has assumed new significance beyond the original one of a competition between two incompatible sets of genetic elements; we now consider phages as segments of bacterial DNA which possess a specific viral function, that is, a genetically determined potentiality for active release and transfer to other cells.

The contribution of phage research to basic genetics has been outstanding. Benzer's (1957) analysis of the fine genetic structure of phage by means of recombination has not only produced clarification of genetic concepts by defining operationally the units of mutation, of recombination, and of genetic function (*muton*, *recon*, and *cistron*), but has also shown the way to the interpretation of genetic specificity in terms of DNA chemistry. The report that specific mutational sites in phage are selectively affected by thymidine analogues (Benzer & Freese, 1958) is a promising beginning.

Along these lines, major advances may be predicted in two directions. First, we expect rapid progress in the correlated studies of DNA biosynthesis and of genetic replication. While DNA provides the basic template for phage production, and while multiplication of phage DNA is the essential outcome of vegetative reproduction of phage, this reproduction entails more than an increase in phage DNA (Hershey, 1957; Stent, 1958). The relative roles of DNA, RNA, and proteins in phage DNA replication, as well as the roles of the recently discovered polynucleotide-synthesizing enzymes (Ochoa & Heppel, 1957; Kornberg, 1957), will be a major area of biochemical virology, tying it to the wider field of nucleic acid biosynthesis.

With viruses other than phages, an essential step should be to correlate the notion of infectious nucleic acid with a description of the early stages in cellular infection. Specifically, the phenomena of eclipse of infectivity, whose reality is now generally accepted, should be interpreted, as with phage, in terms of the cytochemical events in virus penetration and replication.

Second, we expect a rapid advance in the chemical study of virus replication itself. The cytochemical and immunological analysis of the accumulation of viral materials, correlated with biochemical studies, can tell us not only whether nucleic acid, alone or as a nucleoprotein element, plays the central role in the replication of all viruses, but also in which fractions of the cells the various components of viruses are produced, accumulated, and assembled.

Third, we should witness major progress in the analysis of the functional specificity of RNA and, coupled with a clarification of the molecular configuration of RNA, a full-fledged development of 'RNA genetics'. The role of RNA viruses in this new branch of biology will be even more central than that played by phage in the genetics of DNA systems. Purification and chemical analysis of many more animal viruses, and identification of their nucleic acid components, are needed to provide a basis for a correlated genetic and biochemical analysis of viral growth, as well as to define the chemistry of the essential genetic units.

As yet, there is a single example of a unique nucleic acid constituent of viruses, the hydroxymethyldeoxycytidylic acid of the T-even coliphages (Wyatt & Cohen, 1952). Yet, this finding—in itself almost a monstrosity from the standpoint of biochemical evolution—indicates the desirability of a careful search for similar anomalies among other viruses.

VIRUSES AND CELLULAR FUNCTIONS

Virus infection brings into a cell a new genetic element. In the virus-infected cell there occur a number of changes in structure and function. We ask, therefore, which of these changes are by-products of viral replication, which changes reflect the action of viral genes irrespective of replication, and which changes are non-genetic effects of the process of infection itself—for example, of a disruption of the cellular surface, or of the biosynthesis of new cellular enzymes in response to viral materials acting as inducers.

Work with phage provides examples of all these types. Thus, on the one hand, the cellular lysis that accompanies phage release depends on phage-specific enzymes formed only after replication of phage DNA

(Jacob & Fuerst, 1958). On the other hand, early death of a bacterium, probably by surface disruption, may follow even the attachment of an empty phage coat, a clearly non-genetic action (Herriott & Barlow, 1957). Initiation of phage replication requires the active function of a number of phage genes *before replication*, the 'essential cistrons', revealed by radiobiological and other studies (see Bertani, 1958). Among the essential cistrons must be those that control the biosynthesis of new enzymes specifically required for synthesis of viral nucleic acid. The cytosine-hydroxymethylating enzyme, which appears in T2-infected bacteria by an apparently *de novo* biosynthesis (Flaks & Cohen, 1957), is a convenient example, although proof of its phage-controlled specificity is still awaited.

Let us consider two groups of bacterial products produced under phage control: the proteins of the phage particles and certain somatic antigens in *Salmonella*, which are specifically determined by some phages (Iseki & Sakai, 1953), an example of the so-called 'conversion' phenomena by phage. In both cases, the biosynthesis and the intrinsic specificity of these cellular products are determined by phage genes (Streisinger, 1956; Uetake, 1958). Yet one group of products, the somatic antigens, whose presence and function are apparently irrelevant to phage growth and maturation, is formed whenever the controlling phage is present in the cell in any form—vegetative phage, prophage, or even non-multiplying phage element (Uetake, Luria & Burrous, 1958). The other group of products, the phage-coat proteins, whose synthesis and assembly into mature phage particles are essential for the transfer of phage elements from cell to cell, that is, for the viral function, is produced only after vegetative multiplication of the phage genetic elements.

Thus, we see that phage genes control cellular functions necessary for the process of viral transfer as well as cellular functions totally irrelevant to this process. All portions of the bacterial genome are potentially transferable from cell to cell, as shown by transformation experiments with purified DNA. What distinguishes the phage elements is that they possess, among their many genetic functions, those needed to determine the formation of a specific phage coat. In other words, phages are elements of bacterial DNA, genetically and selectively adapted for transfer from cell to cell.

In an admittedly broad extrapolation, supported by current ideas on the biosynthesis of tobacco mosaic virus (Jeener, 1956) and of myxoviruses (Burnet, 1956), I have proposed to define viruses as 'elements of cellular genetic material that can determine, in the cells where they multiply, the biosynthesis of a specific apparatus for their own transfer to other cells' (Luria, 1958). This definition centres our attention on the two essential aspects of viruses; as controllers of genetic functions in the cells, and as specialized agents of infective exchanges of genetic materials among cells.

What contribution can we expect from an awareness of the genetic effects of viruses on cellular properties?

First, at the biochemical level, viruses like phage and TMV should provide the best materials for correlating genetic structure with genetic function; that is, for deciphering the code that translates DNA or RNA structure into the molecular structure of proteins.

Second, if present assumptions are valid, it should be possible to interpret the morphogenesis of all viral particles, like that of phage particles, as a triple process: replication of viral genomes, synthesis of specific accessory constituents, and assembly into mature particles. Advances in this direction have already been made with a number of viruses (Sanders, 1957).

Third, we may expect progress in interpreting cellular alterations as due to specific functions of the viruses. Some cellular damage may be bound to specific steps in the growth cycle of a virus, in the same way as bacterial lysis is bound to phage maturation; and these steps, once visualized, may become amenable to directed chemical or nutritional control. Other cellular alterations, such as the release of cells from normal growth-restraining influences observed in virus-induced tumours, may become understandable in terms of specific effects of viral genes, whose function may be as irrelevant to the replication and maturation of the virus as the control of somatic antigens is apparently irrelevant to the viral function of *Salmonella* phages. That is, we may be able to interpret some of the effects of viruses on their hosts as infective heredity rather than as parasitism.

Such a programme of interpretation of viral action as infective heredity has now become feasible for animal viruses because of the major recent advances in mammalian cell microbiology along genetic, nutritional and biochemical lines (Eagle, 1955; Puck, Cieciura & Fisher, 1957; Simino-vitch, Graham, Leslie & Nevill, 1957). It is apparent that in the study of the genetics and cytochemistry of mammalian cells the animal viruses will play the same role that phage has played in the analogous study of bacteria.

The development of methods for microbiological handling of plant cells is long overdue. For some plant viruses a useful substitute may well be looked for by developing modern tissue culture methods for the cells of their arthropod vectors (Grace, 1958).

VIRUSES AND CELLULAR CONSTITUENTS

The genetic material of phage, in its prophage form, is part of the bacterial chromosome. As prophage, it is materially and functionally integrated with the genetic system of the bacterial cell, even though the material integration is probably less solid than that among other chromosomal elements, as shown by loss or substitution of prophage *in toto* (Bertani, 1958). The details of the integration process and the precise nature of the bonds between prophage and bacterial chromosome are still unclear. Matings between lysogenic bacteria provide one line of attack (Jacob & Wollman, 1957). Another, more exciting one, is provided by certain transduction phenomena in which groups of bacterial genes become stably incorporated into prophages, hence into phage particles, with which they can be transferred to other cells (Morse, Lederberg & Lederberg, 1956; Arber, Kellenberger & Weigle, 1957). In this 'specialized transduction' we see how non-viral chromosomal elements can acquire viral properties, that is, become adapted to infective transfer by recombination with viral elements. In turn, the latter may have acquired their viral function by mutations; as prophages, they may return to pair with their homologous counterparts in the bacterial chromosome. If, even as prophages, they appear to be less completely integrated within the chromosome, this may simply reflect an incompleteness of the residual homology between prophage and the attachment region. Conversion phenomena can easily be interpreted within this framework (Luria, Fraser, Adams & Burrous, 1958).

In bacteria there are several genetic determinants or 'episomes' (Jacob & Wollman, 1958) which appear to have a dual multiplication pattern, as vegetatively reproducing elements on the one hand, and as integrated chromosomal elements on the other. The phage elements should be considered as episomes endowed with the ability to determine a transfer apparatus.

With viruses other than phage, this approach to an experimental analysis of the relationship and interactions between the viruses and the genetic elements of their host cells has barely begun. The study of persistent experimental infections of animal cells in tissue cultures (Puck & Cieciura, 1958; Ackermann, 1958) has revealed a variety of situations, none of which can as yet be interpreted in terms of 'proviruses', that is, of persistent viral genomes harmoniously integrated within the cellular genome. The most promising material is that of tumour viruses, where virus persistence is the primary cause of the abnormal growth pattern. Clearly, progress in the knowledge of the genetic status of proviruses (if they exist) in animal or plant cells will depend on the expected progress in the study of the genetics of these cells.

In this area two specific problems deserve careful attention. First, we need to investigate the nature of the cytogenetic changes that follow, respectively, infection with DNA and RNA viruses. We need to find out whether viral DNA enters into close contact with host-cell DNA or whether it sets up independent and competing centres of DNA synthesis. For example, any DNA entering the cellular cytoplasm might cause cellular damage because of the absence in the cytoplasm of mechanisms for controlling and restraining DNA replication. Conversely, viral RNA or ribonucleoproteins may be prone to replicate first in the cell nucleus, possibly causing specific changes also in the chromosomal DNA. The tools to answer such questions are rapidly being forged by chemical cytology (Brachet, 1957).

Second, we must find out how restricted is the transferability of viral materials. In bacteria all chromosomal elements are transferable from cell to cell as DNA; it is conceivable that in animal and plant cells also some elements endowed with genetic specificity, whether embodied in DNA or in RNA, may be intrinsically transferable, that is, may be capable of functioning if introduced from without into appropriate living cells, even though they do not possess an adaptive mechanism for such transfer. We should search carefully for such transferability of cellular constituents and for what roles it may play, for example, in developmental and regulatory processes in animals and plants. If transferability were a widespread property of cellular constituents, we should beware of considering as viruses all transferable elements encountered in attempts to detect agents of diseases, for example, in cancer research. We should also ask ourselves how much of a genetic change may be required to make a transferable cellular constituent into a virus, that is, to endow it with the ability to direct the biosynthesis of its own vehicle.

VIRUS DISEASES AND INFECTIVE HEREDITY

As we emphasize the genetic aspects of viruses, the study of virus diseases assumes new dimensions. We begin to consider, not only cellular damage accompanying virus multiplication, but also abnormal cell functions reflecting the presence of the viral genome and its function within the framework of the cellular genome. In this sense, virus diseases may be considered as genetic diseases, more akin to metabolic diseases than to bacterial or protozoan infections. Thus, for example, the much debated dichotomy between the somatic mutation theory and the virus theory of cancer loses much of its significance. Clearly, similar results may follow either mutational or infective changes in cellular heredity.

Several other implications may be pointed out. Cellular alterations due to viral gene action can provide new approaches to chemotherapy. It may be possible to control viral infections by acting specifically on the new functions of virus-infected cells rather than directly on viral spread or multiplication. In fact, virus-induced tumours, like other tumours, may be controlled by treatments directed to the growth habits of the cells, not to the viral process.

Some viral phenomena, especially the age dependence of the incidence and course of some virus infections, as observed in lymphocytic chorio-meningitis (Hotchin, 1958) and in many virus-induced tumours (see Gross, 1958) may be mediated by alterations in cellular antigens. These may in turn give rise to abnormal immunological responses, such as immune tolerance or hypersensitivity, depending on the age at which infection occurred (Burnet, 1955).

There are other conceivable mechanisms by which functional changes of cells due to a virus may produce general body alterations. For example, infection of an endocrine organ might, without cell destruction, but by alteration of cellular functions, give rise to metabolic and morphogenetic abnormalities.

VIROLOGY AND MODERN BIOLOGY

The most fascinating aspect of virology to me is the role that virus research is playing in the current revolution in biology. As in the trans-formation of classical physics into modern physics, the current flourish-ing of biology involves the dialectical resolution of conflicting opposites through clarification of basic concepts and of their content. Bio-chemistry is unifying the molecular and the structural levels of organiza-tion. Enzyme action and template action are seen as inseparable aspects of the process of genetic replication at the molecular level. Genetics is bringing about a synthesis of gene replication and gene function as two chemical expressions of the same elements, the coded molecules of nucleic acids, and is dissolving the opposition between heredity and development.

In molecular biology, life becomes the self-propagating pattern of functional organization of selected molecular species into harmonious wholes. By analogy, the cell plays the role of the atom; cellular biology, that of atomic physics. Within the living world natural selection, like the exclusion principles of atomic physics, restricts and stabilizes the states which a cell or organism can successfully assume. Within the cell the basic system of coded macromolecules recalls the atomic nucleus; indeed, it is gathered into a nucleus, whose organization preserves the stable associations of valuable molecular patterns, in the same way as in the atomic nucleus special forces bind together the stable groups of elementary particles.

What role do viruses play? Can we not claim for them, in this analogy, the role of the particulate beams that the physicists use to probe into the organization of atoms and nuclei? And proceeding a step further, may we not feel that in the viruses, in their merging with the cellular genomes and their re-emerging from them, we observe the units and processes which, in the course of evolution, have created the successful genetic patterns that underlie all living cells?

REFERENCES

ACKERMANN, W. W. (1958). Certain factors governing the persistence of poliovirus in tissue culture. In *Symposium on Latency and Masking in Viral and Rickettsial Infections*. Minneapolis: Burgess.

ARBER, W., KELLENBERGER, G. & WEIGLE, J. (1957). La défectuosité du phage lambda transducteur. *Schweiz. Z. allg. Path.* **20**, 659.

BENZER, S. (1957). The elementary units of heredity. In *The Chemical Basis of Heredity*. Edited by W. D. McElroy and B. Glass. Baltimore: Johns Hopkins Univ. Press.

BENZER, S. & FREESE, E. (1958). Induction of specific mutations by 5-bromouracil. *Proc. Nat. Acad. Sci., Wash.* **44**, 112.

BERTANI, G. (1958). Lysogeny. *Advanc. Virus Res.* **5**, 151.

BRACHET, J. (1957). *Biochemical Cytology*. New York: Academic Press.

BURNET, M. (1955). *Principles of Animal Virology*. New York: Academic Press.

BURNET, M. (1956). Structure of influenza virus. *Science*, **123**, 1101.

COLTER, J. S., BIRD, H. H., MOYER, A. W. & BROWN, R. A. (1957). Infectivity of ribonucleic acid isolated from virus-infected tissues. *Virology*, **4**, 522.

EAGLE, H. (1955). The specific amino acid requirements of a mammalian cell (strain L) in tissue culture. *J. biol. Chem.* **214**, 839.

FLAKS, J. & COHEN, S. S. (1957). The enzymic synthesis of 5-hydroxymethyl deoxycytidylic acid. *Biochim. biophys. Acta*, **25**, 667.

FRAENKEL-CONRAT, H. (1956). The role of the nucleic acid in the reconstitution of active tobacco mosaic virus. *J. Amer. chem. Soc.* **78**, 882.

GIERER, A. & SCHRAMM, G. (1956). Die Infektiosität der Nucleinsäure aus Tabakmosaikvirus. *Z. Naturf.* **11**b, 138.

GRACE, T. D. C. (1958). The prolonged growth and survival of ovarian tissue of the promethea moth (*Callosamia promethea*) in vitro. *J. gen. Physiol.* **41**, 1027.

GROSS, L. (1958). Viral etiology of 'spontaneous' mouse leukaemia. *Cancer Res.* **18**, 371.

HERRIOTT, R. M. & BARLOW, J. L. (1957). The protein coats or 'ghosts' of coli phage T2. II. The biological functions. *J. gen. Physiol.* **41**, 307.

HERSHEY, A. D. (1957). Bacteriophages as genetic and biochemical systems. *Advanc. Virus Res.* **4**, 25.

HERSHEY, A. D. & CHASE, M. (1952). Independent functions of viral protein and nucleic acid in growth of bacteriophage. *J. gen. Physiol.* **36**, 39.

HOTCHIN, J. E. (1958). Some aspects of induced latent infection of mice with the virus of lymphocytic choriomeningitis. In *Symposium on Latency and Masking in Viral and Rickettsial Infections*. Minneapolis: Burgess.

HOTCHKISS, R. D. (1955). Bacterial transformation. *J. cell. comp. Physiol.* **45** (Suppl. 2), 1.

ISEKI, S. & SAKAI, T. (1953). Artificial transformation of 0 antigens in *Salmonella* E group. I, II. *Proc. Japan Acad.* **29**, 121 and 127.

JACOB, F. & FUERST, C. R. (1958). The mechanism of lysis by phage studied with defective lysogenic bacteria. *J. gen. Microbiol.* **18**, 518.

JACOB, F. & WOLLMAN, E. L. (1957). Genetic aspects of lysogeny. In *The Chemical Basis of Heredity*. Edited by W. D. McElroy and B. Glass. Baltimore: Johns Hopkins Univ. Press.

JACOB, F. & WOLLMAN, E. L. (1958). Les épisomes, éléments génétiques ajoutés. *C.R. Acad. Sci., Paris*, **247**, 154.

JEENER, R. (1956). Ribonucleic acids and virus multiplication. *Advanc. Enzymol.* **17**, 477.

KORNBERG, A. (1957). Pathways of enzymatic synthesis of nucleotides and poly-nucleotides. In *The Chemical Basis of Heredity*. Edited by W. D. McElroy and B. Glass. Baltimore: Johns Hopkins Univ. Press.

LURIA, S. E. (1950). Bacteriophage: an essay on virus reproduction. *Science*, **111**, 507.

LURIA, S. E. (1958). Viruses as infective genetic materials. In *Symposium on Immunity and Virus Infection* (in the Press).

LURIA, S. E., FRASER, D. K., ADAMS, J. N. & BURROUS, J. W. (1958). Lysogenization, transduction, and genetic recombination in bacteria. *Cold Spr. Harb. Symp. quant. Biol.* **23** (in the Press).

MORSE, M. L., LEDERBERG, E. M. & LEDERBERG, J. (1956). Transduction in *Escherichia coli* K-12. *Genetics*, **41**, 142.

OCHOA, S. & HEPPEL, L. A. (1957). Polynucleotide synthesis. In *The Chemical Basis of Heredity*. Edited by W. D. McElroy and B. Glass. Baltimore: Johns Hopkins Univ. Press.

PUCK, T. T. & CIECIURA, S. J. (1958). Studies on the virus carrier state in mammalian cells. In *Symposium on Latency and Masking in Viral and Rickettsial Infections*. Minneapolis: Burgess.

PUCK, T. T., CIECIURA, S. J. & FISHER, H. W. (1957). Clonal growth *in vitro* of human cells with fibroblastic morphology. *J. exp. Med.* **106**, 145.

SANDERS, F. K. (1957). The multiplication of animal viruses. In *The Nature of Viruses*. Ciba Foundation Symposium. Edited G. E. W. Wolstenholme and E. C. P. Millar. London: Churchill.

SIMINOVITCH, L., GRAHAM, A. F., LESLIE, S. M. & NEVILL, A. (1957). Propagation of L strain mouse cells in suspension. *Exp. Cell Res.* **12**, 299.

STENT, G. (1958). Mating in the reproduction of bacterial viruses. *Advanc. Virus Res.* **5**, 95.

STREISINGER, G. (1956). The genetic control of host range and serological specificity in bacteriophages T2 and T4. *Virology*, **2**, 377.

UETAKE, H. (1958). Mutations affecting the specificity of the somatic antigens determined by *Salmonella* bacteriophage ϵ^{15} (to be published).

UETAKE, H., LURIA, S. E. & BURROUS, J. W. (1958). Conversion of somatic antigens in *Salmonella* by phage infection leading to lysis or lysogeny. *Virology*, **5**, 68.

WATSON, J. D. & CRICK, F. H. C. (1953). The structure of DNA. *Cold Spr. Harb. Symp. quant. Biol.* **18**, 123.

WOLLMAN, E. L., JACOB, F. & HAYES, W. (1956). Conjugation and genetic recombination in *Escherichia coli* K-12. *Cold Spr. Harb. Symp. quant. Biol.* **21**, 141.

WYATT, G. R. & COHEN, S. S. (1952). A new pyrimidine base from bacteriophage nucleic acids. *Nature, Lond.* **170**, 1072.

GROWTH OF BACTERIOPHAGE

EDOUARD KELLENBERGER

Laboratoire de Biophysique, Université de Genève, Switzerland

INTRODUCTION

The developmental cycle of bacteriophage is in essence the same as that of most other viruses; in particular, infection is characteristically followed by the so-called eclipse period in which no infective particles can be found inside the cell. For phage it was possible to show that this eclipse period coincides with the replication of phage DNA. The basic experiments of Hershey & Chase (1952), demonstrating that the protein coat of the infecting phage is left outside the cell, have been followed by still further evidence strengthening the hypothesis that DNA is the sole carrier of genetic information.

Two main problems can be studied with the system of bacterial viruses: (1) the replication of the injected DNA in the form of new phage genomes which are later integrated into the progeny; (2) the direction by that DNA of the synthesis of the phage proteins and the assembly of complete phage particles. These problems have the potentiality of contributing to our knowledge of what is nowadays called the chemical basis of heredity. It is desirable to search out the connexions between all the manifestations of phage reproduction and the genetic information contributed by phage DNA. These questions will be treated in other contributions to this symposium.

Before concentrating on vegetative phage and the formation of mature virus particles, we will briefly recall the main results obtained concerning phage structure and the mechanism of infection, as this knowledge is important for understanding the functional differentiation of phage components. We will not always proceed historically, because newer results have often supplanted the original interpretations.

The author apologizes for putting some exaggerated emphasis on recent morphological results: it is, after all, so satisfactory to see now what was formerly deduced by indirect means.

Most of the experiments concerning phage have been made on the even-numbered *Escherichia coli* T phages. The main reason for this is that the DNA of these phages had been found to be of a composition different from that of the host DNA: cytosine is replaced by 5-hydroxymethylcytosine (Wyatt & Cohen, 1952). It is this property which enables one to follow the metabolism of phage DNA without any confusion with that of bacterial DNA. This fundamental difference is probably reflected in other particular properties; care should therefore be taken in extrapolating results from these T-even phages to other systems.

It is very desirable that our knowledge be extended to other phages, in particular to the temperate phages, which are able to integrate themselves into the host genome, thus forming lysogenic cells. These bacterial viruses are more closely related to the bacteria than are the T-even coliphages, and show even in their lytic cycle a much greater dependence upon the host cell. In the present paper we will consider some observations related to the growth of a temperate coliphage; but the scope of the review does not allow us to go further. For the general problems of lysogeny, we refer the reader to a recent review by Bertani (1958).

STRUCTURE OF BACTERIOPHAGE

The even-numbered T phages can be easily disrupted by osmotic shock into two parts (Anderson, 1950): the DNA moiety, comprising about 40 % of the total phage weight, and the protein (Herriott, 1951), representing the phage head membrane, the tail and some other minor components. In other phages which are not sensitive to osmotic shock, it was possible to show at least that the existence of a head membrane is general, since various methods of inactivation result in the production of empty head membranes (Lark & Adams, 1953; Kellenberger & Kellenberger, 1954).

The structural complexity of the T2-protein has been investigated by electron-microscopy. The tail has been found to consist of several substructures (Kellenberger & Arber, 1955; Williams & Fraser, 1956). At the centre is an inner core, which has recently been found to be a hollow tube (Brenner, Streisinger & Horne, 1958). This core is surrounded by a sheath, which normally covers the whole length of the tail. By chemical means—mainly oxidation, or hydrolysis of thiolester bonds—this sheath can be made to contract to half its length, uncovering the distal part of the tail core (Kellenberger & Arber, 1955; Brown & Kozloff, 1957; Kozloff, Lute & Henderson, 1957). It is not yet known if some other proteins of a 'cement' nature go into solution at the same time. On the tip of the core are fixed the tail fibres. The latter seem to be important in adsorption (Williams & Fraser, 1956). Very recently Brenner (personal communication) succeeded in separating and purifying by chemical means the three main constituents of the tail, namely core, sheath and fibres. This opens the way to more thorough investigations of the chemical structure and physiological functions of these components in relation to the genetic control of their production.

All phages studied so far contain DNA of the usual base composition, with the exception of the T-even phages which contain hydroxy-methyl-cytosine in place of cytosine. No other exceptional base has as yet been observed. The molecular constitution of T2 DNA has been studied in some detail, but without reaching a final conclusion about its significance. It has been found by autoradiography of ^{32}P-containing phage that the DNA is composed of a large piece, representing about 40 % of the total, and several much smaller pieces (Levinthal & Thomas, 1957). Two different DNA fractions had also been found by chromatography (Brown & Martin, 1955). It is interesting to note that the T-even phages contain glucose associated with the hydroxy-methylcytosine, in amounts which are different for the various strains (Sinsheimer, 1956; Jesaitis, 1956), and that the association shows unusual inheritance (Streisinger & Weigle, 1956).

It is not yet clear how the free acid groups of DNA are neutralized. A recent report, however, gives evidence that this role may be taken by basic polyamines. Indeed, spermidine and putrescine have now been found in phage T2 (Ames, Dubin & Rosenthal, 1958).

THE INFECTION OF THE CELL

Since our primary subject is phage growth, we will not discuss in detail our knowledge concerning the adsorption and penetration of bacterial viruses. An extensive review of this subject has been made by Tolmach (1957). We may just mention recent work showing that there is a double interaction between the bacterial wall and the tail of the phage, in the sense that on the one hand contact with the wall seems to induce structural changes in the tail of the phage (Kellenberger & Arber, 1955; Kozloff, Lute & Henderson, 1957), and on the other hand that an enzyme on the phage tail breaks down some of the constituents of the cell wall (Brown & Kozloff, 1957; Weidel & Primosigh, 1957).

One of the most important experiments concerning the infection of a bacterium by a bacteriophage has been made by Hershey & Chase (1952). With ^{35}S used as tracer, only the protein of the phage is made radioactive. When bacteria are infected with such phages and some minutes later sheared in a blender, the following results are found: most of the radioactivity remains in the supernatant when the bacteria are centrifuged down; the resuspended bacteria, however, still form infective centres; observed in the electron microscope (Kellenberger & Arber, 1955) the supernatant is found to contain empty heads alone or associated with half of the tail, so that some very small part of the tail must have been left on the wall or in the bacterium. No sulphur, however, is transmitted to the progeny in measurable amounts (French, 1954). Hence most of the phage protein, composed of the empty head and most of the tail, remains outside the cell after DNA has been injected. Proof of this latter fact is given by ^{32}P-labelling, which is confined to the DNA; after injection, such phosphorus is found bound to the host cell (Hershey & Chase, 1952), and about half of the isotopic label of the injected DNA is found again in the progeny phage (Watson & Maaløe, 1953; French, Graham, Lesley & van Rooyen, 1952; Putnam & Kozloff, 1950; Kozloff, 1953; Hershey, Garen, Fraser & Hudis-Dixon, 1954). The ^{32}P of the isotopically marked DNA is not equally distributed among the progeny, but, as shown by decay experiments (Stent & Jerne, 1955; Stent, 1958), remains confined to a very small number of phages.

Since it is basically important to know whether the injected DNA contains the genetic information, or whether there are some components other than DNA which do so, Hershey (1957) made a detailed investigation of the acid-soluble non-DNA fraction of phage which is injected with the DNA. This fraction, which comprises about 3 % of the total carbon of phage, was found to be composed of a polypeptide and two other substances now identified as polyamines (Ames, Dubin & Rosenthal, 1958). The polypeptide is not transmitted from the parental DNA to the offspring and its synthesis in newly infected bacteria is inhibited by chloramphenicol. The other components, however, are transmitted to the offspring and are formed in the presence of chloramphenicol. But since these substances can be supplied to the offspring through the culture medium, Hershey concludes that they do not play an important role in carrying the genetic information.

THE METABOLISM OF THE PHAGE-INFECTED CELL

Soon after infection with T-even phage the metabolism of the bacterial cell changes markedly: many enzymes are no longer produced, though those already present remain active (Cohen, 1949; Pardee & Williams, 1953), or may even be activated (Kozloff, 1953; Kunkee & Pardee, 1956; Wormser & Pardee, 1957); infected bacteria fail to be induced for adaptive enzymes (Monod & Wollman, 1947); protein synthesis, however, measured as a whole, continues (Cohen, 1948; Hershey, Dixon & Chase, 1953). Antigenically this protein is not related to phage protein (Watanabe, 1957a). It seems important to note, however, that this synthesis seems to be governed by the phage genome: the synthesis of 'non-antigenic protein' is induced by infection in u.v.-irradiated bacteria, in which the synthesis of bacterial protein is largely suppressed (Watanabe, 1957a). The synthesis of bacterial DNA is completely stopped upon infection and the existing DNA becomes progressively degraded. Phage-specific DNA, containing hydroxy-methylcytosine, is found about 8 min. after infection (Cohen, 1948; Hershey, Dixon & Chase, 1953; Vidaver & Kozloff, 1957).

The metabolism of RNA is not yet clearly understood. There is no doubt, however, that after infection with T2, new RNA is synthesized as measured by the assimilation of radioisotopes (Volkin & Astrachan, 1956). Some at least of the bacterial RNA is broken down: purines and pyrimidines may even enter the phage-synthesized DNA (Hershey, Garen, Fraser & Hudis-Dixon, 1954).

Some 5 min. before active intracellular phage appears, phage-specific proteins—precipitating with antiphage serum—begin to appear, and increase almost linearly with time. This protein is produced independently of the other proteins synthesized during the first minutes of infection, that is, there is practically no turnover between them (Kiho & Watanabe, 1957; Watanabe, 1957b).

If the synthesis of an amino acid is missing from an auxotrophic bacterium, phage growth is inhibited unless the amino acid is supplied (Burton, 1955). Phage does not supply the necessary information for the synthesis of amino acids. Phage T2, however, is able to direct the synthesis of thymine (Barner & Cohen, 1954).

THE DNA OF VEGETATIVE PHAGE

DNA and the genetic pool

We have already seen that the DNA of phage T2 begins to increase about 8 min. after infection. It then continues to grow almost linearly (Cohen, 1948; Hershey, Dixon & Chase, 1953; Vidaver & Kozloff, 1957). The measurements include all phage DNA, whether integrated into particles or not. We know, however, that the first intracellular phage, and phage-related structures visible in the electron microscope, do not appear before 10 min., at which time about fifty phage equivalents of DNA can already be measured chemically (Hershey, Dixon & Chase, 1953; Hershey, 1956). Using isotope tracers it has been found that this DNA, formed early, is later incorporated into mature phage (Hershey, 1953); its phosphorus needs about 14 min. for transfer from the inorganic components of the growth medium to the finished, active phage particles (Stent & Maaløe, 1953).

Analysing the data of recombination experiments, Visconti & Delbrück (1953) arrived at the hypothesis of a genetic pool. This notion of a pool was strictly abstract and described a step in phage growth at which matings between the phage genomes are very frequent. From this pool individual genomes are withdrawn to mature into finished phage. It seems fairly obvious that this genetic pool may be identified with the phage-DNA accumulation. A direct proof of this identity, however, has not yet been made, because no phage–bacterium system has yet been found in which both a genetic measurement of the pool size and a chemical measurement of phage DNA can be made. The genetic measurement of the phage pool can be made for some species of phage, such as coliphage λ, in the following way. A superinfecting phage, added at various intervals after the first infection, can enter the pool and contribute to the progeny (Jacob & Wollman, 1956; Whitfield & Appleyard, 1957). The contributions of the two phages will be equal, at the beginning, when the first phage and the superinfecting mutant are in equal numbers. The ratio changes as soon as the first phage has established its pool. By considering the ratios in the progeny from these doubly infected bacteria, the pool size at a given time can be calculated. This genetic measure of pool size is impossible for T2, where the superinfecting phage is mostly lost by virtue of a bacterial reaction (French, Lesley, Graham & van Rooyen, 1951). Conversely, a chemical measure of phage DNA is impossible with λ, because its DNA differs neither in base-composition nor base-ratio from that of the bacterial DNA (Arber, unpublished).

Morphological observations

The genetically predicted phage-DNA pool has recently been revealed by electron microscopy of ultrathin sections of infected bacteria (Pl. 1, fig. 4; Pl. 3, fig. 1) (Kellenberger, Ryter & Séchaud, 1958). It is composed of very fine fibrils at the limit of resolution and contrast of the electron microscope; that is of the order of 30–50 Å. It is cleanly separated from the cytoplasmic granules (ribonucleoprotein), but has an irregular shape. This pool closely resembles, in its fine structure and sometimes even in its form, the nucleoids of normal, uninfected bacteria. Such a fibrillar state of vegetative phage-DNA was previously concluded from physico-chemical studies (Watanabe, Stent & Schachman, 1954).

Electron microscopy furthermore provided the means to follow the sequence of the establishment of the pool of phage T2 (Pl. 1, figs 1–4). Shortly after infection, the bacterial nucleoids migrate slowly towards the cell envelope, and there form marginal vacuoles, as is already well known from previous work (Luria & Human, 1950; and many others, see Kellenberger, Séchaud & Ryter, 1958). This process is completed within 5–6 min. after infection and at about the same time in all cells. From these marginal vacuoles the pool grows out and migrates towards the middle of the cell. This happens 8 min. after infection, exactly at the time when synthesis of phage DNA begins. It is concluded that the establishment of the pool of T2 progresses in two steps, the first being the breakdown of the bacterial nucleus into the marginal vacuoles and the second the formation of the phage-DNA pool. It is not yet clear in what form exactly the Feulgen-positive material of the marginal vacuoles exists, and whether the nuclear breakdown is associated with the observed activation of DNases (Kunkee & Pardee, 1956). For other phages the morphological sequence is not yet known: it is difficult to observe in most cases, since a complete breakdown of the bacterial nucleus has been observed only for the even-numbered T phages and T5 (Murray & Whitfield, 1953).

The role of protein synthesis in the establishment of the pool

It has been found by several different means that protein synthesis is necessary for the initial steps of T2-DNA multiplication. Feeding with 5-methyltryptophan stops the synthesis of proteins and, in infected bacteria, phage-DNA synthesis does not take place (Cohen, 1948). Burton (1955) extended these results by using amino-acid requiring strains and amino-acid analogues. He found, in all cases studied, that phage DNA and protein synthesis are inhibited together as long as the inhibition occurs within the first 7 min. after infection. Phage DNA is synthesized at a nearly normal rate, however, if protein synthesis proceeds for up to 5–8 min. after infection. Finally, Melechen (see Hershey & Melechen, 1957) and Tomizawa & Sunakawa (1956) showed that chloramphenicol, which is well known to inhibit protein synthesis, also inhibits the replication of phage DNA if it is added at the time of, or shortly after, infection. If it is added later, DNA synthesis takes place at a reduced rate, achieving about the normal rate when the chloramphenicol addition is made between 8 and 11 min. after infection. The DNA pool then becomes hypertrophic since no phage particles are made. In the electron microscope this giant pool is easily recognized (Pl. 3, fig. 1). Its fine structure is similar to that of the normal pool, though more densely packed (Kellenberger, Ryter & Séchaud, 1958). By morphological observation it was also found that even the first step of pool formation is affected by chloramphenicol, that is to say, in the presence of this drug the bacterial nucleus is not destroyed and the marginal vacuoles are not produced (Kellenberger, Séchaud & Ryter, 1958).

The Luria–Latarjet experiments

This type of experiment is designed to study intracellular phage or phage subunits by means of inactivations caused by radiations (u.v. or X) or by the decay of radioactive ^{32}P incorporated into the nucleic acid. An extensive review has recently been written by Stent (1958). The basic idea of these experiments was as follows. If an infected cell contains several units, this cell is expected to be killed as a productive centre ('plaque former') only when all or at least most of the identical copies are killed. The radiological analysis of such a system would supply a group of multi-hit (or better, multi-target) curves. With increasing time after infection the number of necessary hits would increase, but the final slope of the curve should theoretically be identical. It is known that this slope is the graphic expression of the radiosensitivity. To the general surprise, the results obtained with T2 by Luria & Latarjet (1947), Benzer (1952) and Stent (1953, 1955, 1958) do not correspond to those expected on the basis of these premises. Soon after infection the cells show a decreased sensitivity to each of the above killing agents, the form of the curve remaining one-hit. At least, when 'shouldered', the curve does not show a normal multi-hit character, with an increase of the target number with time. During the early period after infection, when no DNA synthesis occurs, the sensitivity is already decreasing. Later sensitivity may again increase due to secondary effects (Symonds, 1957). The change of sensitivity can therefore not be directly related to the DNA. T5 gives results comparable to T2 (Luria & Steiner, 1954), while T1, T3, T7 and λ irradiated with u.v. light give results which are closer to those expected (Benzer, 1952; Benzer & Jacob, 1953; Stent, 1953, 1958). Phosphorus decay experiments, however, performed on λ phage, give results which are again comparable to those obtained with T2 (Stent & Fuerst, 1956).

Discussion

In summarizing the results of this section, we can conclude that, undoubtedly for T2, protein synthesis must be possible for phage-DNA synthesis to start. There is no doubt either that freshly injected phage DNA is much more radiosensitive than vegetative phage. Many different working hypotheses can be drawn from this situation. One of the simplest would be to assume that phage DNA is structurally modified, for example by its association with a protein which would give to it additional rigidity, and this would explain both the need of protein synthesis and the decreased radiosensitivity. An alternative hypothesis is to assume that the genetic information of DNA is first transmitted to a template of protein, or ribonucleoprotein, from which it is then transmitted to the new DNA (Stent, 1958). Neither of these hypotheses is yet satisfactorily in agreement with all observations. Preliminary experiments with λ and other phages indicate that here the dependence of DNA synthesis on previous protein synthesis may not be comparable with that in T2 (Crawford, 1958; Séchaud, unpublished results; Thomas, personal communication). Furthermore, the fact that chloramphenicol inhibits the breakdown of the nucleoids in the case of T2 could well indicate that protein synthesis is necessary for some secondary but early action, perhaps not directly concerned with the replication of DNA. The extension of these studies to phages other than T2 will probably go far to clarify this situation. It will be of great importance, also, to determine the chemical state of the DNA in the pool. Electron-microscope studies upon fixation of this sort of DNA tend to exclude the presence of a complete protein, because protein reacts strongly with OsO_4, whereas the units of the pool, as well as those of the bacterial nucleus, react only weakly. Polyamines or simple basic polypeptides could of course neutralize the acid groups of DNA.

FORMATION OF PHAGE PARTICLES

Observation of ultrathin sections with the electron microscope

Improved techniques for obtaining ultrathin sections (Ryter & Kellenberger, 1958) now enable the observation of well-preserved intracellular phage (Pl. 2), and therefore also of the different maturation steps (Kellenberger, Séchaud & Ryter, 1958). Unfortunately, several limitations restrict the information obtainable. The thickness of the sections (about 500 Å) is more than half the diameter of the phage heads. For this reason the phage membrane is visible only exceptionally, when one of the sides of the polyhedral head lies exactly perpendicular to the plane of section. The fact that no membrane is visible around a phage cannot, therefore, be interpreted to mean that it does not possess one. Furthermore, the known techniques do not give enough contrast to the phage tail to make it readily visible on the micrographs. Hence, the formation of the tail cannot yet be followed.

To circumvent some of these deficiencies, observation of sections may be combined with the observation of premature lysates. Quantitative relationships between both of these observations are now established with sufficient precision to be useful (Séchaud, Ryter & Kellenberger,

1958). At 10 min. after infection, some dark bodies with the polyhedral shape of phage heads can be observed in the sections. Upon opening the cells, at least five times fewer empty coats or intact phage are found. The number of these phage-shaped bodies increases with time; at 12 min. (Pl. 1, fig. 4) about thirty such bodies visible on sections are found per cell, but only ten empty heads or intact phages are observed in the lysate. Hence, these bodies must be labile immature phages, produced by a condensation or 'crystallization' of the DNA. If these bodies include any proteins, they are not organized in a form which can 'survive' the opening of the cell and the preparation for electron microscopy, as can be seen from the fact that the number of coat-related structures found in the lysate is much smaller than the number of condensed DNA bodies found intracellularly.

No such phage-shaped bodies appear in the DNA pool formed in the presence of chloramphenicol as long as the drug is present; but they begin to be formed shortly after removal of the drug. Indeed 13–15 min. after this removal about fifty phage-shaped, dark bodies are found per cell; the lysate of disrupted cells, however, contains less than 0·5 morphologically intact phages per cell and only about five empty heads. Again, these DNA condensations are lost upon opening without leaving empty head membranes. It can be concluded that protein synthesis is necessary for condensation of the phage DNA into the first form of immature phage.

The origin of the phage-related structures found in lysates

Since the observation of De Mars, Luria, Fisher & Levinthal (1953) and Levinthal & Fisher (1953) it is well known that empty phage heads, called doughnuts, can be found in lysates of normal and proflavine-treated cells. Later tail-related structures were also found (Kellenberger & Séchaud, 1957). The latter authors found a mean maximum yield of about fifty-five empty heads and twenty-five 'tail-rods', independently of the presence of proflavine. We have already seen from the sectioning work that, at least for normal phage, these empty heads must arise from broken-down, immature phage. This was found to be true also for cells treated with proflavine (Kellenberger, Séchaud & Ryter, 1958). Pl. 3, fig. 2 shows a section of such a proflavine-treated infected cell, containing phage-like particles. In comparing this with Pl. 2, however, we immediately recognize that these particles are not normally 'filled'. The density of the internal material is lower, and the phage membranes frequently detached from it. Counted on sections, about 100 abnormal phages are found, while the premature lysate contains about fifty empty heads and less than 0·1 intact phage particles per cell. On the micrograph of Pl. 3, fig. 2 we find several apparently empty shells; we cannot decide, however, if they are not merely eccentric sections through phage which are incompletely filled. In any case, the number of these empty heads per cell counted on sections (about fifteen) is much lower than the number in lysates. It is not yet known whether the substance filling these phages is DNA.

By the use of a special method of 'embedding' in phosphotungstic acid, Brenner and collaborators (Brenner *et al.* 1958) found that pro-flavine lysates do indeed contain half-filled, tailless particles, which are rather rapidly destroyed upon storage. These findings also corroborate the discovery by Maaløe & Symonds (1953) of inactive particles of approximately the weight of normal phage in premature lysates.

Recently Pardee & Prestidge (1958) produced inactive particles of near normal weight by the use of azatryptophan. These particles show little tendency to be precipitated by antiphage serum; they seem not to be preserved when prepared for the electron microscope, and are generally unstable. They contain, however, phage DNA.

In whole lysates free small particles have been found, endowed with the ability to block antiphage serum (De Mars, 1955). They cannot be identified with the rods (Kellenberger & Séchaud, 1957). It may well be that these particles are the fibres, since purified fibres have strong serum-blocking activity (Brenner, Streisinger & Horne, 1958). Although fibres have been found attached to rods in lysates, free fibres have not as yet been observed because of the background of small particulate components. Purification techniques have not yet been applied to lysates. These serum-blocking particles are probably true precursors: they accumulate, instead of being integrated into phage particles, when phage maturation is inhibited by proflavine.

Conclusions and discussion

It can be concluded from the foregoing that the empty heads or dough-nuts found in lysates are not phage precursors, which later would have to be filled with DNA, but rather a degradation product derived from very sensitive immature phage. This possibility had already been pointed out earlier (Hershey, 1956; Kellenberger & Séchaud, 1957). The major steps of T2-maturation would then be: (1) condensation of phage DNA to phage-head-shaped bodies, a process requiring the action of an unknown form-giving substance probably of protein nature; (2) enveloping of each particle with a membrane, probably still without a tail; (3) formation of the tail, beginning with growth of the inner core and followed by that of the sheath. Since tails cannot be seen in sections, we cannot decide at present whether the rods are built up on the tailless particles, or are assembled separately, and attached later. The fact, however, that rods appear after the head membranes and in smaller numbers (Kellenberger & Séchaud, 1957) is strong evidence in favour of the hypothesis that the tails are formed directly on the already nearly, or completely, finished phage heads. If this were not so, we should expect sometimes to find a large excess of rods.

The situation developed under the influence of proflavine now seems to be more complicated than ever; some precise knowledge about the chemical site of interference of this drug is urgently needed. The use of amino-acid analogues seems a much more promising approach for the study of phage-maturation steps.

ABNORMAL PHAGE GROWTH DUE TO DEFECTIVE GENOME

The defective lysogenic systems

Pathological development is one of the main tools for the study of phage growth. Specific inhibitors are generally used, as we have seen in the preceding sections, in order to obtain information on the process of phage synthesis. A more precise relationship between the genetic information contained in the phage DNA and the synthetic properties directed thereby may be obtained in systems where the phage genome has a genetically localized defect. By such means it will become possible to associate the missing synthetic step with the defective portion of the genome. Since the defect interferes with the synthesis of complete phage, the maintenance of such defective phage is achieved in a lysogenic system, where the prophage, even when defective, divides concurrently with the bacterium.

The first defective-lysogenic strain of *Bacillus megatherium* was observed by Lwoff & Siminovitch (1951). U.v. induction initiates lysis of such a culture, but no phages are produced, and DNA synthesis seems to be inhibited (Siminovitch, 1951). A great number of defective-lysogenic strains has since been derived mainly from *Escherichia coli* K 12 (λ). For some of them the defect has been localized on the genetic map of the phage (Jacob & Wollman, 1956; Arber, 1958). These defective-lysogenic strains form three main groups when their characteristics are considered. The first is composed of strains which always produce a few active phages with a large amount of coat-related structures (Appleyard, 1954, 1956; Jacob & Wollman, 1956; Jacob, Fuerst & Wollman, 1957; Whitfield & Appleyard, 1957; Arber & Kellenberger, 1958). It is believed that the few active phages in the output result from back-mutations of the genetic defect (Jacob & Wollman, 1956). The defective-lysogenic strains of the second group do not produce either active phage or coat-related structures. They may, however, be induced to lyse. The best-studied phage of this group is the Gal-transducing phage λ (Morse, Lederberg & Lederberg, 1956; Weigle, 1957). It has been found that any phage λ which can transduce the ability of bacteria to ferment galactose is always defective (Arber, Kellenberger & Weigle, 1957; Campbell, 1957; Arber, 1958). Transducing phage P22 of *Salmonella* is also defective (Starlinger, personal communication), as well as P1 of *Shigella* (Luria, Fraser, Adams & Burrous, 1958). Campbell (discussion to Luria *et al.* 1958) has recently discovered a third group of defectives, where the manifestation of the defect is host-dependent: on some hosts it behaves defectively while on others it yields normal phage. This interaction opens a new field, by introducing the possibility of genetic control in both host and virus.

All defective strains studied have been found to be able to produce phage particles carrying a defective genome, when a superinfecting normal phage introduces the missing functions (Arber, Kellenberger & Weigle, 1957; Jacob, Fuerst & Wollman, 1957; Arber & Kellenberger, 1958).

Phage coat-related structures produced by defective strains

The lysates of several defective-lysogenic strains able still to produce a few infective phages have been observed under the electron microscope (Arber & Kellenberger, 1958). Empty heads are found in all cases. Frequently free tails are also found. Ultrathin sectioning of induced bacteria has not yet been applied here to test whether the empty heads are breakdown products of immature phage. Lysates of defective-lysogenic strains may contain serum-blocking ability not necessarily associated with an organized tail. Of further particular interest are the defects which affect the production of an endolysin responsible for lysis of the induced cells (Jacob, Fuerst & Wollman, 1957; Jacob & Fuerst, 1958).

Prophage defects interfering with DNA synthesis

Since the base ratio of λ-DNA is not different from that of the bacterium (Arber, unpublished results) it is impossible to distinguish the two DNAs by chemical means. The increase of the λ phage pool has to be measured genetically. Jacob, Fuerst & Wollman (1957) and Whitfield & Appleyard (1957) found some defective strains of the first group, where the formation of the genetic pool is inhibited. Most extensively studied in this respect is the Gal-defective phage λ, where a segment representing about one-quarter of the genetic map is missing (Arber,

Kellenberger & Weigle, 1957; Arber, 1958). This explains why no coat-related structures are found for this strain. Neither does the genetic pool increase at all after induction. The question arose whether DNA synthesis itself is inhibited in such defective strains where the genetic pool does not increase. Whitfield (personal communication) has shown that this is not the case; after induction of such strains general DNA synthesis proceeds as in irradiated non-lysogenic and lysogenic cells, that is, after a small latent period depending upon the dose of irradiation (Kelner, 1953). Hence, if phage DNA is produced, it is genetically not accessible. It seems, however, much more probable that what we observe is bacterial DNA, phage DNA not having monopolized the DNA metabolism. An increase of defective genomes can be produced by superinfection with another phage. This superinfecting phage may be normal or defective providing its defect is not in the same region as that of the first phage. The fact that previous recombination of both parental phages does not seem to be necessary, supports the hypothesis that this Gal-defective genome lacks something necessary at a very early stage of vegetative multiplication.

Conclusion and discussion

Defective prophages can be found which interfere either with the establishment of the genetic pool or with phage-specific protein synthesis and the process of maturation. The function missing for the increase of the pool can be provided by a superinfecting phage. This defect is totally different from a u.v. lesion in irradiated phage since in this latter case the function cannot be provided by superinfection (Kellenberger & Arber, unpublished results). All the evidence indicates that u.v.-treated phage is unable to serve as a template for the replication of DNA, whereas defective phage can serve as a template but lacks information for a synthetic step necessary for building up the copy. Nothing is known as yet about this function. The other known defects, interfering with maturation, are certainly of a very different nature, as indicated by the production of electron-microscopically visible phage-related structures.

GENERAL DISCUSSION

Phage growth has been described as a 'parasitism on the genetic level' (Luria, 1954). The host-dependence of this parasitism may, however, be very different for the various phage species. In speculating I would tend to postulate two main types of parasitism. The first, represented by the T-even phages and T5, would be totalitarian: the infected bacteria contribute the amino-acid syntheses and the energy supply, but all new syntheses would be directed by the phage genome. To take command, the infecting phage first has to destroy all genetic information contained in the bacteria. Many observations are in favour of this view, such as those regarding the protein and RNA metabolisms, the breakdown of the bacterial nucleus and DNA.

The second type, represented mainly by the temperate phages, as for example coliphage λ, gets the necessary advantage over bacteria simply by a shift of the metabolic equilibrium. The shift produced by the virus infection is probably rather small and its extent variable, so that there is a rather high proportion of cells which can recover and integrate the phage as prophage. The imbalance of metabolism may have as a principal result the multiplication mainly of phage DNA, instead of bacterial DNA. That the latter, together with its genetic information, is not destroyed seems to be indicated by several observations: the bacterial nucleus is maintained during a rather long portion of the latent period; nucleases are not activated, in contrast with T2 infection (Wormser & Pardee, 1957); and the ability to form adaptive enzymes during the latent period persists (Siminovitch & Jacob, 1952). Once a sufficient amount of phage DNA is present, it is natural enough that synthesis of phage-specific proteins takes place. The metabolic advantage given to the phage by the shift would also explain the induction of lysogenic cells, for which no satisfactory theory is as yet established (Lwoff, 1953). It is known that u.v. irradiation produces what is called an unbalanced growth (Barner & Cohen, 1956). This imbalance would favour again the production of phage instead of bacterial substance. Indeed, in u.v.-irradiated bacteria, phage λ multiplies normally in all cells, and no lysogeny becomes established (Lieb, 1953). Furthermore, the normal course of phage multiplication begins only 20–30 min. after induction, indicating that an intervening period is necessary for the prophage to 'segregate' from the bacterial genome (Jacob & Wollman, 1953). This period would represent the delay necessary for the new metabolism to become established.

These two main types of parasitism should manifest themselves mainly on the level of DNA synthesis. As we have seen in the foregoing paragraphs, the observations with regard to these two types would indeed indicate fundamental differences. In the case of temperate phage, it would seem that most of the apparatus used for the synthesis of bacterial DNA should fit immediately for the synthesis of virus DNA, with the exception perhaps of one essential enzyme or substance. It is of course possible that bacterial and viral DNA differ from each other in the sugar moiety, or in the basic substance used for neutralizing the phosphoric-acid groups, and that such difference is responsible for the advantage of one over the other.

The comparative studies of virulent T2 and temperate phage may also help us to gain a clearer idea about the direct or indirect replication of DNA. The most simple and straightforward hypothesis is to assume that DNA replicates as such by splitting between the bases of the double DNA helix, each branch reforming a duplicate daughter strand. Many recent experiments favour such a semi-conservative mechanism of replication (Meselson & Stahl, 1958; Delbrück & Stent, 1957). Genetic recombination would occur during the replication process by a sort of 'switching over' of the two reforming strands between two parents. This mechanism of copy-choice is considered, among others, in a review by Delbrück & Stent (1957).

We have already seen that two arguments can be brought forward against this direct replication: (1) the need of protein synthesis to precede DNA replication; (2) the decrease in sensitivity to radiation and ^{32}P decay in vegetative phage during replication. Therefore a new hypothesis has been formulated (Stent, 1958) suggesting that information is transmitted first to an insensitive template (either of ribonucleoprotein or protein) from which fresh DNA is then synthesized. One important advantage of the RNA-template hypothesis would be that it includes automatically the transfer of information to RNA which would be used not only for the synthesis of new phage DNA but also for protein synthesis. In the direct replication of DNA, the pathway of RNA to protein has to be considered separately. There are, however, several weak points in this theory. If recombinants are made when the information is still in the template form, the genetic pool must contain these templates, i.e. the morphologically observed pool should then be composed of RNA or protein in addition to DNA. This is contrary to the morphological evidence, because proteins would behave in quite a different way during fixation than does the observed pool (Kellenberger, Ryber & Séchaud, 1958). Hence we have to conclude that complete proteins are not present. It could still be, however, that RNA is associated with a very simple polyamine or something similar. But then the RNA thread would so much resemble DNA that the argument would become somewhat sophisticated. But even without these morphological observations, the template theory is still faced with the objections raised in interpretations of the radiation analyses. We think that the first observation to explain is not the decrease in sensitivity of the virus-infected cell, but the incomprehensible persistence of one-hit, or at the most two- or three-hit inactivation curves, even when the number of targets becomes as large as forty vegetative particles. This can mean either that the basic radiobiological theory is wrong, or that there are only one or very few weakly sensitive templates producing DNA. In the latter case we would have to assume that recombination did not occur in the intermediate phase but only in the accumulation of no-longer-multiplying DNA. Recombination would then be a final event, having no influence on the copies still to be made. But this contradicts the results of recombination experiments, where an early recombinant is the presumptive source of a clone of recombinants. We cannot get out of this difficulty by assuming that every new DNA strand again forms a template which will be used only once before destruction, because it would then be rather difficult to have only a very restricted number of active templates.

How else can the need of protein synthesis to precede DNA synthesis be explained? Several rather obvious arguments can be advanced. To build up the copies of DNA some new enzymes are needed. Information for these is brought by the phage. Obviously protein synthesis must still be possible, in order to synthesize such enzymes. Protein synthesis is also needed for breakdown of the bacterial nucleus. If destruction of bacterial information is a necessary condition for growth of T2, then this breakdown is already a sufficient condition for DNA synthesis to depend upon protein synthesis.

Thus, the need of protein synthesis can easily be taken into account without assuming a template containing mostly protein. But the results of radiation analysis remain to be explained. It is true that bacteria which have undergone previous irradiation or ^{32}P decay have mostly unchanged capacity to support growth of phage (Stent, 1958). These control experiments, however, become less significant when it is realized that the RNA formed during phage growth is probably different from the bacterial RNA. It could well be, then, that it is this new RNA whose protein synthesizing function is disturbed by the radiation or the ^{32}P decay. But in this hypothetical scheme too few experimental facts are yet known, as we will now see.

If we consider the pathway of protein synthesis, some observations seem in agreement with the hypothesis that virulent T2 immediately takes over the direction of all syntheses of the cell, without having to wait until numerous copies have been made. Indeed, the fact that dissolution of the bacterial nucleus follows rapidly the injection of T2 DNA, and that this process is inhibited by chloramphenicol, seems strong evidence for a synthetic ability of the injected DNA. We know that this breakdown is also initiated by u.v.-irradiated phage (Luria & Human, 1950) when no replication of DNA occurs (Hershey & Burgi,

1956). Another piece of evidence is the observation of Uetake, Luria & Burrous (1958) that a transducing temperate phage is already able to express the phenotype of the transported gene a few minutes after infection.

The question whether protein synthesis needs a ribonucleoprotein as an intermediate carrier of information is not yet answered definitely. Treatment of uninfected as well as of T4-infected bacteria with ribonuclease stops protein synthesis very promptly (Jerne & Maaløe, 1957). In the case of a temperate phage, ribonuclease, and base analogues which are incorporated only into RNA, are more effective inhibitors of phage than of bacterial protein synthesis (Jeener, 1958). The evidence that the base ratio of RNA changes upon infection is a further indication that the new RNA is made under the direction of the virus. This RNA almost certainly has a metabolic function, either in protein synthesis or as a template for DNA.

Let us consider finally the formation of phage particles. A general outline of the sequence of the maturation steps is now known. It will be of particular interest to discover and isolate the substance or substances responsible for the condensation of DNA out of the pool into bodies of the characteristic polyhedral shape. This 'condensation principle' may act in producing cross-links between different coils or layers of DNA, thus permitting the establishment of a regular DNA array which is stable against thermal agitation. It could be, however, that this array is obtained by an extremely thin, labile membrane; but it would be difficult in this case to understand why the DNA suddenly becomes organized into a state different from that present in the pool.

There will be many more difficulties to be overcome when the different steps of assembly of the coat and tail are studied. It would probably be profitable to isolate and purify some of the known precursor proteins, in order to relate them to the genetic information contained in the phage DNA. This would complement the investigations made on the disassembled parts of mature phage (Brenner, Streisinger & Horne, 1958).

In sum, then, we may conclude as follows:

(1) The evidence pointing to the occurrence of an intermediate template made of protein or ribonucleoprotein is not strong enough to allow the template theory of DNA replication to be preferred to the theory of replication by some direct mechanism.

(2) The results of the Luria–Latarjet experiments, as well as the need for protein synthesis prior to DNA replication, may be satisfactorily explained on other grounds than the intermediate template theory.

(3) It is thought that the T-even phages are parasites of a particularly independent nature and that further studies using temperate phages will help to clarify the fundamental problem of DNA replication.

(4) The hypothesis that protein synthesis goes obligatorily through RNA is in agreement with the different observations, but cannot yet be regarded as more than tentative.

(5) Maturation of phage begins with the condensation of DNA out of the pool. A 'condensation principle' of protein nature (or related to protein synthesis) is postulated.

The experimental work done in our laboratory with the help of several collaborators was greatly aided by a research grant from the 'Fonds National Suisse pour la Recherche scientifique', and by the gift of some laboratory equipment from the Rockefeller Foundation.

REFERENCES

AMES, B. N., DUBIN, D. T. & ROSENTHAL, S. M. (1958). Presence of polyamines in certain bacterial viruses. *Science*, **127**, 814.

ANDERSON, T. F. (1950). Destruction of bacterial viruses by osmotic shock. *J. appl. Physiol.* **21**, 70.

APPLEYARD, R. K. (1954). Segregation of new lysogenic types during growth of a doubly lysogenic strain derived from *Escherichia coli* K12. *Genetics*, **39**, 440.

APPLEYARD, R. K. (1956). The transfer of defective Lambda lysogeny between strains of *Escherichia coli*. *J. gen. Microbiol.* **14**, 573.

ARBER, W. (1958). Transduction des caractères Gal par le bactériophage Lambda. *Arch. Sci., Genève*, **11**, 259.

ARBER, W. & KELLENBERGER, G. (1958). Study of the properties of seven defective-lysogenic strains derived from *Escherichia coli* K12 (λ). *Virology*, **5**, 458.

ARBER, W., KELLENBERGER, G. & WEIGLE, J. (1957). Le défectuosité du phage lambda transducteur. *Schweiz. Z. Path.* **20**, 659.

BARNER, H. D. & COHEN, S. S. (1954). The induction of thymine synthesis by T2 infection of a thymine-requiring mutant of *Escherichia coli*. *J. Bact.* **68**, 80.

BARNER, H. D. & COHEN, S. S. (1956). The relation of growth to the lethal damage induced by ultraviolet irradiation in *Escherichia coli*. *J. Bact.* **71**, 149.

BENZER, S. (1952). Resistance to ultraviolet light as an index to the reproduction of bacteriophage. *J. Bact.* **63**, 59.

BENZER, S. & JACOB, F. (1953). Étude du développement du bactériophage au moyen d'irradiations par la lumière ultra-violette. *Ann. Inst. Pasteur*, **84**, 186.

BERTANI, G. (1958). Lysogeny. *Advanc. Virus Res.* **5**, 151.

BRENNER, S., STREISINGER, G. & HORNE, R. W. (1958). Personal communication.

BROWN, D. D. & KOZLOFF, L. M. (1957). Morphological localization of the bacteriophage tail enzyme. *J. biol. Chem.* **225**, 1.

BROWN, G. L. & MARTIN, A. V. (1955). Fractionation of the deoxyribonucleic acid of T2r bacteriophage. *Nature, Lond.* **176**, 971.

BURTON, K. (1955). The relation between the synthesis of deoxyribonucleic acid and the synthesis of protein in the multiplication of bacteriophage T2. *Biochem. J.* **61**, 473.

CAMPBELL, A. (1957). Transduction and segregation in *Escherichia coli* K12. *Virology*, **4**, 366.

COHEN, S. S. (1948). The synthesis of bacterial viruses. I. The synthesis of nucleic acid and protein in *Escherichia coli* B infected with T2r+ bacteriophage. *J. biol. Chem.* **174**, 218.

COHEN, S. S. (1949). Growth requirements of bacterial viruses. *Bact. Rev.* **13**, 1.

CRAWFORD, L. V. (1958). Deoxyribonucleic acid synthesis in phage-infected *Bacillus megaterium* KM. *Biochim. Biophys. Acta*, **28**, 208.

DELBRÜCK, M. & STENT, G. S. (1957). On the mechanism of DNA replication. In: *The Chemical Basis of Heredity*. Edited by W. D. McElroy and B. Glass, p. 699. Baltimore: Johns Hopkins Univ. Press.

DE MARS, R. I. (1955). The production of phage-related materials when bacteriophage development is interrupted by proflavine. *Virology*, **1**, 83.

DE MARS, R. I., LURIA, S. E., FISHER, H. & LEVINTHAL, C. (1953). The production of incomplete bacteriophage particles by the action of proflavine and the properties of the incomplete particles. *Ann. Inst. Pasteur*, **84**, 113.

FRENCH, R. C. (1954). The contribution of protein from parent to progeny in T2 coliphage. *J. Bact.* **67**, 45.

FRENCH, R. C., GRAHAM, A. F., LESLEY, S. M. & VAN ROOYEN, C. E. (1952). The contribution of phosphorus from T2r+ bacteriophage to progeny. *J. Bact.* **64**, 597.

FRENCH, R. C., LESLEY, S. M., GRAHAM, A. F. & VAN ROOYEN, C. E. (1951). Studies on the relationship between virus and host cell. III. The breakdown of P^{32} labelled T2r+ bacteriophage adsorbed to *E. coli* previously infected by other coliphages of the T group. *Canad. J. med. Sci.* **29**, 144.

HERRIOTT, R. M. (1951). Nucleic-acid-free T2 virus 'ghosts' with specific biological action. *J. Bact.* **61**, 752.

HERSHEY, A. D. (1953). Nucleic acid economy in bacteria infected with bacteriophage T2. II. Phage precursor nucleic acid. *J. gen. Physiol.* **37**, 1.

HERSHEY, A. D. (1956). Chemistry and viral growth. In *Currents in Biochemical Research*. Edited by D. E. Green. New York: Interscience.

HERSHEY, A. D. (1957). Some minor components of bacteriophage T2 particles. *Virology*, **4**, 237.

HERSHEY, A. D. & BURGI, E. (1956). Genetic significance of the transfer of nucleic acid from parental to offspring phage. *Cold Spr. Harb. Symp. quant. Biol.* **21**, 91.

HERSHEY, A. D. & CHASE, M. (1952). Independent functions of viral protein and nucleic acid in growth of bacteriophage. *J. gen. Physiol.* **36**, 39.

HERSHEY, A. D., DIXON, J. & CHASE, M. (1953). Nucleic acid economy in bacteria infected with bacteriophage T2. I. Purine and pyrimidine composition. *J. gen. Physiol.* **36**, 777.

HERSHEY, A. D., GAREN, A., FRASER, D. K. & HUDIS-DIXON, J. (1954). Growth and inheritance in bacteriophage. *Carnegie Inst. Wash. Year Book*, no. 53, p. 210.

HERSHEY, A. D. & MELECHEN, N. E. (1957). Synthesis of phage-precursor nucleic acid in the presence of chloramphenicol. *Virology*, **3**, 207.

JACOB, F. & FUERST, C. R. (1958). The mechanism of lysis by phage studied with defective lysogenic bacteria. *J. gen. Microbiol.* **18**, 518.

JACOB, F., FUERST, C. R. & WOLLMAN, E. L. (1957). Recherches sur les bactéries lysogènes défectives. II. Les types physiologiques liés aux mutations du prophage. *Ann. Inst. Pasteur*, **93**, 724.

JACOB, F. & WOLLMAN, E. L. (1953). Induction of phage development in lysogenic bacteria. *Cold Spr. Harb. Symp. quant. Biol.* **18**, 101.

JACOB, F. & WOLLMAN, E. L. (1956). Recherches sur les bactéries lysogènes défectives. I. Déterminisme génétique de la morphogenèse chez un bactériophage tempéré. *Ann. Inst. Pasteur*, **90**, 282.

Jeener, R. (1958). The action of ribonuclease, thiouracil and azaguanine on the synthesis of phage proteins by an induced lysogenic bacterium. *Biochim. Biophys. Acta*, **27**, 665.

Jerne, N. K. & Maaløe, O. (1957). The effects of ribonuclease on the bacteriophage T4, its host cell, *E. coli* B, and on infected *coli* cells. *Acta path. microbiol. scand.* **40**, 362.

Jesaitis, M. A. (1956). Differences in the chemical composition of the phage nucleic acids. *Nature, Lond.* **178**, 637.

Kellenberger, E. & Arber, W. (1955). Die Struktur des Schwanzes der Phagen T2 und T4 und der Mechanismus der irreversiblen Adsorption. *Z. Naturf.* **10**b, 698.

Kellenberger, E. & Kellenberger, G. (1954). The process of filtration on agar used for electron microscopical studies of bacteriophages in lysates and in single bacterial bursts. Proc. III. Intern. Conf. Electron Microscopy, London 1954, p. 268.

Kellenberger, E., Ryter, A. & Séchaud, J. (1958). Electron microscope study of DNA-containing plasmas. II. Vegetative and mature phage DNA as compared with normal bacterial nucleoids in different physiological states. *J. biophys. biochem. Cytol.* (in the Press).

Kellenberger, E. & Séchaud, J. (1957). Electron microscopical studies of phage multiplication. II. Production of phage-related structures during multiplication of phages T2 and T4. *Virology*, **3**, 256.

Kellenberger, E., Séchaud, J. & Ryter, A. (1958). To be submitted to *Virology*.

Kelner, A. (1953). Growth, respiration, and nucleic acid synthesis in ultraviolet-irradiated and in photoreactivated *Escherichia coli*. *J. Bact.* **65**, 252.

Kiho, Y. & Watanabe, I. (1957). Protein and ribonucleic acid synthesis induced by bacteriophage infection. *Intern. Symp. Enzyme Chemistry, Japan*.

Kozloff, L. M. (1953). Origin and fate of bacteriophage material. *Cold Spr. Harb. Symp. quant. Biol.* **18**, 209.

Kozloff, L. M., Lute, M. & Henderson, K. (1957). Viral invasion. I. Rupture of thiol ester bonds in the bacteriophage tail. *J. biol. Chem.* **228**, 511.

Kunkee, R. E. & Pardee, A. B. (1956). Studies on the role of deoxyribonuclease in T2 bacteriophage development. *Biochim. Biophys. Acta*, **19**, 236.

Lark, K. G. & Adams, M. H. (1953). The stability of phages as a function of the ionic environment. *Cold Spr. Harb. Symp. quant. Biol.* **18**, 171.

Levinthal, C. & Fisher, H. W. (1953). Maturation of phage and the evidence of phage precursors. *Cold Spr. Harb. Symp. quant. Biol.* **18**, 29.

Levinthal, C. & Thomas, C. A. (1957). Molecular autoradiography: The β-ray counting from single virus particles and DNA molecules in nuclear emulsions. *Biochim. Biophys. Acta*, **23**, 453.

Lieb, M. (1953). The establishment of lysogenicity in *Escherichia coli*. *J. Bact.* **65**, 642.

Luria, S. E. (1954). Genetic functions and developmental processes of bacterial viruses. In: *The Dynamics of Virus and Rickettsial Infections*. Edited by Hartman, Horsfall and Kidd. New York: Blakiston.

Luria, S. E., Fraser, D. K., Adams, J. N. & Burrous, J. W. (1958). Lysogenization, transduction and genetic recombination in bacteria. *Cold Spr. Harb. Symp. quant. Biol.* (in the Press).

Luria, S. E. & Human, M. L. (1950). Chromatin staining of bacteria during bacteriophage infection. *J. Bact.* **59**, 551.

Luria, S. E. & Latarjet, R. (1947). Ultraviolet irradiation of bacteriophage during intracellular growth. *J. Bact.* **53**, 149.

Luria, S. E. & Steiner, D. L. (1954). The role of calcium in the penetration of bacteriophage T5 into its host. *J. Bact.* **67**, 635.

Lwoff, A. (1953). L'induction. *Ann. Inst. Pasteur*, **84**, 225.

Lwoff, A. & Siminovitch, L. (1951). Induction de la lyse d'une bactérie lysogène sans production de bactériophage. *C.R. Acad. Sci., Paris*, **233**, 1397.

Maaløe, O. & Symonds, N. (1953). Radioactive sulfur tracer studies on the reproduction of T4 bacteriophage. *J. Bact.* **65**, 177.

Meselson, M. & Stahl, F. W. (1958). The replication of DNA in *Escherichia coli*. *Proc. Nat. Acad. Sci., Wash.* (in the Press).

Monod, J. & Wollman, E. (1947). L'inhibition de la croissance et de l'adaptation enzymatique chez les bactéries infectées par le bactériophage. *Ann. Inst. Pasteur*, **73**, 937.

Morse, M. L., Lederberg, E. M. & Lederberg, J. (1956). Transduction in *Escherichia coli* K-12. *Genetics*, **41**, 142.

Murray, R. G. E. & Whitfield, J. F. (1953). Cytological effects of infection with T5 and some related phages. *J. Bact.* **65**, 715.

Pardee, A. B. & Prestidge, L. S. (1958). Effects of azatryptophan on bacterial enzymes and bacteriophage. *Biochim. Biophys. Acta*, **27**, 330.

Pardee, A. B. & Williams, I. (1953). Enzymatic activity and bacteriophage infection. III. Increase of deoxyribonuclease. *Ann. Inst. Pasteur*, **84**, 147.

Putnam, F. W. & Kozloff, L. M. (1950). Biochemical studies of virus reproduction. IV. The fate of the infecting virus particles. *J. biol. Chem.* **182**, 243.

Ryter, A. & Kellenberger, E. (1958). Étude au microscope électronique de plasmas contenant de l'acide désoxyribonucléique. I. Les nucléoïdes des bactéries en croissance. *Z. Naturf.* (in the Press).

Séchaud, J., Ryter, A. & Kellenberger, E. (1958). Considérations quantitatives sur des coupes ultraminces de bactéries infectées par un bactériophage. In preparation.

Siminovitch, L. (1951). Relation entre le développement abortif du prophage chez *Bacillus megatherium* 91(1) et la synthèse de l'acide désoxyribonucléique. *C.R. Acad. Sci., Paris*, **233**, 1694.

Siminovitch, L. & Jacob, F. (1952). Biosynthèse induite d'un enzyme pendant le développement des bactériophages chez *Escherichia coli* K12. *Ann. Inst. Pasteur*, **83**, 745.

Sinsheimer, R. L. (1956). The glucose content of the deoxyribonucleic acids of certain bacteriophages. *Proc. Nat. Acad. Sci., Wash.* **42**, 502.

Stent, G. S. (1953). Mortality due to radioactive phosphorus as an index to bacteriophage development. *Cold Spr. Harb. Symp. quant. Biol.* **18**, 255.

Stent, G. S. (1955). Decay of incorporated radioactive phosphorus during reproduction of bacteriophage T2. *J. gen. Physiol.* **38**, 853.

Stent, G. S. (1958). Mating in the reproduction of bacterial viruses. *Advanc. Virus Res.* **5**, 95.

Stent, G. S. & Fuerst, C. R. (1956). Decay of incorporated radioactive phosphorus during development of a temperate bacteriophage. *Virology*, **2**, 737.

Stent, G. S. & Jerne, N. K. (1955). The distribution of parental phosphorus atoms among bacteriophage progeny. *Proc. Nat. Acad. Sci., Wash.* **41**, 704.

Stent, G. S. & Maaløe, O. (1953). Radioactive phosphorus tracer studies on the reproduction of T4 bacteriophage. II. Kinetics of phosphorus assimilation. *Biochim. Biophys. Acta*, **10**, 55.

Streisinger, G. & Weigle, J. (1956). Properties of bacteriophages T2 and T4 with unusual inheritance. *Proc. Nat. Acad. Sci., Wash.* **42**, 504.

Symonds, N. (1957). Effects of ultraviolet light during the second half of the latent period on bacteria infected with phage T2. *Virology*, **3**, 485.

Tolmach, L. J. (1957). Attachment and penetration of cells by viruses. *Advanc. Virus Res.* **4**, 63.

PLATE 1

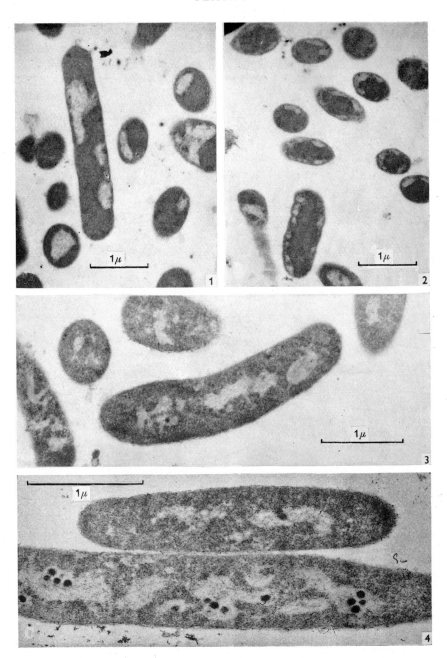

(*Facing p.* 32)

PLATE 2

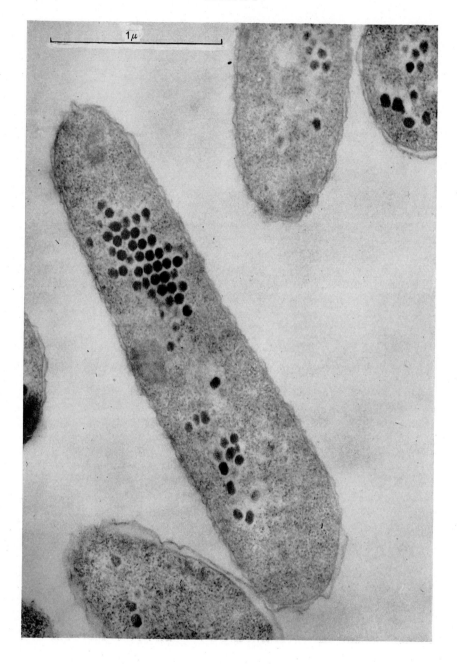

PLATE 3

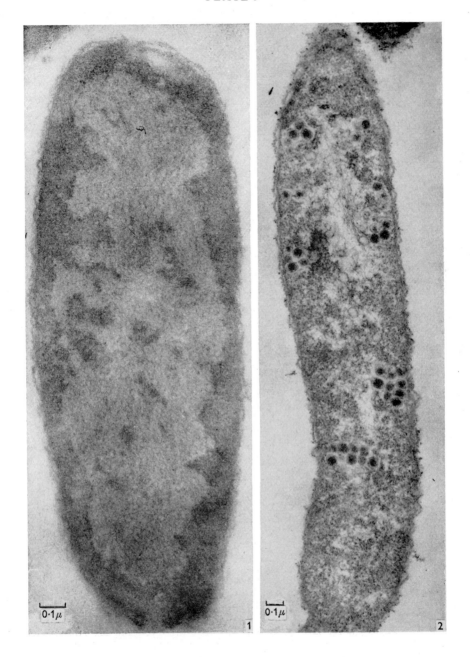

0·1μ

0·1μ

1

2

Tomizawa, J. I. & Sunakawa, S. (1956). The effect of chloramphenicol on deoxy-ribonucleic acid synthesis and the development of resistance to ultraviolet irradiation in *E. coli* infected with bacteriophage T2. *J. gen. Physiol.* **39**, 553.

Uetake, H., Luria, S. E. & Burrous, J. W. (1958). Conversion of somatic antigens in *Salmonella* by phage infection leading to lysis or lysogeny. *Virology*, **5**, 68.

Vidaver, G. A. & Kozloff, L. M. (1957). The rate of synthesis of deoxyribonucleic acid in *Escherichia coli* B infected with T2r+ bacteriophage. *J. biol. Chem.* **225**, 335.

Visconti, N. & Delbrück, M. (1953). The mechanism of genetic recombination in phage. *Genetics*, **38**, 5.

Volkin, E. & Astrachan, L. (1956). Phosphorus incorporation in *Escherichia coli* ribonucleic acid after infection with bacteriophage T2. *Virology*, **2**, 149.

Watanabe, I. (1957a). Formation of non-phage-antigenic protein in *E. coli* infected with T2 phage. *Biochim. Biophys. Acta*, **25**, 665.

Watanabe, I. (1957b). The effect of ultraviolet light on the production of bacterial virus protein. *J. gen. Physiol.* **40**, 521.

Watanabe, I., Stent, G. S. & Schachman, H. K. (1954). On the state of the parental phosphorus during reproduction of bacteriophage T2. *Biochim. Biophys. Acta*, **15**, 38.

Watson, J. D. & Maaløe, O. (1953). Nucleic acid transfer from parental to progeny bacteriophage. *Biochim. Biophys. Acta*, **10**, 432.

Weidel, W. & Primosigh, J. (1957). Die gemeinsame Wurzel der Lyse von *Escherichia coli* durch Penicillin oder durch Phagen. *Z. Naturf.* **12b**, 421.

Weigle, J. (1957). Transduction by coliphage λ of the galactose marker. *Virology*, **4**, 14.

Whitfield, J. F. & Appleyard, R. K. (1957). Formation of vegetative pool by induced defective and healthy lysogenic strains of *Escherichia coli*. *J. gen. Microbiol.* **17**, 453.

Williams, R. C. & Fraser, D. (1956). Structural and functional differentiation in T2 bacteriophage. *Virology*, **2**, 289.

Wormser, E. H. & Pardee, A. B. (1957). Deoxyribonuclease activity in *Escherichia coli* K12(λ) after bacteriophage induction with ultraviolet irradiation. *Virology*, **3**, 76.

Wyatt, G. R. & Cohen, S. S. (1952). A new pyrimidine-base from bacteriophage nucleic acids. *Nature, Lond.* **170**, 1072.

EXPLANATION OF PLATES

All figures show electron-micrographs of ultrathin sections of bacteria embedded in Vestopal W, observed with an RCA EMU 2D electron microscope. I am greatly indebted to Antoinette Ryter and Janine Séchaud for providing them.

Plate 1. Sequence of the intracellular development of phage T2.

Fig. 1. 2 min. after infection: the bacterial nucleoids move towards the cell margins.

Fig. 2. 4 min. after infection: formation of the typical marginal vacuoles.

Fig. 3. 10 min. after infection: the pool is formed.

Fig. 4. 12 min. after infection: condensation of the DNA to the polyhedral, phage-shaped bodies.

Plate 2. Mature intracellular T2 phage observed 30 min. after infection.

Plate 3

Fig. 1. Giant T2 DNA pool observed 75 min. after infection when 25 μg./ml. chloramphenicol was added at the 8th minute.

Fig. 2. Pathological T2 phage growth in the presence of 7 μg./ml. proflavine added at the time of infection. Observed 30 min. after infection: some empty heads and 'badly filled' phages can be seen.

THE MULTIPLICATION OF VIRUSES IN PLANTS

B. D. HARRISON

Rothamsted Experimental Station, Harpenden, Herts

Although it is convenient to separate viruses into types which infect either plants, animals or bacteria, evidence is accumulating which suggests that the modes of multiplication of these groups of viruses may not be so very different. There seem to be many similarities between plant and animal viruses, and indeed, some viruses multiply both in plants and in their insect vectors (Maramorosch, 1952). Additional similarities are that some animal viruses, like all the plant viruses which have been analysed, contain nucleic acid of the ribose type, and that certain plant and animal viruses have particles of similar shape and size. No plant virus, however, has been found with the tadpole shape which is characteristic of bacteriophages, and the two groups also differ chemically, for phages contain deoxyribonucleic acid. But despite these differences, there are also important similarities between plant viruses and phages, for the multiplication of both seems to be initiated by only the nucleic acid part of the virus particles.

Although there are these similarities between viruses which infect plants, animals or bacteria, individual plant viruses have particles with very different shapes—rods, flexuous threads or spheres (Pl. 1, figs. 1–8)—and it would be naïve to assume that they all replicate in a precisely similar manner. The plant viruses whose multiplication has been studied, however, have not been chosen with these differences in mind. Instead, they are mostly viruses that occur in relatively large amounts in infected plants, are stable and easily purified, and of which the prime example is tobacco mosaic virus (TMV). In fact, little is known about the multiplication of viruses which have not these properties. But though many of the phenomena of virus multiplication have been studied with only a few viruses and hosts, different workers have used different host-virus combinations and environmental conditions, and piecing together the story of plant virus multiplication is not straightforward.

INFECTION OF CELLS BY INOCULATION

By comparison with bacterial and some animal viruses, the methods of assaying plant viruses are insensitive, as some thousands of particles must be inoculated to plants to obtain an infection. Plant viruses will not infect their host plants unless provided with a wound through which to enter, although once they have entered and multiplied in one cell, they readily invade adjacent cells of the tissue without further help. The inability of viruses to infect unwounded plants was often attributed to the impermeability of the cuticle which coats most plant organs, but callus cells, which have no cuticle, also rarely become infected when immersed in virus preparations (Kassanis, Tinsley & Quak, 1958): this suggests that the rather rigid walls which most plant cells possess are also impermeable to virus unless they are pierced by plasmodesmata, which were not found in these callus cells. For infection to occur, a cell must be wounded but not so severely that it dies without the virus introduced into it multiplying. Indeed, the rather low proportion of cells from which lesions develop after injection with virus using a micromanipulator is most plausibly explained as being due to excessive damage to many of the injected cells (Sheffield, 1936). A similar effect is seen when leaves are repeatedly inoculated by rubbing a virus preparation over their upper surfaces with the forefinger; increasing numbers of lesions usually result from the first few applications, but in subsequent applications the rubbing appears to destroy more potential lesion sites than it establishes, and a decreased number of lesions develops. The number of rubs that can be made before the maximum number of lesions is reached, or passed, depends on the robustness and physiological state of the plants, and is smaller with delicate than with tough plants. Both with tough and with delicate leaves, however, nearly all the infections seem to occur in epidermal cells, for such infections are prevented from developing by irradiating leaves with ultraviolet light soon after inoculation, and only a small proportion of the ultraviolet light passes through the epidermis and enters mesophyll cells (Bawden & Harrison, 1955; Benda, 1955).

A major factor limiting the number of infections in inoculated leaves is the number of suitably wounded cells, and this can be greatly increased by mixing an abrasive with the inoculum. The abrasives used for this purpose seem to increase the number of suitable wounds in the epidermal cells and not to make infection of deeper tissues possible. The use of abrasives increases the number of infections with all the viruses which have been tested, but there is some evidence suggesting that a cell wounded in such a way that it can support the multiplication of one virus may not be suitable for that of another. For instance, TMV often causes more lesions in old than in young leaves of *Nicotiana glutinosa*, whereas in comparable leaves of the same species, tomato bushy stunt virus causes more lesions in the younger leaves. However, an equally plausible explanation is that different viruses infect plants through the same kind of wound but their chances of multiplying once they have entered the host cell are differently affected by its physiological state. Further evidence of the different effects of the state of the host when different infecting agents are used is provided by comparing the numbers of lesions caused by the nucleic acid of TMV with those caused by whole TMV. Unlike whole TMV, the nucleic acid causes more lesions in young than in old leaves of summer-grown *Nicotiana glutinosa*, and the number of infections caused by the nucleic acid is increased more by keeping plants at high temperatures before inoculation than when whole virus is used as the inoculum (Bawden, in the Press). This, of course, means that the result of comparing the infectivity of preparations of TMV-nucleic acid and whole TMV depends on the kind of assay plants used. The nucleic acid is more susceptible to inactivating agents of many kinds than is whole TMV and it is reasonable to suggest that differences in its infectivity for different kinds of leaves relative to that of whole TMV, may be caused by differences among inactivating systems in the leaves. In infectivity assays the behaviour of certain viruses, tomato bushy stunt for example, closely resembles that of TMV-nucleic acid. This suggests that such viruses are more likely than whole TMV to be inactivated in the cell, during the processes leading to virus multiplication.

It has been assumed that the number of cells in which virus multiplies after being introduced at inoculation can be estimated by the number of lesions which develops, although for a lesion to develop, virus must not only multiply in the initially invaded cell, but must also then invade and multiply in surrounding cells in the leaf. Treatments that affect lesion number may therefore act by preventing any of the sequence of events. Most treatments applied before inoculation, however, probably affect the ease with which wounds suitable for infection are made, or the chance that the virus particles which enter cells at inoculation will multiply, or both. Mixing an abrasive in the inoculum, or growing plants in conditions that favour the formation of delicate leaves, will obviously affect the number of suitable wounds produced at inoculation, whereas other treatments, such as keeping plants in darkness, or at a high temperature for only a day before inoculation, although often greatly increasing the number of lesions, probably act in some other way. Indeed, Nienhaus (1957), using potato virus *Y* and *Physalis floridana*, found that keeping plants in darkness or at a high temperature decreased the amount of substances in the sap, which, when extracted and mixed with virus, abolish its infectivity for test plants. Hence he suggested that such substances tend to prevent the infection of plants which contain them.

Besides those present in the sap of higher plants, many other substances, when incorporated in an inoculum, decrease the number of lesions caused in inoculated leaves. These include serum components, enzymes, and growth products of bacteria and fungi (see Bawden, 1954). Inhibitors of infection in the sap of certain species of plants are often responsible for the difficulty in transmitting viruses from these to other species, although they mostly have little effect on infection of other plants of the same species. The chemical nature of only a few of these inhibitors has been established; for example, that in *Phytolacca decandra* is a glycoprotein (Kassanis & Kleczkowski, 1948). Many of the inhibitors mentioned above combine with viruses *in vitro*, but, except in the instances of virus antiserum and tannins, it is doubtful if the combination is responsible for the inhibition because efficiency in decreasing the number of lesions caused depends on the species of plant inoculated and is independent of the virus used. An inhibitor in the sap of New Zealand spinach plants not only decreases lesion number, but also delays the movement of virus from initially infected cells of cowpea to others, perhaps by delaying virus multiplication (Benda, 1956). Substances that delay some initial stage in virus multiplication presumably increase the time that an introduced virus particle is exposed to inactivating systems in the cell and thus increase the chance that the virus will be inactivated before beginning to multiply. But there is no reason to assume that all inhibitors act in the same way; others may simply stimulate virus-inactivating systems or prevent virus from multiplying by altering virus–host interaction in many other ways.

Lesion numbers can often be increased by adding potassium phosphate or sodium oxalate to the inoculum, and two explanations of this action have been proposed. In the first, Yarwood (1955) suggests that attachment of virus particles to part of the cell precedes their separation into protein and nucleic acid, and is dependent upon the presence of certain ions, as it is with bacteriophages. In contrast, Benda (1956) points out that both phosphate and oxalate are calcium precipitants and suggests that their action may be to delay the repair of wounded cells or to increase the permeability of protoplasm to virus, in short to promote the entrance of virus into and its distribution within wounded cells.

Even under optimal conditions, methods of inoculation are inefficient as judged by the number of virus particles applied for each lesion that develops. One reason for this is that the number of wounds suitable for infection is limited: another may be that many of the virus particles are not infectious. Indeed, it has long been known that virus preparations could be fractionated in such a way that some of the fractions had little or no infectivity. But usually such non-infective fractions contain particles of different size or mass from the major constituent of the most infective fractions, and there is little to indicate what proportion of particles in the highly infective fractions is infectious. The number of virus particles which initiates each infection is still uncertain. Statistical evidence allows two alternative hypotheses. In the first, the dose hypothesis, a large number of particles is assumed to act together at each site, whereas in the second, only one particle, of many which may enter the cell, is assumed to initiate the multiplication process (Kleczkowski, 1950; Kleczkowski & Kleczkowski, 1951). But by analogy with animal and bacterial viruses, the hypothesis that infections are each initiated by one virus particle would seem the more reasonable one. Another reason for the inefficiency of inoculation is that little of the virus inoculated on to leaves enters the wounded cells. Indeed, 95 % of the inoculum can be washed off leaves after inoculation with little effect on lesion number, and this proportion is not altered by mixing an abrasive with the inoculum, although use of the abrasive greatly increases the number of lesions caused. It follows that much of the virus retained by washed leaves when an abrasive is not used plays no obvious part in infection. Thus, although more than one virus particle may be needed to cause a lesion, and many of the virus particles in the most infective preparations may be non-infectious, these possibilities have not been proved, and the inefficiency of inoculation may be due solely to the limited number of suitably wounded cells made available and the failure to put much of the inoculum into them.

THE SEQUENCE OF EVENTS IN INOCULATED CELLS

By analogy with the multiplication of bacteriophages, the nucleic acid of plant viruses can reasonably be expected to separate from the virus protein at infection, and to initiate synthesis of new virus-nucleic acid and protein, which subsequently combine to form new infectious particles. The evidence for these stages with plant viruses, however, is far from complete, and much of it is indirect and open to other interpretations.

Assays of the virus content of sap, extracted at intervals from leaves which have been inoculated and washed, show that infectivity decreases for several hours before it begins to increase. It is, however, uncertain whether the decrease in infectivity has any relevance to virus multiplication, for the proportion of the inoculum in these leaves which actually multiplies is probably so small that any changes it undergoes will be undetectable or masked by changes in the virus that is not actively infecting. Alternatively, many of the virus particles in such leaves may go through the first of the processes which must occur to initiate virus multiplication, but not through subsequent ones, so that most of the potential infections abort: if this is true, then the early fall in infectivity of the leaf extracts represents a stage in infection. The fact that the initial decrease in infectivity also occurs with species of plants in which no virus multiplication can be detected, does not help to distinguish between the two possibilities, because the mechanism of the immunity of such plants to infection is unknown. Thus, although the virus particles which initiate multiplication may very possibly enter a state in which they are not infectious or in which their infectivity is unstable, experiments of this kind cannot be taken to provide critical evidence in favour of such possibilities.

The initial decrease in infectivity of leaf extracts after inoculation seems to continue until virus starts to accumulate in secondarily infected cells, suggesting that the amount of virus formed in primarily infected cells is too small to detect in the presence of residual inoculum. Supporting evidence for this suggestion comes from experiments in which leaves were exposed to ultraviolet radiation at intervals after inoculation. The time at which infections became very resistant to inactivation by ultraviolet (u.v.) radiation was about half that needed for detection of an increase in infectivity of extracts from leaves rubbed with concentrated inocula and kept in conditions optimal for virus accumulation. This degree of resistance to u.v. inactivation probably means that the virus is no longer confined to the epidermal cells infected at inoculation, presumably because it has multiplied and spread to the mesophyll. Infectivity measurements therefore seem to give little information about the sequence of events in inoculated cells, although they are useful for studying subsequent multiplication and will be referred to later (Harrison, 1956a).

The changes in the ability of certain treatments to affect lesion number when applied at different intervals after inoculation presumably reflect events in inoculated cells, for few treatments can arrest lesion development after the virus has multiplied in the inoculated cells and spread to others. The most detailed evidence for different stages in the multiplication process in inoculated cells has been obtained by adapting the u.v.-irradiation technique of Luria and Latarjet (1947) to plant-virus systems. However, a word of caution should be said about interpreting these results. The method assumes that all cells infected at inoculation are epidermal, and that doses of u.v. radiation (2537 Å) which have no significant effect on the host will completely inactivate virus in the epidermis without affecting virus in deeper tissues; none of these assumptions is quite true, but the errors involved do not seem great enough to invalidate the main conclusions. Leaves are given a range of doses of u.v. radiation at intervals after inoculation and curves plotted showing the proportion of potential lesions which survive irradiation. From these curves, four phases can be distinguished both with tobacco necrosis virus in French bean and with TMV in *Nicotiana glutinosa*, but the phases occupy different periods with the two viruses (Bawden & Harrison, 1955; Siegel & Wildman, 1956; Table 1).

Table 1. *Duration of initial phases of virus infection in inoculated leaves, estimated by the u.v.-irradiation method*

	Inoculum and host plant		
	Tobacco necrosis virus and French bean at 25°*	Tobacco mosaic virus (U2 strain) and *Nicotiana glutinosa* at 20°†	Nucleic acid from tobacco mosaic virus (U2 strain) and *Nicotiana glutinosa* at 20°‡
Phase 1	0–1 hr.	0–2 hr.	Absent
Phase 2	1–2 hr.	2–3·5 hr.	
Phase 3	2–3 hr.	3·5–5 hr.	0–3 hr.
Phase 4	3 hr. onwards	5 hr. onwards	3 hr. onwards
Phase 5	4 hr. onwards	Not determined	Not determined

* Bawden & Harrison (1955).   † Siegel & Wildman (1956).
‡ Siegel, Ginoza & Wildman (1957).

Phase 1

During the first phase, the reaction to irradiation does not change and the inactivation line is exponential. Siegel, Ginoza & Wildman (1957) found that this first phase is abolished when nucleic acid from TMV is inoculated instead of whole TMV, and therefore suggested that it is the time needed for the *in vivo* separation of protein from nucleic acid. If this is so, formation of new virus might be expected to be detected sooner after inoculation with nucleic acid than with whole virus, as Schramm & Engler (1958) have claimed with TMV in tobacco. There are great differences in the length of phase 1 with different viruses. Thus, in *Nicotiana glutinosa* leaves kept at 25° it lasts about 2 hr. with the U2 strain of TMV, at least 6 hr. with tomato bushy stunt virus, and about 12 hr. with tomato spotted wilt virus (Harrison, unpublished). There are also differences between different strains of TMV; phase 1 is twice as long with the U1 strain as with the U2 strain (Siegel & Wildman, 1956). These two strains also have different sensitivities to u.v. inactivation *in vitro* when intact, but their separated nucleic acids are equally sensitive; this suggests that the protein-nucleic acid linkage in the two strains differs (Siegel, Wildman & Ginoza, 1956), and that one kind of linkage may be broken in host cells more readily than the other, which could explain the difference in length of the first phase with the two strains.

The presence of the protein part of the virus at infection probably has several different effects. First, it probably protects the virus-nucleic acid from inactivation within the cell, for, *in vitro*, the infectivity of TMV-nucleic acid is very much less stable than that of whole TMV, and the infectivity of the best fresh nucleic acid preparations is only about 1% of that of whole virus containing the same amount of nucleic acid (Gierer & Schramm, 1956). Indeed, when the nucleic acid in such preparations is recombined with virus protein to make virus-like particles, and in such a way that infectivity can no longer be destroyed by ribonuclease, infectivity is stabilized and may increase as much as 25-fold (Fraenkel-Conrat & Singer, 1957; Fraenkel-Conrat, 1957), suggesting that such stabilization aids the establishment of infection. The low infectivity of the nucleic acid preparations therefore seems due, not to inactivation of nucleic acid during the preparative procedures, but to the small chance that an infectious unit of nucleic acid has of initiating an infection. The virus protein may also, perhaps, aid attachment of the virus particles to potential sites of virus multiplication, and this could be another reason for the greater number of lesions caused by native or recombined TMV nucleoprotein as compared with TMV-nucleic acid. Hence, the ability of virus protein and of u.v.-inactivated whole virus to prevent infection by untreated whole virus could be the result of competition for attachment sites in the cell (Bawden & Kleczkowski, 1953; Bawden & Pirie, 1957a). The ability of u.v.-inactivated virus preparations to inhibit infection seems virus specific for tobacco mosaic and tobacco necrosis viruses, suggesting that different viruses perhaps have different attachment sites in the cell. When combined with TMV-nucleic acid, however, the protein from some strains of TMV seems to aid infection more than that from others, for although the infectivity per unit weight of native virus of Holmes's ribgrass strain for *Nicotiana glutinosa* is only about a twentieth of that of a green mosaic strain, the infectivity per unit weight of their nucleic acids is similar. Moreover, when nucleic acid from the ribgrass strain is recombined with protein from the green mosaic strain, a product is obtained which has a greater infectivity per unit weight than native ribgrass virus (Fraenkel-Conrat & Singer, 1957). Whether the protein from the green mosaic strain aids infection more because it protects the nucleic acid better from inactivation within the cell, because it assists virus attachment to multiplication sites more efficiently, or because it is more readily split from the nucleic acid at an early stage of infection, is unknown. Indeed, there is no reason to suppose that maximum infectivity is achieved when TMV-nucleic acid is combined with protein of the type found in the green mosaic strain. Judged in terms of the number of virus particles inoculated per lesion caused, infection with the green mosaic strain is still very inefficient.

Although the sensitivity of potential lesions to u.v. inactivation does not change appreciably during the first phase of infection, other kinds of evidence indicate that changes occur in virus-inoculated leaves at this time. Within the first hour after inoculating tobacco leaves with TMV, their respiration rate increases and their rate of photosynthesis decreases. The change in rate of photosynthesis suggests that the metabolism of cells that do not contain virus is disturbed, because although there is indirect evidence that at this time virus is restricted to the epidermis, epidermal cells contain no chlorophyll. Such rapid effects of infection on rates of photosynthesis and respiration have been noted only with TMV in tobacco; tobacco etch and potato X viruses had no effects for some days, until they had multiplied and symptoms had appeared (Owen, 1955, 1957a, 1957b, 1958). During the first hour after inoculation, repair of the wounded cells seems to begin; immediately after rubbing, many infections can be caused by spraying the leaves with virus suspensions, but spraying an hour later causes few, suggesting that by then many of the holes through which virus particles enter cells have sealed up. Similarly, many infections can be prevented by dipping leaves in ribonuclease solutions during the first hour after inoculation, but not later, perhaps because the enzyme cannot penetrate the cells when the damage is repaired (Bawden & Harrison, 1955). However, the end of the ribonuclease-sensitive phase may mark a change in state of the infecting particle, because a similar phase was also observed when the enzyme was introduced into leaves by infiltration (Hamers-Casterman & Jeener, 1957); in these experiments, however, it is not clear whether inhibition was caused by infiltrated enzyme or by enzyme that entered leaves through wounds in the epidermis during the infiltration process.

Several, but not all, plant viruses show the phenomenon of photo-reactivation; that is, when virus preparations are irradiated with u.v. light so that less than 1 % of their original infectivity remains, the residual infectivity is greater when the test plants are kept in daylight after inoculation than when they are kept in darkness. The particles of potato virus X which multiply only in the presence of daylight are not in a light-sensitive state *in vitro*, nor immediately after inoculation, although most of them enter it within the next 30 min. (Bawden & Kleczkowski, 1955). The initial light-insensitive phase may perhaps correspond with the first phase of infection with unirradiated virus determined using the u.v.-irradiation method of Bawden & Harrison (1955).

Phase 2

During the second phase after inoculation, it becomes increasingly diffi-cult to prevent the appearance of lesions by exposing leaves to u.v. light. But because the inactivation line remains exponential, it seems probable that the number of infecting particles in each infected cell remains un-changed. The possibility that the first phase ends when the virus-nucleic acid separates from virus protein has already been mentioned. If this does occur, sensitivity to u.v. inactivation would be expected to increase, because in *in vitro* tests, nucleic acid from TMV is more easily inactivated than native TMV: however, sensitivity to u.v. inactivation in fact decreases during the second phase. The paradox can be readily explained if the separation of the nucleic acid immediately leads either to its associ-ation with a host component that absorbs ultraviolet, or to the synthesis of u.v.-absorbing substances. Observations made by Zech & Vogt-Köhne (1955) perhaps support the second possibility, because these indicated that u.v.-absorbing substances accumulated in cells of tobacco leaves soon after inoculation with TMV. By analogy with phages, such u.v.-absorbing substances may be precursors of virus, possibly purines and pyrimidines. Alternatively, association of virus nucleic acid with a host component could explain the end of the period of sensitivity to ribonuclease.

It seems possible that phase 2 may correspond in time to the light-sensitive phase which those particles of potato virus X which are potentially photoreactivable enter 30 min. after inoculation. Reactiva-tion most likely consists of the repair of damaged virus particles by a light-requiring process, and if repair does not occur, infection proceeds no further. If damaged infecting particles are not reactivable by light until their protein and nucleic acid have separated, the fact that they lose their ability to be reactivated within 2 hr. of acquiring it would not be surprising, for naked nucleic acid would probably soon be in-activated.

Lesion formation is also prevented by immersing leaves in water at 50° for 30 sec. soon after inoculation, but the efficacy of this treatment decreases within 2 hr. of inoculating bean leaves with TMV (Yarwood, 1958). How the heat treatment works is unknown; perhaps the infect-ing particle passes through a state in which it is readily inactivated by high temperature, or by inactivating systems that are stimulated at 50°. Alternatively, the host cell may be destroyed as a potential virus producer when placed at high temperatures soon after wounding.

Phase 3

Whether the third phase occurs as a distinct stage in the course of infection is doubtful, but both with TMV in *Nicotiana glutinosa* and with tobacco necrosis virus in French bean there seems to be a time at the end of phase 2 when the u.v. sensitivity stays constant, for about an hour at an environmental temperature of 20–25°.

Phases 4 and 5

At the beginning of phase 4, u.v. sensitivity decreases and the course of the u.v. inactivation line changes from being exponential to a hump-backed, or 'multiple-hit', curve, suggesting that new infectious particles have formed. Soon after the beginning of the fourth phase, phase 5 starts, in which even large doses of u.v. radiation do not prevent lesions forming, presumably because new infectious particles have spread from epidermal to mesophyll cells. The infectivity of leaf extracts, however, does not increase until about twice the time needed for the fourth phase to end, perhaps, as already mentioned, because until then there is too little new virus to detect in the presence of residual inoculum, or perhaps because the first virus to spread from cell to cell is not extracted in sap or is in a form which is unstable *in vitro* and thus is not detected by infectivity tests on extracts from leaves.

SUBSEQUENT VIRUS MULTIPLICATION IN INOCULATED LEAVES

Although the form in which infection spreads from cell to cell is unknown, estimates have been made of the rate of spread of virus infection through tissue, presumably as the result of multiplication in a series of cells. For instance, Rappaport & Wildman (1957) estimated that the edge of a TMV lesion in a *Nicotiana glutinosa* leaf advanced 8μ/hr. Infection is generally supposed to spread from cell to cell by way of the plasmodesmata, although there is little direct evidence for this view. Indeed, the uncertainty has recently been emphasized by the finding that TMV multiplies and moves through tobacco callus tissue at about 5μ/hr. although no plasmodesmata were found in such tissue (Kassanis *et al.* 1958). Little is known of the effects of variations in environmental conditions on the movement of infectious particles from cell to cell, as distinct from multiplication and movement, nor of the way environmental factors affect the delay between synthesis of new infectious particles and their movement into other cells. That the delay can be quite short is suggested by the observation that, at 25°, the fourth phase of infection with tobacco necrosis virus in French bean, described above, is succeeded by the fifth within an hour or two. The time needed for this virus to multiply and move out of the epidermis into the mesophyll decreases with increase of temperature, but most of the decrease probably reflects the effect of temperature on the time needed for virus to be synthesized. Thus, although the period required for virus to move out of the epidermis decreases above the optimum temperature for virus accumulation, at such temperatures the rate of virus accumulation is less than the rate of virus synthesis (Harrison, 1956 b). The time required for virus to multiply and move from the inoculated epidermis into the mesophyll has also been studied by removing the epidermis from leaves at intervals after inoculation (Welkie & Pound, 1958 a). The effect of temperature on the movement of cucumber mosaic virus from the epidermis of cowpea leaves is remarkably similar to that indicated by the u.v.-irradiation method for tobacco necrosis virus in French bean (Table 2).

Table 2. *Effect of temperature on the time required for virus to spread from epidermal to mesophyll cells in inoculated leaves*

Virus and host plant	Optimum temperature for virus accumulation	Hours required for virus to spread to the mesophyll at half the infection sites				Method of estimation
		16°	20°	24°	28°	
Tobacco necrosis virus and French bean	22°	12·2	8·2	6·0	5·0	U.v. irradiation (Harrison, 1956 b)
Cucumber mosaic virus and cowpea	—	13·6	7·5	5·8	4·2	Removing the epidermis (Welkie & Pound, 1958 a)

Various assay methods have been used to follow the accumulation of viruses in inoculated leaves, including infectivity, serological and particle-counting methods. These methods have usually given similar results with TMV in tobacco and show that, after the initial phase, in which progressively decreasing amounts of virus are recovered, the curve of virus concentration with time at first rises steeply and then flattens out. Similar results have been obtained with several other viruses, but with a few, lucerne mosaic for example, virus concentration falls rapidly after reaching a maximum (Ross, 1941), perhaps because virus is inactivated *in vivo.* The early part of curves obtained by plotting virus concentration against time might be expected to show 'steps' corresponding to the virus produced at each new set of sites. However, the first new virus to be detected in infectivity tests, the most sensitive of the assay methods, is probably produced in secondarily infected cells, which may not have become infected synchronously, and whose virus content usually continues to increase for a period several times longer than that needed for the first particles to be formed. These factors militate against finding 'steps' in curves showing the increase of virus concentration with time. With hosts which react to infection by forming localized necrotic lesions, the position is different. Thus, Harrison (1956a) suggested that TMV lesions in *N. glutinosa* leaves were mainly formed by the death of secondarily infected cells, and that, because infection remained localized, the curve of virus concentration with time represented the virus formed in these cells, which, moreover, died a few hours after virus started to accumulate in them. Rappaport & Wildman (1957), however, found that TMV continued to accumulate in inoculated *N. glutinosa* leaves for several days, but in their experiments the size of the lesions also increased over this period.

The extent to which different viruses multiply in inoculated leaves varies enormously: the concentration of TMV may exceed 2000 mg./l. in tobacco sap whereas that of some other viruses probably never reaches more than 2 mg./l. Indeed, over half the total protein in tobacco leaves may be in the form of TMV. In such plants the cells contain about 100 particles/μ^3, so that each mesophyll cell contains 10^5–10^6 and each large hair cell in the epidermis up to 10^8 particles (Nixon, 1956). With any one virus and host species, virus concentration is liable to be greatly affected by environmental conditions. The nutrition of the host plants, and the light intensity and photoperiod to which they are exposed all have an influence, but that of temperature is much the greatest. For instance, 3 days after inoculating French bean leaves with tobacco necrosis virus, the virus concentration in leaves kept at 22° was 5000 times greater than that at 10° and 1000 times greater than that at 30°. Such variations in environmental conditions also affect the symptoms caused by viruses, and, moreover, with any one host and virus, the most severe symptoms are often associated with the highest virus content of infected cells (Harrison, 1956b).

Effects of virus infection on host metabolism may be seen in many different ways. In tobacco leaves inoculated with TMV the respiration rate increases and the rate of photosynthesis decreases, both by a constant amount and within an hour after inoculation, showing that the size of these effects is independent of the number of cells in which the virus is multiplying. However, as already mentioned, this behaviour may not be at all general, for with tobacco etch virus, rates of respiration and photosynthesis are not affected until symptoms appear in the tobacco leaves several days after inoculation. Thus, the early stages of multiplication of tobacco etch virus seem to make smaller demands on the host than do those of TMV. The effects on the nitrogen metabolism of tobacco caused by infection with TMV have been studied using disks cut from recently infected leaves, floated on water or nutrient solution, kept at 23° and continuously illuminated. Infected disks contained less non-protein nitrogen than healthy disks, and the deficit was greatest in tissue synthesizing virus most rapidly. Most of the deficit was in the ammonia fraction, and the total amide and amino-acid contents were not greatly affected, suggesting that much of the virus nitrogen came from the ammonia fraction (Commoner & Dietz, 1952). Indeed, when disks were floated on ammonium-rich nutrient, most of the virus nitrogen came from the nutrient (Commoner, Schieber & Dietz, 1953).

Virus infection usually seems to result in the synthesis of a range of anomalous proteins, although the possibility that some of those found in extracts of virus-infected leaves are produced from other proteins during the preparative procedures should not be forgotten. Preparations of TMV and potato virus X contain particles of different lengths, and those of the Rothamsted tobacco necrosis virus and of turnip yellow mosaic virus each contain spheres of two sorts (Bawden & Pirie, 1945; Kleczkowski & Nixon, 1950; Bawden & Nixon, 1951; Markham & Smith, 1949). When TMV preparations are made by ultracentrifugation, a relatively gentle method, the commonest particle length is about 300 mμ, although longer particles and others no longer than their width of 15 mμ are also present. The small particles, which are incompletely sedimented by ultracentrifugation, precipitate with virus antiserum, and they readily aggregate to form long rods. They have little or no infectivity and contain little or no phosphorus. Although there is also some evidence to the contrary, some workers have found fewer of the long particles in preparations from leaves infected for several weeks than in those from leaves infected recently, and also that the nucleic acid content of preparations from long-infected leaves is lower (Takahashi & Rawlins, 1948; Zech & Vogt-Köhne, 1956). This suggests that some, at least, of the shorter particles may be formed by breakage of longer ones.

Three other non-infectious proteins, which contain little or no phosphorus and precipitate with TMV antiserum, have been isolated from infected tobacco leaves. They are not sedimented after an hour of ultracentrifugation at 100,000 g and pH 7, but they all aggregate at pH 5 to form virus-like rods, irreversibly in the case of one of the proteins (Takahashi & Ishii, 1952; Commoner, Yamada *et al.* 1953). These proteins only occur in small amounts in infected plants and they do not appear until about 200 hr. after inoculation, well after the first infectious virus. Commoner, Yamada *et al.* (1953) also found that an insoluble nucleo-protein accumulated in leaves about 100 hr. after infection, and that it subsequently decreased again in amount until it reached the level in uninfected leaves: at this time the three proteins described above began to appear. Commoner, Yamada *et al.* therefore suggested that virus-nucleic acid synthesis may not keep step with virus-protein synthesis, so that in the later stages of infection, virus protein accumulates in addition to virus nucleoprotein. However, it seems equally possible that these three proteins may be produced in small amounts in all infected cells, and that their appearance at 200 hr. after inoculation simply means that not until then are enough cells infected for the protein concentrations to reach a detectable level. Indeed, Van Rysselberge & Jeener (1957) found that when tobacco leaves inoculated 3–4 days previously were exposed to radio-active carbon dioxide for 2 hr. and extracts made from them, the protein which was not sedimented by ultracentrifugation but was precipitated by virus antiserum had a much higher specific radioactivity than the sero-logically active material which was sedimented. They therefore suggested that the unsedimented protein is the precursor of virus nucleoprotein.

A similar situation exists with turnip yellow mosaic virus, prepara-tions of which contain two kinds of spherical particles with the same external dimensions but different sedimentation rates. One kind is an infectious nucleoprotein with its nucleic acid carried centrally and the other is a non-infectious, hollow, protein shell. Although the ratio of the number of particles of one kind to that of the other is similar in virus preparations made at different times after infection (Matthews, 1958), Jeener (1954) found that exposing infected leaves for a few hours to radioactive carbon dioxide resulted in a greater specific radioactivity of the protein than of the nucleoprotein. This observation is again com-patible with the view that the protein particles are the precursors of the nucleoprotein ones. This kind of interpretation, however, assumes that the proteins are at least as stable *in vivo* as the nucleoproteins, which seems questionable. Indeed, the nucleic acid-free 'A-protein' obtained from TMV (Schramm, Schumacher & Zillig, 1955), which resembles the 'X-protein' found in infected leaves, is hydrolysed by proteolytic enzymes which have no effect on TMV nucleoprotein (Kleczkowski, unpublished). At present, therefore, no decision can be reached on whether the virus proteins found in leaves are precursors or breakdown products of virus nucleoprotein, whether they are auxiliary products of virus-infected cells, or whether they are formed in more than one of these ways. These possibilities have been fully discussed by Bawden & Pirie (1953).

That some viruses can be broken down in infected cells has long been obvious from the fact that plants could be freed from such viruses by prolonged exposure to 35–40° (Kunkel, 1936). Some of these viruses have high thermal inactivation points *in vitro* and seem to be inactivated more rapidly *in vivo* than in sap, suggesting that the host may play an important part in the inactivation (Kassanis, 1952; Harrison, 1956*b*). Synthesis and breakdown of tobacco necrosis virus both occur in French bean leaves at 30° and probably at lower temperatures also. The rate of accumulation of virus in the leaves therefore depends on the balance between synthesis and inactivation, and this in turn depends on the temperature and on the virus content of the leaf (Harrison, 1956*b*). Little is known about the mechanism of virus inactivation *in vivo*, but it may be caused by the system isolated in the mitochondrial fraction of tobacco leaves infected with tobacco necrosis or tobacco ring spot viruses (Bawden & Pirie, 1957*b*). This system requires air, is inhibited by the presence of azide and appears to produce an unknown substance of low molecular weight, which, once produced, inactivates virus whether or not air or azide is present. Tobacco necrosis and tobacco ring spot viruses, which are both inactivated in plants at 35° and are therefore unstable *in vivo*, are both inactivated by this system, but TMV is not; nor does infection with TMV stimulate the system. Thus, two viruses which are relatively unstable *in vivo* stimulate a virus-inactivating system in their host plant, whereas a more stable virus does not.

It seems unlikely that the low rate at which some viruses accumulate at 35° stems from a high rate of inactivation at that temperature. Many strains of TMV accumulate little at such temperatures, although, once formed, these viruses are resistant to inactivation in leaves kept at 35°. Spread of infection from cell to cell in leaves of *Nicotiana* spp. is, however, not stopped at 35°, and large chlorotic lesions may develop in inoculated leaves, although little TMV can be extracted from them. When leaves with these lesions are placed at lower temperatures, the lesions become necrotic and large quantities of virus can be extracted after a day, and even after 2 hr. at 28° the infectivity of leaf extracts can have increased 20-fold or more (Sukhov, 1956; Kassanis, 1957*b*). It is not known whether TMV precursors are formed at 35°, and, if they are formed, whether they accumulate or are broken down, but it seems

4

probable that different viruses fail to accumulate at 35° for different reasons.

The range of substances present in virus-infected leaves and the possibility that some of them may be virus precursors have been indicated, but there is no direct evidence on how such precursors may become incorporated into virus nucleoprotein in the leaf. Observations on mixtures of similar substances *in vitro*, however, suggest some possible stages. All these observations were made using A-protein and nucleic acid, both made by disrupting TMV particles. Substances resembling these appear to occur *in vivo*, for A-protein is similar to, though perhaps not identical with, X-protein, and Cochran & Chidester (1957) claim to have isolated TMV-nucleic acid from infected plants. Preparations of A-protein contain no typical virus rods, and TMV-nucleic acid preparations contain only very fine threads: both A-protein and TMV-nucleic acid are electrophoretically distinct from TMV nucleoprotein. At pH 5 the A-protein aggregates spontaneously to form virus-like rods, but these rods break up again at pH 7. In the presence of TMV-nucleic acid, however, virus-like nucleoprotein rods are formed which are stable at pH 7. Their nucleic acid cannot be removed nor their infectivity destroyed by ribonuclease and they are electrophoretically similar to native TMV (Fraenkel-Conrat & Singer, 1957; Kleczkowski, in the Press). Formation of such infectious nucleoprotein particles is favoured by increase of temperature from 5° to 20°. Thus, were free virus-nucleic acid and A-protein to come together in infected cells, they would probably aggregate quickly, apparently without requiring the assistance of enzymes, and the nucleoprotein formed would be more stable than either of its constituents. Here then is a possible model for a final stage in the formation of TMV nucleoprotein.

The sites of virus multiplication in plant cells are unknown. Nixon & Sampson (1956) found that some chloroplasts in electron micrographs of thin sections of TMV-infected leaves were degenerate and associated with virus inclusion-bodies. But even if chloroplasts are sites of virus synthesis, they cannot be the only ones, for viruses multiply in many types of cells which contain plastids but not chloroplasts. Recent work, moreover, suggests that synthesis of normal plant proteins is associated with the microsomes, which could be sites of virus synthesis. Perhaps some speculations may not be out of place. A first stage might be for an infecting virus particle to become associated with a cell organelle (nucleus, plastid, mitochondrion or microsome), where the virus-nucleic acid would separate from its protein coat and pass into the organelle. The virus-nucleic acid would be potentially able to act as a pattern for the synthesis of more virus-nucleic acid and virus protein; within the organelle, however, only virus-nucleic acid synthesis would occur and here the nucleic acid would be protected from inactivation. In time, virus-nucleic acid from the pool formed in this way would begin to escape from the organelle: outside, it would act only as a pattern for virus protein, which would coat it to form virus nucleoprotein particles. The protein might be built up on the surface of the nucleic acid from simple molecules, and the large fragments of anomalous protein, such as X-protein, found in extracts of infected leaves, might be pieces that became detached from combination with the nucleic acid when in the process of coating it. The dependence of virus multiplication on such organelles could explain the absence of virus in meristematic cells, in which they are not fully developed, and there seems nothing inherently unlikely in the possibility that the nucleic acid and protein parts of virus are formed in different parts of the cell.

VIRUS SYNTHESIS IN SYSTEMICALLY INFECTED LEAVES

Although the quantity of virus produced in systemically infected leaves far exceeds in total that produced in inoculated leaves, systemically infected leaves are much poorer experimental subjects, and their study has provided much less information of relevance to the processes of virus multiplication.

Viruses seem to begin moving out of inoculated leaves and invading other parts of plants soon after they have multiplied in secondarily infected cells, presumably because virus particles then escape into phloem vessels, through which they are relatively rapidly transported to the root and shoot tips. There is, however, no evidence that viruses multiply in the phloem vessels. Plants which have only one lesion in their inoculated leaves often become infected systemically, but when several hundred lesions are present, systemic infection seems to originate from virus produced in only a few of them (Cohen *et al.* 1957). The most plausible explanation is that the first virus particles to invade young shoots multiply and soon greatly outnumber the particles that arrive subsequently from inoculated leaves by way of the phloem; the chance that a virus particle arriving in the phloem will multiply to any considerable extent then becomes negligible. Although the young regions of roots and shoots are the first parts of the plant to be invaded systemically, the virus concentration in the meristematic parts always remains much below that reached in mature leaf tissues. Indeed, the extreme tips of shoots often seem free from virus, and virus-free plants can be obtained from infected ones by excising and culturing such meristems (Kassanis, 1957 a). It is not clear whether virus fails to invade these meristematic tissues, perhaps because newly formed cell walls are impermeable to it, or whether it invades but does not multiply.

The concentration of many viruses, after reaching a maximum in the first leaves to be infected systemically, is lower in those formed later. The virus concentration may fall in this way to a tenth or less of the maximum value, and the decrease is often reflected by a decrease in the severity of leaf symptoms. With viruses which cause symptoms of the ring-spot type in leaves present at the time of inoculation, leaves produced subsequently are often almost symptomless, although they contain virus and appear immune to reinfection by inoculation with the same or a closely related virus strain. This change in symptoms seems to coincide with the maturation of the first cells formed after establishment of virus in or near the growing point. Even when the change in symptoms is less dramatic, as with many other viruses, there is often an appreciable decrease in virus concentration. The cause of these changes is unknown.

Environmental factors affect greatly not only the concentration of virus in systemically infected leaves, and the size and rapidity of its fluctuations in successively formed leaves, but also symptoms. Many of the changes in nutrition, temperature or light that favour plant growth also favour the development of severe symptoms and a high virus concentration. These correlations, however, do not always hold. For instance, increasing the manganese content of nutrient mixtures supplied to plants can increase growth but decrease the concentration reached by TMV: also, in cabbage the optimum temperatures for accumulation of viruses A and B are very different (Pound & Walker, 1945; Welkie & Pound, 1958 b). The optimum temperature for virus accumulation, however, does not depend solely on the identity of the virus, for the concentration of cabbage virus A is differently affected by temperature in cabbage and horseradish (Pound & Walker, 1945; Pound, 1949). In general, for any one combination of host and virus, the severity of symptoms is correlated with the amount of virus per infected cell, but some viruses which seem to be present in only small amounts may cause very severe symptoms. Presumably, viruses cause disease symptoms by producing aberrations in the nucleoprotein metabolism of their hosts, and it would be naïve to assume that only one kind of aberration can occur. Also, it is worth pointing out that virus concentration is a measure of virus accumulation, and with viruses which are unstable *in vivo*, virus concentration may give a poor indication of the rate or amount of virus synthesis, which, in turn, may be more accurate measures of the extent to which the host's metabolic systems are diverted from their normal pathways. Thus, viruses which accumulate in only relatively small amounts in plants may actually be synthesized more rapidly than others which are more stable *in vivo* and accumulate in larger amounts.

The presence of one virus in a plant often decreases the concentration reached by a second unrelated virus, as might be expected were the two competing for metabolites or potential multiplication sites. When potato virus X multiplies in the presence of potato virus Y, however, it appears to reach a greater concentration than when it multiplies alone (Rochow & Ross, 1955). At the other extreme, it is common for plants already infected with one virus not to develop additional symptoms when inoculated with a closely related strain. Indeed, the plant-protection test, which is based on this phenomenon, is probably the most widely used method of grouping unknown virus isolates, and with only few exceptions the relationships indicated by such tests agree well with those determined serologically, i.e. by the most reliable method. The suggestion that the specificity of the plant-protection phenomenon can be explained by competition for metabolites or multiplication sites is unconvincing, for all the plant viruses which have been analysed chemically have very similar constituents, and the idea that a plant, such as tobacco, that is susceptible to more than fifty viruses which do not protect plants from one another, could have different multiplication sites for each, has little appeal. Also, although infection with TMV results in the accumulation of large quantities of anomalous nucleoprotein, it does not make plants immune to other viruses. Best (1954) has suggested that when plants already infected with one strain of a virus are inoculated with another strain, particles of the second strain enter cells and go through an initial stage of multiplication, perhaps the separation of virus-nucleic acid from virus protein, and that this nucleic acid 'crosses' with the much larger quantity of nucleic acid of the first strain which is already present in the cells. This process would be analogous to the 'recombination' which occurs during the 'vegetative' phase of phage multiplication. Virus of the second strain would therefore be so rapidly diluted genetically with the first strain that it would not be detectable in assays. A corollary of Best's ideas would be that as closely related virus strains evolved into forms whose nucleic acids recombined with each other less readily, there would be less protection between the viruses in plants, until, when there was no recombination, there would also be no plant protection.

PRODUCTION OF VARIANTS

As with the multiplication of other biological entities, the multiplication of plant viruses occasionally results in the production of variants which are imperfect copies of the original, infecting particles. Study of the way such variants arise may help in understanding virus multiplication. The variants can differ from their parents in each of many different properties, but most are recognized because they cause distinctive symptoms: indeed, the best known of all variants is the one that can be isolated from the yellow spots that often occur in tobacco leaves infected with the green mosaic strain of TMV. Usually the proportion of variants that can be recognized is less than 1 % of the total virus population; it is not known how precisely the structure of the non-variant particles resembles that of their parents. An interesting example of a virus that seems much less genetically stable than most is a strain of tobacco rattle virus (Cadman & Harrison, unpublished). This strain multiplies well when transferred from tobacco to tobacco by bulk inocula: when single-lesion isolates are made, however, at least half will scarcely maintain themselves in successive subcultures in tobacco, whereas most of the others multiply readily. Also, few of the single-lesion isolates, which multiply readily cause symptoms identical with those caused by the parent culture, and when a further series of single-lesion isolates is made from them, a similar range of variants, good multipliers and poor multipliers, is again obtained. Infection with this virus therefore gives rise to the production of obvious variant types more frequently than to that of the original type, and, as many of these variants can scarcely maintain themselves on subculture in tobacco, it seems unlikely that they appear because they outgrow the parent type. Serological tests, too, have shown that this strain of tobacco rattle virus varies unusually rapidly when successive subcultures are made. This is a soil-borne virus and it may have a host to which it is well adapted among soil organisms, so that its great variability when propagated in tobacco may be due to a comparative inability to replicate exactly in the new host.

Changes in pathogenicity that occur when plant viruses are propagated in new hosts or in new environmental conditions are well known. For example, a tobacco necrosis virus, which causes small black lesions in French bean leaves when first isolated from plants grown in the field, may, after repeated subculturing, form larger lesions, and then variants appear which spread along the leaf veins and soon predominate in the culture. A frequently occurring variation was also observed when a tobacco necrosis virus recently obtained from tobacco roots was propagated in cowpea (Fulton, 1952). Red areas often developed at the periphery of the white lesions formed in cowpea leaves, a phenomenon resembling the appearance of mutant forms of fungi as sectors of colonies grown on agar plates. From the red areas, Fulton isolated variant forms which caused only red lesions in cowpea leaves, showing that such variants were more stable in cowpea than the type which caused white lesions. A change in ability to be transmitted by aphid vectors when propagated in different hosts has been recorded with potato virus *C* (Watson, 1956). When isolated from potato this virus was not transmitted by aphids, but after several years of subculturing in *Nicotiana glutinosa* it was. Moreover, most of the isolates returned by aphids from *N. glutinosa* to potato soon lost their aphid transmissibility. Indeed, loss of insect transmissibility has been recorded with other viruses subcultured for several years without the use of insect vectors and in general loss seems more common than gain. The features of virus particles that make one strain transmissible by a certain insect, and another not, are unknown. Variations of the kinds mentioned in this paragraph most probably occur because some of the variants produced by chance have a selective advantage in plants over their parent types and also differ from them in other easily recognized properties.

A far more rapid and dramatic change is shown by the cowpea strain of TMV on transference from tobacco to French bean and vice versa (Bawden, 1958). The two forms of the virus, purified from tobacco and French bean respectively, differ in chemical and antigenic constitution, in their ability to invade tobacco and French bean systemically, and in the symptoms they cause in other species. The bean form is highly infective for bean, as also is the tobacco form for tobacco, but when one form is inoculated to the other host, systemic infection results only when highly concentrated inocula are used, and, when it does occur, the virus present in such systemically infected leaves is not of the form used as inoculum. Two possible explanations of this phenomenon are, first, that this virus is always a mixture of the two forms and these are differentially favoured in the two hosts, or secondly, that one form mutates to the other, and back, with a low frequency, and that the different forms are differentially selected in the two hosts. All attempts to detect small amounts of one form in preparations of the other failed, and when each form was passed through a series of four single lesions, a method which resolves mixtures of other viruses, and the final single-lesion isolates cultured, they behaved in every way like their parent cultures. Also, when tobacco leaves are sampled at intervals after inoculation with the bean form, the latter increases for some days before the tobacco form appears.

The most probable explanation of this behaviour is that each form occasionally mutates to the other, but that virus preparations obtained from one host usually contain too few of the mutants for these to infect the other host directly. Only when virus from one host multiplies to a limited extent in the other host are enough mutants produced for one or more of these to outgrow their parent and appear as the new form. It is, however, an open question whether the production of the variants is directed by the new host or whether the new host merely applies a strong selection pressure to variants produced by chance.

It has long been known that propagation of the type strain of TMV at 35° results in the appearance of forms which multiply well at such temperatures, but rather less rapidly than the type strain at 25°, and which cause only very slight symptoms in tobacco. At 35°, such forms can be detected in leaves 20 hr. after inoculation with the type strain, suggesting that they are produced and multiply in the first few lots of cells to become infected. Here, too, there is no more reason to suppose that production of the new form is directed by the new conditions, high temperature, than that a variant, occurring by chance, has a strong selective advantage at 35° (Sukhov, 1956; Kassanis, 1957b).

There is as yet little evidence that plant viruses interact genetically during multiplication, but results obtained by Best & Gallus (1955) with tomato spotted-wilt virus are most simply explained by assuming that they do. Plants were inoculated with a mixture of two virus strains, each of which had remained stable for several years, and variants combining characters of each strain (recombinants) were subsequently isolated from the mixedly infected plants. What may be a similar phenomenon was observed by Benda (1957), who noted that although a yellow aucuba strain of TMV would rarely invade *Nicotiana sylvestris* plants systemically, it lead to the production of numerous white spots in systemically infected leaves when inoculated together with a green mosaic strain that readily becomes systemic in this plant. However, no tests were made to show whether the white spots contained the yellow aucuba strain or a recombinant type with only some of the yellow aucuba characters. If such white spots contain the ordinary yellow aucuba type of virus, the interesting possibility exists that they were infections initiated by particles composed of nucleic acid of the yellow aucuba type and protein of the green mosaic type, comparable with composite particles made artificially (Fraenkel-Conrat & Singer, 1957), and that the protein part of the virus particle determines the ability to invade plants systemically. Such particles would be analogous to the phenotypic variants produced by phages. However, a third, more orthodox, interpretation is that infection with the green mosaic strain alters the physiological state of the host in a way which favours the systemic movement of virus of the yellow aucuba type.

Mutation and selection are well known in plant viruses, but enough work has been done to suggest that variant forms may also arise in other ways. Thus, recombination and phenotypic variation may, perhaps, both occur in plant viruses, although they would probably not be suspected had they not been described with phages.

CONCLUSION

At the beginning of this article I suggested that plant viruses resemble some animal viruses more closely than bacteriophages. Despite their differences in structure, however, the modes of multiplication of plant viruses and bacteriophages seem to have many similarities. The fact that these similarities exist, suggests we can be confident that the multiplication of many of the plant viruses of which we know nothing resembles that of the few of which we do know something. This is no argument for continuing to study only a few plant viruses, for exceptional behaviour should prove at least as interesting as is the normal.

REFERENCES

BAWDEN, F. C. (1954). Inhibitors and plant viruses. *Advanc. Virus Res.* 2, 31.

BAWDEN, F. C. (1958). Reversible changes in strains of tobacco mosaic virus from leguminous plants. *J. gen. Microbiol.* 18, 751.

BAWDEN, F. C. (in the Press). The multiplication of viruses. In *Plant Pathology*. Edited by J. G. Horsfall and A. E. Dimond. New York: Academic Press.

BAWDEN, F. C. & HARRISON, B. D. (1955). Studies on the multiplication of a tobacco necrosis virus in inoculated leaves of French-bean plants. *J. gen. Microbiol,* 13, 494.

BAWDEN, F. C. & KLECZKOWSKI, A. (1953). The behaviour of some plant viruses after exposure to ultraviolet radiation. *J. gen. Microbiol.* 8, 145.

BAWDEN, F. C. & KLECZKOWSKI, A. (1955). Studies on the ability of light to counter-act the inactivating action of ultraviolet radiation on plant viruses. *J. gen. Microbiol.* 13, 370.

BAWDEN, F. C. & NIXON, H. L. (1951). The application of electron microscopy to the study of plant viruses in unpurified plant extracts. *J. gen. Microbiol.* 5, 104.

BAWDEN, F. C. & PIRIE, N. W. (1945). The separation and properties of tobacco mosaic virus in different states of aggregation. *Brit. J. exp. Path.* 26, 294.

BAWDEN, F. C. & PIRIE, N. W. (1953). Virus multiplication considered as a form of protein synthesis. *Symp. Soc. gen. Microbiol.* 2, 21.

BAWDEN, F. C. & PIRIE, N. W. (1957a). The activity of fragmented and reassembled tobacco mosaic virus. *J. gen. Microbiol.* 17, 80.

BAWDEN, F. C. & PIRIE, N. W. (1957b). A virus-inactivating system from tobacco leaves. *J. gen. Microbiol.* 16, 696.

BENDA, G. T. A. (1955). Some effects of ultra-violet radiation on leaves of French bean (*Phaseolus vulgaris* L.). *Ann. appl. Biol.* 43, 71.

BENDA, G. T. A. (1956). The effect of New Zealand spinach juice on the infection of cowpeas by tobacco ringspot virus. *Virology*, **2**, 438.

BENDA, G. T. A. (1957). White spots in *Nicotiana sylvestris* following mixed infection with TMV strains. *Virology*, **3**, 601.

BEST, R. J. (1954). Cross protection by strains of tomato spotted wilt virus and a new theory to explain it. *Aust. J. Biol. Sci.* **7**, 415.

BEST, R. J. & GALLUS, H. P. C. (1955). Further evidence for the transfer of character-determinants (recombination) between strains of tomato spotted wilt virus. *Enzymologia*, **17**, 207.

COCHRAN, G. W. & CHIDESTER, J. L. (1957). Infectious nucleic acid in plants with tobacco mosaic. *Virology*, **4**, 390.

COHEN, M., SIEGEL, A., ZAITLIN, M., HUDSON, W. R. & WILDMAN, S. G. (1957). A study of tobacco mosaic virus strain predominance and an hypothesis for the origin of systemic virus infection. *Phytopathology*, **47**, 694.

COMMONER, B. & DIETZ, P. M. (1952). Changes in non-protein nitrogen metabolism during tobacco mosaic virus biosynthesis. *J. gen. Physiol.* **35**, 847.

COMMONER, B., SCHIEBER, D. L. & DIETZ, P. M. (1953). Relationships between tobacco mosaic virus biosynthesis and the nitrogen metabolism of the host. *J. gen. Physiol.* **36**, 807.

COMMONER, B., YAMADA, M., RODENBERG, S. D., WANG, T-Y. & BASLER, E. (1953). The proteins synthesized in tissue infected with tobacco mosaic virus. *Science*, **118**, 529.

FRAENKEL-CONRAT, H. (1957). The infectivity of tobacco mosaic virus nucleic acid. In *Cellular Biology, Nucleic Acids, and Viruses*. New York: New York Academy of Sciences.

FRAENKEL-CONRAT, H. & SINGER, B. (1957). Virus reconstitution. II. Combination of protein and nucleic acid from different strains. *Biochim. biophys. Acta*, **24**, 540.

FULTON, R. W. (1952). Mutation in a tobacco necrosis virus strain. *Phytopathology*, **42**, 156.

GIERER, A. & SCHRAMM, G. (1956). Infectivity of ribonucleic acid from tobacco mosaic virus. *Nature, Lond.* **177**, 702.

HAMERS-CASTERMAN, C. & JEENER, R. (1957). An initial ribonuclease-sensitive phase in the multiplication of tobacco mosaic virus. *Virology*, **3**, 197.

HARRISON, B. D. (1956a). The infectivity of extracts made from leaves at intervals after inoculation with viruses. *J. gen. Microbiol.* **15**, 210.

HARRISON, B. D. (1956b). Studies on the effect of temperature on virus multiplication in inoculated leaves. *Ann. appl. Biol.* **44**, 215.

JEENER, R. (1954). A preliminary study of the incorporation in growing turnip yellow mosaic virus and its related non-infective antigen of labelled amino acids. *Biochim. biophys. Acta*, **13**, 307.

KASSANIS, B. (1952). Some effects of high temperature on the susceptibility of plants to infection with viruses. *Ann. appl. Biol.* **39**, 358.

KASSANIS, B. (1957a). The use of tissue cultures to produce virus-free clones from infected potato varieties. *Ann. appl. Biol.* **45**, 422.

KASSANIS, B. (1957b). Some effects of varying temperature on the quality and quantity of tobacco mosaic virus in infected plants. *Virology*, **4**, 187.

KASSANIS, B. & KLECZKOWSKI, A. (1948). The isolation and some properties of a virus-inhibiting protein from *Phytolacca esculenta*. *J. gen. Microbiol.* **2**, 143.

KASSANIS, B., TINSLEY, T. W. & QUAK, F. (1958). The inoculation of tobacco callus tissue with tobacco mosaic virus. *Ann. appl. Biol.* **46**, 11.

KLECZKOWSKI, A. (1950). Interpreting relationships between the concentrations of plant viruses and numbers of local lesions. *J. gen. Microbiol.* **4**, 53.

KLECZKOWSKI, A. (in the Press). Aggregation of the protein of tobacco mosaic virus with and without combination with the virus-nucleic acid. *Virology*.

KLECZKOWSKI, A. & KLECZKOWSKI, J. (1951). The ability of single phage particles to form plaques and to multiply in liquid cultures. *J. gen. Microbiol.* 5, 346.

KLECZKOWSKI, A. & NIXON, H. L. (1950). An electron-microscope study of potato virus *X* in different states of aggregation. *J. gen. Microbiol.* 4, 220.

KUNKEL, L. O. (1936). Heat treatments for the cure of yellows and other virus diseases of peach. *Phytopathology*, 26, 809.

LURIA, S. E. & LATARJET, R. (1947). Ultraviolet irradiation of bacteriophage during intracellular growth. *J. Bact.* 53, 149.

MARAMOROSCH, K. (1952). Direct evidence for the multiplication of aster-yellows virus in its insect vector. *Phytopathology*, 42, 59.

MARKHAM, R. & SMITH, K. M. (1949). Studies on the virus of turnip yellow mosaic. *Parasitology*, 39, 330.

MATTHEWS, R. E. F. (1958). Studies on the relation between protein and nucleoprotein particles in turnip yellow mosaic virus infections. *Virology*, 5, 192.

NIENHAUS, F. (1957). Untersuchungen über den Einfluss von Temperatur und Licht auf die Empfänglichkeit der Pflanzen für das Kartoffel-Y-virus. *Phytopath. Z.* 30, 189.

NIXON, H. L. (1956). An estimate of the number of tobacco mosaic virus particles in a single hair cell. *Virology*, 2, 126.

NIXON, H. L. & SAMPSON, J. (1956). A study of healthy and virus-infected plant cells by thin-section methods. *Proc. Third Internat. Conf. on Electron Microscopy*, *London*, 1954. Royal Microscopical Society, p. 251.

OWEN, P. C. (1955). The respiration of tobacco leaves in the 20-hour period following inoculation with tobacco mosaic virus. *Ann. appl. Biol.* 43, 114.

OWEN, P. C. (1957a). The effects of infection with tobacco mosaic virus on the photosynthesis of tobacco leaves. *Ann. appl. Biol.* 45, 456.

OWEN, P. C. (1957b). The effects of infection with tobacco etch virus on the rates of respiration and photosynthesis of tobacco leaves. *Ann. appl. Biol.* 45, 327.

OWEN, P. (1958). Photosynthesis and respiration rates of leaves of *Nicotiana glutinosa* infected with tobacco mosaic virus and of *N. tabacum* infected with potato virus *X*. *Ann. appl. Biol.* 46, 198.

POUND, G. S. (1949). The effect of air temperature on virus concentration and leaf morphology of mosaic-infected horseradish. *J. Agric. Res.* 78, 161.

POUND, G. S. & WALKER, J. C. (1945). Effect of air temperature on the concentration of certain viruses in cabbage. *J. Agric. Res.* 71, 471.

RAPPAPORT, I. & WILDMAN, S. G. (1957). A kinetic study of local lesion growth on *Nicotiana glutinosa* resulting from tobacco mosaic virus infection. *Virology*, 4, 265.

ROCHOW, W. F. & ROSS, A. F. (1955). Virus multiplication in plants doubly infected by potato viruses *X* and *Y*. *Virology*, 1, 10.

ROSS, A. F. (1941). The concentration of alfalfa-mosaic virus in tobacco plants at different periods of time after inoculation. *Phytopathology*, 31, 410.

SCHRAMM, G. & ENGLER, R. (1958). The latent period after infection with tobacco mosaic virus and virus nucleic acid. *Nature, Lond.* 181, 916.

SCHRAMM, G., SCHUMACHER, G. & ZILLIG, W. (1955). Über die Struktur des Tabakmosaikvirus. III. Mitt.: Der Zerfall in alkalischer Lösung. *Z. Naturf.* 10b, 481.

SHEFFIELD, F. M. L. (1936). The susceptibility of the plant cell to virus disease. *Ann. appl. Biol.* 23, 498.

SIEGEL, A., GINOZA, W. & WILDMAN, S. G. (1957). The early events of infection with tobacco mosaic virus nucleic acid. *Virology*, 3, 554.

SIEGEL, A. & WILDMAN, S. G. (1956). The inactivation of the infectious centers of tobacco mosaic virus by ultraviolet light. *Virology*, 2, 69.

SIEGEL, A., WILDMAN, S. G. & GINOZA, W. (1956). Sensitivity to ultra-violet light of infectious tobacco mosaic virus nucleic acid. *Nature, Lond.* **178**, 1117.

SUKHOV, K. S. (1956). The problem of hereditary variation of phytopathogenic viruses. *Reprint by Akad. Nauk S.S.S.R., Moscow*, pp. 29.

TAKAHASHI, W. N. & ISHII, M. (1952). An abnormal protein associated with tobacco mosaic virus infection. *Nature, Lond.* **169**, 419.

TAKAHASHI, W. N. & RAWLINS, T. E. (1948). An electron microscope study of tobacco mosaic virus extracted from pulp and juice after various periods of infection. *Phytopathology*, **38**, 279.

VAN RYSSELBERGE, C. & JEENER, R. (1957). Plant virus synthesis and the abnormal protein constituents of infected leaves. *Biochim. biophys. Acta*, **23**, 18.

WATSON, M. A. (1956). The effect of different host plants of potato virus *C* in determining its transmission by aphids. *Ann. appl. Biol.* **44**, 599.

WELKIE, G. W. & POUND, G. S. (1958 *a*). Temperature influence on the rate of passage of cucumber mosaic virus through the epidermis of cowpea leaves. *Virology*, **5**, 362.

WELKIE, G. W. & POUND, G. S. (1958 *b*). Manganese nutrition of *Nicotiana tabacum* L. in relation to multiplication of tobacco mosaic virus. *Virology*, **5**, 92.

YARWOOD, C. E. (1955). Deleterious effects of water in plant virus inoculations. *Virology*, **1**, 268.

YARWOOD, C. E. (1958). Heat activation of virus infections. *Phytopathology*, **48**, 39.

ZECH, H. & VOGT-KÖHNE, L. (1955). Ultraviolettmikrospektrographische Untersuchungen an Tabakmosaikvirus *in situ*. *Naturwissenschaften*, **11**, 337.

ZECH, H. & VOGT-KÖHNE, L. (1956). Untersuchungen zur Reproduktion des Tabakmosaikvirus. I. Elektronenmikroskopische Beobachtungen. *Exp. Cell Res.* **10**, 458.

EXPLANATION OF PLATE

Figs. 1–8. Particle shapes and sizes of several plant viruses. All magnified × 24,500. Fig. 1. Tobacco mosaic virus. Fig. 2. Potato virus *X*. Fig. 3. Tobacco rattle virus. Fig. 4. Henbane mosaic virus. Fig. 5. Tobacco necrosis virus (Rothamsted culture). Fig. 6. Tomato spotted wilt virus. Fig. 7. Clover wound tumour virus. The black line is equivalent to 1μ. Fig. 8. Potato yellow dwarf virus. (Figs. 1–5 are by courtesy of H. L. Nixon; Figs. 6 and 7 by courtesy of L. M. Black, M. K. Brakke and A. E. Vatter; Fig. 8 by courtesy of M. K. Brakke and A. E. Vatter.)

PLATE 1

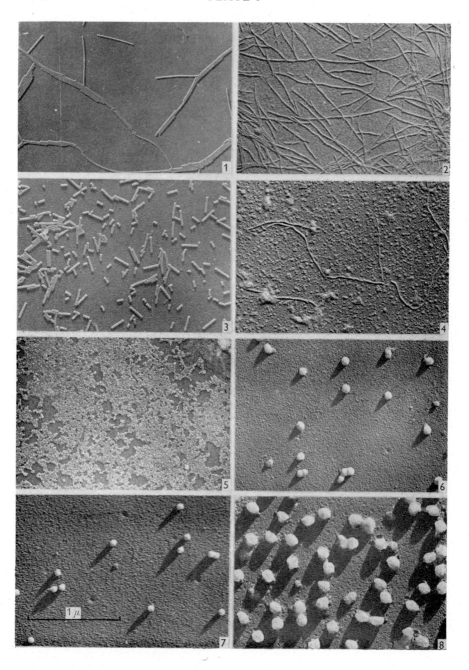

SOME OBSERVATIONS CONCERNING THE REPRODUCTION OF RNA-CONTAINING ANIMAL VIRUSES

WERNER SCHÄFER

Max-Planck-Institut für Virusforschung, Tübingen, Germany

In presenting some results concerning a biological process which has not yet been fully explored, a research worker is somewhat like an archaeologist who has found some of the stones originally composing a mosaic. He is certainly tempted to fill in the holes in a manner he supposes to be right. This leads to the danger that someone who is not familiar with the findings cannot immediately recognize which part of the picture presented is well established and which a matter of suggestion. The worker himself may also be so impressed by the picture gained that he overlooks the holes really present. Nevertheless, I would like to integrate some of our group's results on the biological process of virus multiplication in this way, since I believe that an understanding of the working concepts being employed at present will provide a better basis for discussion. Such dangers as those mentioned above will be avoided as far as possible by pointing out what can be considered as fact and what is more or less a matter of hypothesis.

Only RNA-containing animal viruses will be considered in this paper and an integration of the results will be attempted only with fowl plague virus, where more factual information is available.

PROPERTIES OF ISOLATED VIRUS RNA

The isolation of an infectious RNA from tobacco mosaic virus (TMV) by Gierer & Schramm (1956*a*, 1956*b*) stimulated similar investigations with some RNA-containing animal viruses, in order to see if the isolated RNA from these agents also contains all the information the host cell needs for the production of new virus particles. Colter, Bird & Brown (1957) were successful in this field first, isolating an infectious RNA fraction from mouse brains infected with Mengo-encephalitis virus. A short time later a corresponding infectious principle was extracted in our institute (Wecker & Schäfer, 1957*b*) using EE-infected tissues. Recently a comparable RNA fraction has been obtained from some other small animal viruses (Colter, Bird, Moyer & Brown, 1957; Alexander *et al.* 1958). In all these cases the method of preparation was that developed by Gierer & Schramm (1956*a*, 1956*b*), that is, extraction of the RNA fraction by shaking with phenol at 0–4°.

The *EE-virus*, adopted for use in our investigations, is a spherical particle of about 50 mμ in diameter, containing about 4·4 % RNA, 54 % lipid, and protein (cf. Beard, 1948). It is questionable if carbohydrates other than the ribose of RNA are present. Infected mouse brains or infected chick embryos served as starting material in our early experiments. The infectivity of the fractions obtained was tested by intracerebral injection in mice, but later by intra-allantoic injection of embryonated eggs. The infectious principle isolated was characterized by various methods (Table 1) (Wecker, in preparation).

Table 1. *Behaviour of virus particles in comparison with the 'RNA' fraction isolated from EE-infected tissue. Extraction method: phenol, 0°–4°*

Treatment of the material	Virus particles Log$_{10}$ LD$_{50}$/ml.†	'RNA' Log$_{10}$ LD$_{50}$/ml.†
Control	3·7	3·8
25 μg/ml. RNase 20 min. 20°	3·6	‡
25 μg/ml. DNase 20 min. 20°	3·8	‡
Control	—	2·9
0·01 μg./ml. RNase 15 min. 10°	—	‡
0·01 μg./ml. DNase 15 min. 10°	—	3·5
Normal horse serum*		
1/400	6·0	1·2
1/200	6·4	1·3
1/100	6·2	0·9
1/50	6·1	0·6
Control	8·1	3·0
Ethanol precipitate	‡	3·5
Control	3·7	3·8
55 min. 144,700 g	1·0	3·6

* To each virus- or 'RNA'-dilution the appropriate amount of serum was added.
† Infectivity test in embryonated eggs.
‡ 10 embryos survived inoculation with 0·2 ml. of undiluted material.

Incubation with RNase destroyed its infectivity completely, whereas that of a preparation of virus particles was not diminished under the same conditions. The effect observed with normal horse serum is probably a reflection of its RNase content (Alexander *et al.* 1958). A certain amount of RNase seems also to have been present in the specimen of 'DNase' used since a relatively high dose (25 μg./ml.) of this specimen destroyed the infectivity of the infectious material, whereas no inactivation occurred with 0·01 μg./ml. of this 'DNase'. A corresponding dose of RNase, however, resulted in complete loss of infectivity.

Ethanol inactivated the virus particles but precipitated the isolated active principle without any loss in infectivity. The redissolved material regularly possessed a higher biological activity than the untreated preparation, suggesting that some inhibitory substances are removed by precipitation with ethanol. The u.v. absorption ratio $E_{258 m\mu}/E_{280 m\mu}$ of the preparations after ethanol precipitation was 1·95–2·19, indicating that very little protein could be present. According to nitrogen determinations, no excess of N was present compared with the expected amount of nucleic acid N.

These results thus suggest that the isolated infectious material is different from the virus particles and behaves like RNA. This was supported by ultracentrifugal studies in which the sedimentation rate of each material was followed by biological determinations (Table 1). The extracted infectious principle sedimented much more slowly than the virus particles. In this experiment the virus particles were suspended in a phenol extract of normal embryos (having about the same viscosity as the infective fraction) in order to have comparable conditions for the sedimentation of the virus and the extracted infectious material. The molecular weight of the latter has not yet been determined exactly. But some preliminary experiments by Wecker (in preparation) indicate that it is of the order of 2×10^6. This is about the same value as was determined by Gierer (1957) for the infectious RNA of TMV. It corresponds to the absolute amount of RNA present in TMV and EE, polio, influenza, and fowl plague viruses (Table 2); and it seems that this is the RNA mass these viruses need for inducing their multiplication.

Table 2. *The absolute amount of RNA of various viruses*

Virus	Particle weight	RNA content (%)	Absolute RNA-content
TMV	40×10^6	5·6	$2·2 \times 10^6$
Polio	$6·7 \times 10^6$	22–30	$1·5$–$2·0 \times 10^6$
EE	c. 50×10^6*	c. 4·4	c. $2·2 \times 10^6$
KP	150×10^6	c. 1·8	c. $2·7 \times 10^6$
Influenza	280×10^6	0·7–1·0	$2·0$–$2·8 \times 10^6$

* Calculated from the diameter found by electron microscopy.

The question arose as to the origin of the active 'RNA' isolated from EE-infected tissues. Is it liberated from virus-particles, from another RNA-containing virus-specific product such as s-antigen or from a RNA structure which may exist free in the infected cells or combined with some non-viral, that is, cellular protein? It is most unlikely that virus particles are the source of the infectious 'RNA' since the amount of extractable active fraction is much reduced when the phenol is added after homogenization of the tissue, and becomes nil when the homogenate is treated with RNase before the phenol treatment (Table 3). Phenol was therefore added to EE-infected mouse brains or chick embryos before homogenization. In this way the factor disturbing the isolation of the infective principle, probably cellular RNase, was denatured as quickly as possible.

Table 3. *Infectivity of 'RNA' fractions from EE-infected tissues isolated by phenol in the cold under varied conditions. (Wecker, E., in preparation)*

Treatment of EE-infected chick embryo material	Infectivity of the material obtained (Log_{10} LD_{50}/ml.)
Phenol added *before* homogenization	3·1–3·7
Phenol added *after* homogenization	2·0
Homogenate first treated with RNase then phenol added	*

Table 4. *Influence of temperature on the extraction efficiency. Starting material: purified EE-virus concentrate*

Temperature during phenol-treatment (° C.)	Total RNA extracted (μg.)	Infectivity of the material obtained (Log_{10} LD_{50}/ml.)	
		Before RNase treatment	After RNase treatment
0	0	*	*
40	72	2·35	*
50	710	3·24	*

* 10 embryos survived inoculation with 0·2 ml. of undiluted material.

The second supposition—that a type of s-antigen is present in the cells—is also unlikely since no such structure has as yet been described for EE. Thus it seems most probable that the infectious 'RNA' isolated in the cold is derived either from a free viral RNA occurring in the host cells or from RNA which was originally associated with some cell component.

Further evidence that the infective RNA isolated from infective tissue did not come from the virus particles was found when purified virus preparations were available (Wecker, in preparation). Phenol treatment of such preparations in the cold yielded no infectious principle (Table 4). But since it appeared possible that the lipid of the virus particle prevented the liberation of RNA, the phenol extraction was performed at a higher temperature (40–50°), in the hope that the lipids might then be removed. Under these conditions an active RNA fraction was also obtained from purified EE-virus (Table 4).

Unfortunately, the amount of 'RNA' derived from purified EE-virus has not yet been high enough to allow extensive characterization. In some preliminary experiments, however (Wecker, unpublished), its reactions to enzyme and ethanol treatment, as well as its behaviour in the centrifuge, have been very similar to those of the infective principle described above. The same is true for the biologically active material derived by the new method from EE-infected tissues.

For comparative purposes, similar experiments were performed with a strain of *mouse encephalomyelitis virus* (*ME*) isolated by Dr Gönnert-Bayer, Elberfeld (Franklin, Wecker & Henry, in preparation). The ME virus is about the size of polio virus and, because it is resistant to ether and other lipid solvents, it probably does not contain any surface lipid. This is presumably the reason why an infective principle could be isolated from partially purified preparations of this virus by cold as well as by warm phenol. Here also the principle obtained by phenol treatment was destroyed by RNase but not by DNase. It was precipitated without loss of infectivity by ethanol as well as by M-NaCl. No indication was found that the ME-infected mouse brain contains any source of viral 'RNA' other than the virus particles themselves.

The efficiency of the warm and cold phenol extractions has been further compared in some experiments with *TMV* (Wecker, in preparation). These showed that infective RNA can also be obtained from this plant virus by shaking with phenol at higher temperatures (40 and 60°). The yield was equal to or even higher than that obtained by the original method of Gierer & Schramm (1956*a*, 1956*b*). Thus viral RNA from three different sources seems to be somewhat resistant to the influence of higher temperatures.

The present studies, as well as those of other workers, seem to indicate that the RNA of animal viruses can, like that of TMV, contain all the information for the production of new virus units. Another interesting feature of the experiments with EE is the demonstration that an active viral RNA, or RNA-containing product, is present in the infected tissues in addition to the RNA contained in the infectious particles. Further studies are necessary to determine whether this is a breakdown product of virus particles, a product of abnormal virus synthesis, or an essential intermediate stage in the formation of new virus.

This product recalls the virus-specific products which are found along with infective virus particles in cells infected with myxoviruses. Since a good deal is already known about the multiplication of the myxoviruses it would seem of value to consider the significance of such products in connection with these viruses.

FOWL PLAGUE VIRUS AND ITS MULTIPLICATION

The virus particle and its composition

Detailed studies on the fowl plague myxovirus (KP) have been made in our laboratory in recent years (see Schäfer, 1957). Like all other myxoviruses, the KP-virus is able to agglutinate red cells and possesses a receptor-destroying enzyme. This virus is a rather complex unit compared with the smaller viruses mentioned previously. It is a spherical particle, about 70–80 mμ in diameter (Pl. 1, fig. 1 a) and contains protein, RNA, lipids, and carbohydrates. According to our most recent determinations its RNA content is about 1·8 %. About 25 % of its weight is lipid.

By degrading the particles one can show that they contain at least two types of subunits, which differ physically, chemically, and biologically (Schäfer & Zillig, 1954; Zillig, Schäfer & Ullmann, 1955; Schäfer, 1957). One of the two structures so liberated is called *gebundenes* (g)-*antigen*. It is composed of protein and 10–15 % RNA. All the viral RNA appears to be associated with it. Purified preparations of g-antigen are electrophoretically relatively homogeneous (Schäfer & Zillig, 1954), but in the analytical ultracentrifuge show up to six gradients. The heterogeneity in the centrifuge correlates well with the microscopic appearances, for electron micrographs show small spherical units with a diameter of 10–15 mμ and elongated elements apparently composed of from two to six spheres (Pl. 1, fig. 1 b). The g-antigen can be identified as virus-specific material serologically. It reacts with antibody produced by infection, which corresponds to s-antigen antibody; g-antigen is not infectious and possesses no haemagglutinating activity. Our preparations have shown a small capacity to immunize chickens against infection which is probably due to contamination with very small amounts of the second virus component.

The second component contains both protein and carbohydrate and consists of fairly uniform spherical particles about 30 mμ in diameter (Pl. 1, fig. 1c). Since it agglutinates red cells it was named *haemagglutinin*. The haemagglutinin contains the virus receptor-destroying enzyme and behaves serologically like the V-antigen; in other words, it has the serological specificity of the intact virus particle. No serological relationship could be detected between g-antigen and haemagglutinin. The haemagglutinin is non-infectious either alone or mixed with g-antigen, but it will immunize chickens very efficiently. In fact, if the specific immunizing activity is referred to the nitrogen content of the antigens, it shows about the same specific immunizing activity in chickens as formolized intact virus.

The following evidence on the arrangement of the subunits suggests that the g-antigen is located inside the spherical unit and that the haemagglutinin is a part of its surface. The haemagglutination- and receptor-destroying-enzyme-reactions, in addition to the sero-immunological reactions of the surface of the intact virus particle, can be reproduced with isolated haemagglutinin. The g-antigen *in situ*, however, can neither be reached by its specific antibody nor induce the production of that antibody. The antigenicity of g-antigen is demonstrable only when the virus particle is split (Schäfer, 1957). From the results of Valentine & Isaacs (1957) one gains the impression that the g-antigen in the virus particle is arranged in a ring-like form. After degradation of the outer part of the virus particle with proteolytic enzymes a nucleoprotein ring could be demonstrated. The ring resists degradation by such enzymes because its RNA is wrapped around the protein core. Apparently, during the ether treatment of the virus particle, this nucleoprotein ring is broken down into pieces of various sizes. As would be expected with such breakdown products, the RNA of the pieces is exposed and susceptible to digestion by RNase (Schäfer & Wecker, 1958).

The entire virus particle is held together by lipids since their removal by ether leads to liberation of the different virus subunits. Although no preparation of virus particles has been obtained completely free from an antigen corresponding to a normal component from egg fluid (Munk & Schäfer, 1951), this has been possible for g-antigen. Our haemagglutinin preparations contained a relatively small amount of such a normal component.

The multiplication of fowl plague virus

The multiplication of KP-virus was studied in various cell systems: allantoic membranes of chick embryos, cultures of chicken macrophages, giant cells formed from these macrophages, and principally in tissue cultures of chick embryo cells. Monolayers of giant cells were produced from macrophages by lowering slightly the pH of the medium (Franklin, 1958 *a*). The virus behaved similarly during the multiplication cycle in all these systems.

Behaviour of the infecting virus particle

To initiate its reproduction, the virus particle itself, or at least its genetic material, has first to enter the host cell. Attachment of virus to the cell surface and penetration into the cell could be mediated by the haemagglutinins since they are known to attach themselves to receptors of the red cell membrane and destroy these enzymically. Studies on influenza virus, an agent similar in structure to KP-virus, support this idea because destruction of the receptor sites of host cells, by the receptor-destroying enzyme (RDE) of *Vibrio cholerae*, renders the cells incapable of being infected by some strains of influenza virus (Stone, 1948*a*, 1948*b*). It is doubtful, however, if the two viruses resemble each other in this respect because no comparable effect has been observed with KP-virus. Indeed, tissue cultures of chicken embryo cells treated before infection with either large amounts of RDE or a haemagglutinin preparation of high enzymic activity produced KP-virus nearly as efficiently as untreated control cultures. Thus infection with KP-virus may be initiated without participation of such surface receptors and without action of their counterpart, the haemagglutinin of the virus.

Several lines of approach were employed to follow the multiplying virus further. As with other viruses, a drop in infectivity occurs shortly after adding KP-virus particles to the host cell system (Schäfer & Munk, 1952); and it seemed possible that this may result from breakdown of the invading virus particles into subunits similar to those obtained by ether treatment. In order to see if such subunits occur, ^{32}P-labelled KP-virus was prepared. The isotope is mainly in the virus RNA and lipid fractions (Wecker & Schäfer, 1956, 1957*a*). The specific activity of highly purified preparations was about 200–300 counts/min./haemagglutinating unit. Their log plaque-forming unit-haemagglutination ratio (PFU/HA) was about 6·0 against about 6·7 in our most infectious preparations. Large numbers of embryonic chicken cells were infected with such 'hot' virus at a multiplicity between 1 and 2. After incubation for 30–180 min. the infected cells were thoroughly washed and then homogenized. To allow extraction of virus material from the cell debris, the homogenates were held for 30 min. at 4° and the cell debris then removed by centrifuging. The supernates ('infected extracts') contained about 35 % of the total radioactivity originally present in the homogenates and characterization of the ^{32}P carriers in the extracts was attempted. Hot virus particles were also added to extracts of normal cells after removal of the cell debris and these were used as controls. Additional balance experiments showed that no significant transfer of virus ^{32}P to cell material occurred in our system during the period of observation.

Centrifugation experiments showed that a considerable amount (25–61 %) of the ^{32}P-carriers of the 'infected extracts' could not be sedimented by gravitational forces which sedimented 84–93 % of the hot virus particles in the controls. The labelled material in extracts of cells infected 30 min. earlier sedimented in the same way as those of cells infected for a longer time. Thus the non-sedimentable ^{32}P of cells amounted to as much as 25–60 % as early as 30 min. after infection.

A fraction of this non-sedimentable ^{32}P from infected cells could be precipitated by rabbit antiserum to g-antigen (Schäfer, 1957). Unlabelled g-antigen was added to both extracts to produce larger precipitates. The precipitates were thoroughly washed (4-times) to remove any non-specific radioactive material. The precipitates from 'infected extracts' contained about 11 % of the ^{32}P originally present whereas precipitates of the controls contained only about 1 %. The radioactive fraction of the 'infected extracts' that remained after precipitating g-antigen contained labelled lipids and nucleic acid. The nucleic acid was identified as RNA by digestion with RNase. The RNA enclosed in the virus particle cannot be attacked by the enzyme.

A clear-cut interpretation of these experiments is difficult, since only the extractable ^{32}P-carriers, representing about 35 % of the viral ^{32}P originally associated with the cells, could be characterized and, furthermore, the PFU/HA ratio of 6·0 shows that not all the labelled particles were infectious; nevertheless the findings seem to indicate that a considerable proportion of the infecting virus particles is degraded soon after contact with the host cells. They show further that g-antigen and RNA not associated with a corresponding antigenic component are liberated by this process. This RNA was probably detached from the g-antigen.

The biological activity of KP-viral RNA

Since infectious RNA can be isolated from some animal viruses and since the RNA of KP-virus is apparently liberated inside the host cell, it seemed reasonable to suppose that an isolated RNA from this virus might also be able to initiate infection. Therefore KP-infected tissues and purified KP-virus preparations were treated with phenol. Although both the cold and warm phenol methods were employed, no infectious RNA fraction has yet been obtained (Wecker & Schäfer, unpublished).

The reason for these disappointing results is not evident. It may be that the isolated RNA is only able to initiate the formation of one of the KP-virus subunits, for example, the g-antigen, and that some sort of further inducer is needed for production of the second subunit. It would be very difficult to establish the biological activity of the RNA under these circumstances since the tests for the two subunits of the virus are relatively insensitive compared with the infectivity test, and, further, the chances of introducing both these inducers into the same cell, and thereby producing new infective particles, are remote. The same difficulties would be expected if, as an alternative hypothesis, a special RNA were necessary for the production of each virus subunit. But this is not very likely since a single particle of KP-virus only contains an amount of RNA (see Table 2) corresponding, in the case of TMV (Gierer, 1957), to one biologically active RNA molecule. A third possibility is that the RNA of KP-virus is relatively unstable compared with that of other viruses. This is suggested by the fact that the ring-like structure of the KP-virus (g-antigen) and with this the viral RNA strand, is apparently destroyed by ether treatment. Therefore it seems worth while to look for further extraction methods, enabling us to isolate the KP-RNA as an intact molecule.

Appearance and properties of s-antigen and its relation to g-antigen

We have also attempted to explore the multiplication process of KP-virus by means of complement-fixation tests. These have shown that an antigenic substance behaving like g-antigen, and commonly called *s-antigen*, is the first virus material to increase and that it does so about 3 hr. after infection (Schäfer & Munk, 1952b; Breitenfeld & Schäfer, 1957). Accordingly the isolation of s-antigen has been carried out in order to compare this substance more carefully with g-antigen (Schäfer & Munk, 1952a; Schäfer, Munk & Mussgay, 1956). Since it was impossible to get suitable amounts of s-antigen from cells which had been infected for only 3 hr., cells were taken as starting material after a longer period of infection, on the assumption that all the s-antigen produced in an infected cell has the same properties. Infective virus-particles and other haemagglutinating units were first removed from the cell extracts by adsorption on red cells and by high-speed centrifuging. The further steps of the purification procedure are described elsewhere (Schäfer & Munk, 1952a; Schäfer, Munk & Mussgay, 1956).

The particles obtained could not be distinguished physically from g-antigen. Particles of different sizes were observed, the smallest spherical units having a diameter of 10–15 mμ (Pl. 1, fig. 1d). The longer ones seem to be made up of several such units. These structures are composed of ribonucleoprotein, like the g-antigen. Their RNA content was found to vary between 6 and 14 %, the relatively high variation probably being due to occasional losses of nucleic acid during purification.

Further evidence for the close relationship between the two antigens came from precipitation experiments. Neither g- nor s-antigen was precipitated by anti-KP-haemagglutinin serum nor by serum against KP-virus particles. But precipitation of both antigens occurred with KP-g-antigen antibody and also with serum against the corresponding antigen from influenza FM/1-virus. The antigenic relationship between these two viruses is limited to their g-antigens (Figs. 1 and 2). The only difference observed between our purified g- and s-antigen prepara-

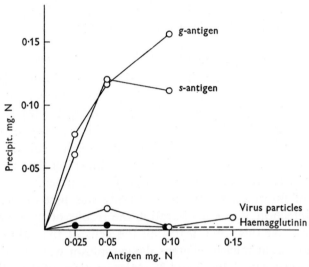

Fig. 1. Precipitation of KP-units by KP-g-antigen-antiserum prepared in a rabbit.

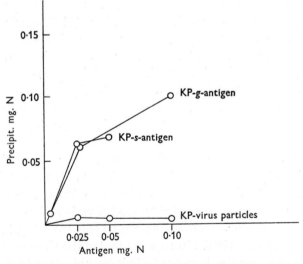

Fig. 2. Precipitation of KP-units by FM/1-g-antigen-antiserum prepared in a rabbit.

tions has been in their immunizing capacities (Schäfer, 1957). In contrast to the g-antigen preparations, the s-antigen preparations have failed to immunize chickens against infection. But this difference might have been due to small amounts of haemagglutinin still contained in our g-antigen preparations, especially since the respective specific immunizing activity found with the g-antigen samples was, as already mentioned earlier, relatively low. Thus it appears that the g-antigen, liberated from virus particles by treatment with ether, and the s-antigen, contained in infected cells, are identical or at least very similar.

Localization of the s-antigen inside the cell

An attempt to discover the site of s-antigen formation has been made by using Coons' (see Coons & Kaplan, 1950) fluorescent antibody technique (Breitenfeld & Schäfer, 1957; Franklin, 1958 b). Monolayer cultures of embryonic chicken cells and of multinucleate giant cells from chicken macrophages were treated with virus doses just sufficient to infect nearly all the cells. At different times after infection the cultures were stained with fluorescent antibody specific for g-antigen.

Binding of fluorescent-g-antigen-antibody was first observed about 3 hr. after infection, thus corroborating the results of the complement-fixation tests. At this time nearly all the cells of the culture showed brightly fluorescent nuclei, whereas the cytoplasm was practically free from fluorescence (Pl. 2, figs 2 and 3). Microsections of the cells showed that the s-antigen is situated inside and not around the nuclei (Breitenfeld, unpublished). The nuclear fluorescence increased with time; fluorescence also occurred later in the cytoplasm (Pl. 2, figs 4 and 5), and finally the entire cell fluoresced strongly on staining with fluorescent g-antigen antibody (Pl. 2, fig. 6). From these observations one gains the impression that the antigenically active material of the g- or s-antigen is formed in the nucleus and that subsequently it migrates to the cytoplasm. But another possibility is that there are also centres of s-antigen formation in the cytoplasm which start to function later than those in the nucleus.

It would be of great value to know the path of formation of the RNA contained in the g- or s-antigen. Wecker (1957) has obtained some information about this from ^{32}P labelling experiments. He incubated tissue cultures with equal doses of ^{32}P added at various times, from 48 hr. before up to the time of infection. As can be seen from Fig. 3, there was no significant difference in the isotope content of the virus nucleic acid of the various virus samples harvested. This would scarcely be expected if considerable amounts of P-containing material of the host cell were used for synthesis of viral RNA.

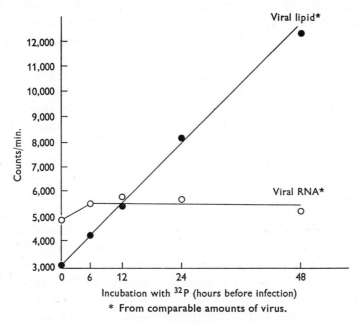

Fig. 3. Virus ³²P distribution as a function of preincubation of the host cell with the isotope.

Appearance and properties of haemagglutinating material

Haemagglutinating activity of the infected system generally rises shortly after the complement fixation test shows an increase of g- or s-antigen. In most of our experiments the increase of haemagglutination titre has occurred between 3 and 4 hr. after infection. At this stage only a relatively small or no rise of infectivity was demonstrable (Schäfer & Munk, 1952b; Breitenfeld & Schäfer, 1957). To see if particles similar to the haemagglutinin subunit of the virus occur inside the cells we have isolated the haemagglutinating particles from infected cell homogenates by adsorption to, and elution from, red cells and, if need be, by separation from whole virus using differential centrifuging (Schäfer, Zillig & Munk, 1954; Schäfer, 1957).

The particles obtained in this way were quite different from the haemagglutinin units we had expected to find. Morphologically they somewhat resembled the microsomes of normal cells as described by Palade & Siekevitz (1956). Flattened circular bodies between about 50 and 550 mμ in diameter could be seen in the electron microscope (Pl. 1, fig. f). Some of these contained denser masses. The shells of the bodies were sometimes ruptured. Although they were mostly prepared from cells after longer infection times, it could be shown that particles with the same morphology, and similarly adsorbable on to red cells, were also present in homogenates of cells 4 hr. after infection (Munk, unpublished). At this time structures of the size and shape of virus particles were relatively scarce. The isolated particles had a lower sedimentation rate than the virus particles, and they could also be separated from these by electrophoresis. Our purest preparations of such units showed a low LD_{50}/HA ratio compared with samples of fully infectious virus. The ratio was sometimes 2·0, whereas preparations of infective particles showed a ratio of about 7·4. The residual infectivity is probably due to the presence of a few virus particles, even though the possibility that the particular units themselves possess some low probability of initiating infection cannot at present be fully excluded. Although they are precipitated by antiserum against virus particles (Schäfer, 1955), their antigenic structure seems to differ somewhat from that of the virus surface and of the viral haemagglutinin subunits since their immunizing capacity in chickens appeared extremely low in comparison with that of virus particles or isolated haemagglutinin (Schäfer, 1955). It corresponded indeed to the content of infectious units in the preparations. No particles of this type could be isolated from infected allantoic fluid.

Particles which are characterized by a lower sedimentation rate and a lower LD_{50}/HA ratio than the respective myxoviruses are frequently called 'incomplete forms'. The units described here resemble morphologically those isolated by Werner & Schlesinger (1954) from tissues infected with influenza virus, but seem to differ from those first found by Von Magnus (see 1954) in allantoic fluid after undiluted passages. The latter, according to Von Magnus (1954), are morphologically similar to the virus particles of influenza and like these possess an immunizing ability. Units comparable with the 'incomplete forms' of Von Magnus could not be produced with KP-virus by repeated undiluted passages.

More extensive comparative studies are desirable, especially of the chemistry of the units. Relatively little is known about the chemical composition of the KP-'incomplete forms'. The high lipid content (about 60 %) of our preparations is most striking. RNA is present but the amount has not yet been determined exactly. These findings, as well as the morphological resemblance of the particles to microsomes, stimulated us to see if they possessed glucose-6-phosphatase activity characteristic of microsomes.

From homogenates of infected chick embryos, particles adsorbable to red cells were removed with the help of washed chicken erythrocytes. The latter were then washed three times in the cold and the particles eluted by adding RDE. For each experiment fifteen infected chicken embryos were used as starting material. After the eluted material had been concentrated by high-speed centrifuging it was examined for enzyme activity by a modification of the method employed by Ashmore & Nesbett (1955), as follows: the concentrates were incubated with glucose-6-phosphate as a substrate for 1 hr. at 30° and the total inorganic P determined. From the values obtained, the content of inorganic phosphorus present in two controls (one substrate only, the other concentrate only) was subtracted. To avoid larger losses of enzyme-activity the embryos were taken from eggs shortly before dying; for the same reason infective virus particles were not removed from the concentrates by further cycles of centrifuging. Material obtained by the same procedure from normal embryos and from infectious allantoic fluid served as further controls.

Table 5. *Glucose-6-phosphatase activity of particles adsorbable on red cells*

Origin of the preparation	Inorganic P liberated (μg./ml.)
Homogenate of infected chick-embryos	12·2
	12·5
	17·5
	28·0
	32·5
	35·0
	51·5
Homogenate of normal embryos	0
	4·5
	5·0
Infectious egg fluid	0

Some typical results of such experiments are presented in Table 5. They show that glucose-6-phosphatase activity was present in the samples obtained from infected embryos but to only a negligible degree in the controls. This indicates that there are particles in homogenates from infected embryos which can be adsorbed on to red cells and which carry a glucose-6-phosphatase. It is not yet possible to decide definitely whether these are really the so-called 'incomplete forms'. The control experiment with material from allantoic fluid is not quite convincing since the adsorbable viral units present here—mostly virus particles—were exposed extracellularly to the influence of the incubation temperature. This could lead to inactivation of glucose-6-phosphatase. Furthermore one has to consider that that enzyme might have been only superficially adsorbed to the particles contained in the infected cell homogenates. Nevertheless, these preliminary results seem compatible with the hypothesis that the 'incomplete forms' of KP are microsomes of the infected cells.

Localization of haemagglutinin-antigen inside the cell

If this hypothesis were correct one would expect to find haemagglutinin-antigen in the cytoplasm of the host cells. Investigations with fluorescent antibody specific for haemagglutinin showed that this is indeed the case (Breitenfeld & Schäfer, 1957; Franklin, 1958b). The corresponding antigen was usually first detected about 4 hr. after infection, just at the time when the haemagglutination titre was rising. In chick embryo cells a brightly fluorescing, juxtanuclear locus was often observed in addition to the fluorescence distributed throughout the entire cytoplasm (Pl. 2, fig. 7). The significance of this locus is unknown. As the multiplication cycle progresses, fluorescence produced by fluorescent antibody to haemagglutinin-antigen becomes more pronounced at the cell periphery and sometimes fine thread-like fluorescent projections reaching out into the surroundings can be seen at high magnification (Pl. 3, fig. 8).

The cell nuclei do not seem to contain haemagglutinin-antigen. This can best be verified by observing multinucleate giant cells derived from macrophages (Pl. 3, fig. 9). The form of these cells is similar to that of a fried egg: the central cytoplasm is relatively thick and the peripheral quite thin. Hence nuclei at the periphery are only covered by a thin layer of cytoplasm.

In interpreting these findings one has to remember that intact virus particles also bind haemagglutinin-antibody. But it seems improbable that they contribute a significant amount to the cytoplasmic fluorescence observed after treatment with fluorescent anti-haemagglutinin serum. Ultrahistological investigations (Hotz & Schäfer, 1955) indicate that particles of this type are never visible in the cytoplasm of infected chicken allantoic cells during the viral multiplication cycle, and it seems likely that this is also the case with chick embryo cells and chicken macrophages in cultures. Further, 4 hr. after infection, when a clear fluorescence of the cytoplasm can be observed, infectivity tests reveal the presence of only relatively few new infective virus particles. The ultrahistological investigations are described in more detail below.

The information available suggests that the various components of the virus particles are produced at different sites in the host cell: the g-antigen in the nucleus, and at least some part of the haemagglutinin in the endoplasmic reticulum from which, according to Palade & Siekevitz (1956), the microsomes are released during homogenization.

The suggestion that at least two different synthetic centres of the cell are concerned with the production of virus material has been further strengthened by experiments with proflavine. Franklin (1958 c) has shown that low concentrations suppress the formation of haemaggluti-nating material but not the production of the substance which behaves serologically like g- or s-antigen (Fig. 4).

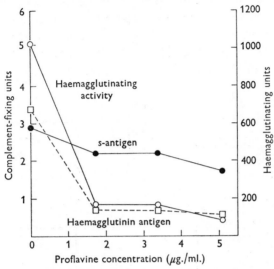

Fig. 4. Effect of proflavine on the production of virus material in tissue culture of embryonic chicken cells. Haemagglutinating activity measured by haemagglutination test, haemagglutinin antigen and s-antigen by complement fixation test.

Appearance of new infectious virus particles and origin of their lipid

The infectivity titre of the infected cell systems rises shortly after the haemagglutinating titre starts to increase (Schäfer & Munk, 1952 b; Breitenfeld & Schäfer, 1957; Franklin, in preparation). Some indication how and where the *infective virus particles* are formed was gained from the ultrahistological studies made some years ago with infected allantoic membranes (Hotz & Schäfer, 1955). As already mentioned, no particles resembling the 70–80 mμ spherical virus particles were found inside the cells at any stage of the multiplication cycle. The first visible change was the appearance and subsequent growth of fine protrusions on the free surface of the cells at about 4 hr. after infection (Pl. 3, fig. 10 b). At about 5 hr. after infection particles resembling virus particles could be seen at the top of these protrusions (Pl. 3, fig. 10 c), and later the margin of the cells was completely covered by such particles (Pl. 3, figs 10 d and e). The observed protrusions apparently correspond to the fine strands seen in the investigations with fluorescent anti-haemagglutinin serum and also to the filaments, which can occasionally be detected in the fluids surrounding the infected cells (Pl. 1, fig. e).

The lipid, which holds the virus subunits together, does not appear to be specially produced for the virus. It seems likely that it is part of the original cellular lipid. This idea is supported by the ^{32}P labelling experiments in which cell-cultures were pre-incubated with the isotope at various times before infection (Wecker, 1957). When lipids of the newly formed virus were tested for radioactivity it was found that, in contrast to RNA, the labelling of the lipids increased with duration of pre-incubation of the cells with ^{32}P (Fig. 3).

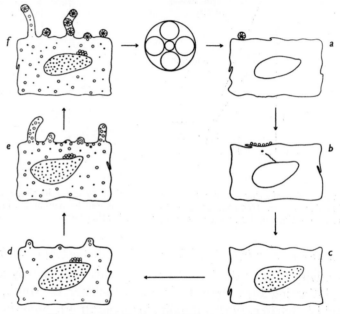

Fig. 5. Hypothetical cycle of KP-virus reproduction.

Our present information can be summarized in the scheme of KP-virus multiplication presented in Fig. 5. The infecting virus particle, containing g-antigen, haemagglutinin and lipids, adsorbs to the host cell (a) and then becomes degraded in some unknown way (b). During this process its g-antigen nucleoprotein is released and probably from this its RNA. It is not known how the genetic material enters the cell nor what happens to the haemagglutinin and lipid components. The g-antigen is the first new virus material which can be detected inside the cell (c) and is followed by the haemagglutinin (d). These materials appear to be produced in separate systems of the cell: the g-antigen in the nucleus and the haemagglutinin in the endoplasmic reticulum. How these systems are induced is not at all clear. But we know from more simply constructed viruses that RNA can initiate the production of viral nucleoprotein. It seems therefore to be a reasonable hypothesis that the RNA of the KP-virus also induces the formation of viral ribonucleoprotein, that is the g-antigen, in the nucleus. The haemagglutinin contains an enzyme not normally occurring in the cells and it is conceivable that this material, like an adaptive enzyme, requires another inducer. This hypothetical inducer might well be coupled to the haemagglutinin of the infecting particle.

After their production, the two viral components seem to diffuse to the cell margin (d, e) where they are finally assembled in fine protrusions of the cell wall to become the new infective virus particles (f). From the electron-microscopic appearances one could well imagine that a lipid of the cell wall, and perhaps some other material of the cell (normal component), envelops the viral subunits in these protrusions.

CONCLUDING REMARKS

The picture presented here is certainly only a preliminary and very rough sketch, whose main purpose is to stimulate further investigations. It contains many uncertainties, reveals detail at only a few points, and gives no information as to how the viral nucleic acid multiplies, takes part in the reproduction of viral protein and transfers the stamp of viral specificity. At these points virology is now approaching the main problems in which contemporary biochemistry is engaged. To attack these problems in the virological field one should simplify the systems as far as possible. With respect to the virus a very important step forward was made by the isolation of biologically active viral RNA, and with respect to the host cells it seems most desirable to follow the biochemist and work with cell fractions. Even now there is reason to hope that such studies will eventually unearth enough stones for the mosaic of animal virus multiplication to be made into a generally convincing picture.

Most of the work presented was supported by the 'Deutsche Forschungs-gemeinschaft'.

REFERENCES

ALEXANDER, H. E., KOCH, G., MOUNTAIN, I. M., SPRUNT, K. & VAN DAMME, O. (1958). Infectivity of ribonucleic acid of poliovirus on HeLa cell monolayers. *Virology*, **5**, 172.
ASHMORE, J. & NESBETT, F. B. (1955). Effect of bile acids on activity of glucose-6-phosphatase. *Proc. Soc. exp. Biol. Med.* **89**, 78.

BEARD, J. W. (1948). Review: Purified animal viruses. *J. Immunol.* **58**, 49.

BREITENFELD, P. M. & SCHÄFER, W. (1957). The formation of fowl plague virus antigens in infected cells, as studied with fluorescent antibodies. *Virology*, **4**, 328.

COLTER, J. S., BIRD, H. H. & BROWN, R. A. (1957). Infectivity of ribonucleic acid from Ehrlich ascites tumour cells infected with Mengo encephalitis. *Nature, Lond.* **179**, 859.

COLTER, J. S., BIRD, H. H., MOYER, A. W. & BROWN, R. A. (1957). Infectivity of ribonucleic acid isolated from virus-infected tissues. *Virology*, **4**, 522.

COONS, A. H. & KAPLAN, M. H. (1950). Localization of antigen in tissue cells. II. Improvements in a method for the detection of antigen by means of fluorescent antibody. *J. exp. Med.* **91**, 1.

FRANKLIN, R. M. (1958a). Some observations on the formation of giant cells in tissue cultures of chicken macrophages. *Z. Naturf.* **13b**, 213.

FRANKLIN, R. M. (1958b). The growth of fowl plague virus in tissue cultures of chicken macrophages and giant cells. *Virology*, **6**, 81.

FRANKLIN, R. M. (1958c). The synthesis of fowl plague virus products in a pro-flavine-inhibited tissue culture system. *Virology*, **6**, 525.

GIERER, A. (1957). Structure and biological function of ribonucleic acid from tobacco mosaic virus. *Nature, Lond.* **179**, 1297.

GIERER, A. & SCHRAMM, G. (1956a). Infectivity of ribonucleic acid from tobacco mosaic virus. *Nature, Lond.* **177**, 702.

GIERER, A. & SCHRAMM, G. (1956b). Die Infektiosität der Nucleinsäure aus Tabakmosaikvirus. *Z. Naturf.* **11b**, 138.

HOTZ, G. & SCHÄFER, W. (1955). Ultrahistologische Studie über die Vermehrung des Virus der klassischen Geflügelpest. *Z. Naturf.* **10b**, 1.

MAGNUS, P. VON (1954). Incomplete forms of influenza virus. *Advanc. Virus Res.* **2**, 59.

MUNK, K. & SCHÄFER, W. (1951). Eigenschaften tierischer Virusarten untersucht an den Geflügelpestviren als Modell. II. Serologische Untersuchungen über die Geflügelpestviren und über ihre Beziehungen zu einem normalen Wirtsprotein. *Z. Naturf.* **6b**, 372.

PALADE, G. E. & SIEKEVITZ, P. (1956). Liver microsomes. An integrated morphological and biochemical study. *J. Cytol.* **2**, 171.

SCHÄFER, W. (1955). Sero-immunologische Eigenschaften 'Inkompletter Formen' des Virus der Klassischen Geflügelpest. *Arch. exp. vet. Med.* **9**, 218.

SCHÄFER, W. (1957). Units isolated after splitting fowl plague virus. In *Ciba Foundation Symposium*: '*The Nature of Viruses*'. London: Churchill.

SCHÄFER, W. & MUNK, K. (1952a). Reinigung und Eigenschaften eines löslichen Antigens der klassischen Geflügelpest. *Z. Naturf.* **7b**, 573.

SCHÄFER, W. & MUNK, K. (1952b). Eigenschaften tierischer Virusarten untersucht an den Geflügelpestviren als Modell. IV. Untersuchungen über den Ablauf der Vermehrung beim Virus der klassischen Geflügelpest. *Z. Naturf.* **7b**, 608.

SCHÄFER, W., MUNK, K. & MUSSGAY, M. (1956). Physikalisch-chemische und biologische Eigenschaften des gereinigten 'löslichen Antigens' der klassischen Geflügelpest. *Z. Naturf.* **11b**, 330.

SCHÄFER, W. & WECKER, E. (1958). Über die Wirkung von Ribonuklease auf ^{32}P-markiertes 'gebundenes Antigen' des Virus der klassischen Geflügelpest. *Arch. exp. vet. Med.* **12**, 418.

SCHÄFER, W. & ZILLIG, W. (1954). Über den Aufbau des Virus-Elementarteilchens der klassischen Geflügelpest. I. Gewinnung, physikalisch-chemische und biologische Eigenschaften einiger Spaltprodukte. *Z. Naturf.* **9b**, 779.

PLATE 1

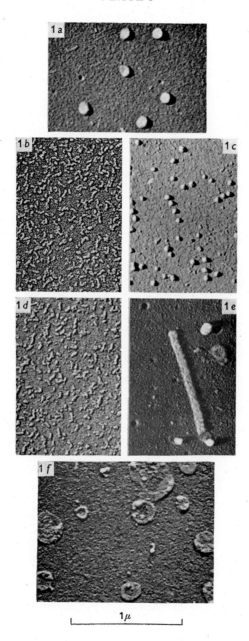

1 a

1 b

1 c

1 d

1 e

1 f

1μ

(*Facing p.* 80)

PLATE 2

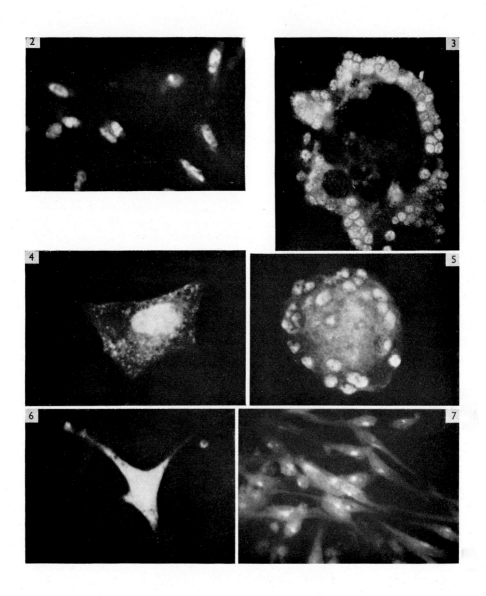

PLATE 3

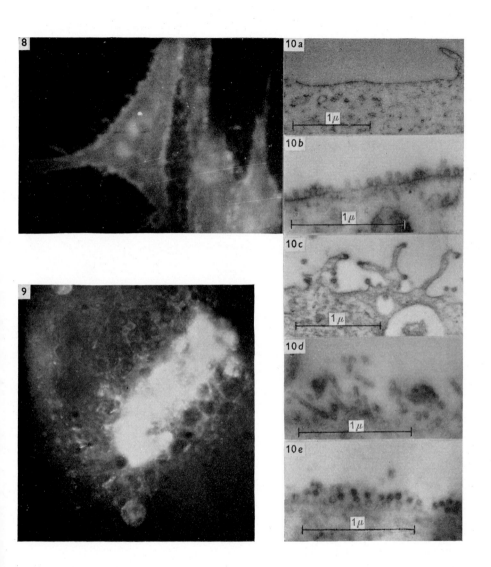

SCHÄFER, W., ZILLIG, W. & MUNK, K. (1954). Isolierung und Charakterisierung hämagglutinierender, nicht-infektiöser Einheiten bei klassischer Geflügelpest. *Z. Naturf.* **9***b*, 329.

STONE, J. D. (1948*a*). Prevention of virus infection with enzyme of *V. cholerae*. I. Studies with viruses of mumps-influenza group in chick embryos. *Aust. J. exp. Biol. med. Sci.* **26**, 49.

STONE, J. D. (1948*b*). Prevention of virus infection with enzyme of *V. cholerae*. II. Studies with influenza virus in mice. *Aust. J. exp. Biol. med. Sci.* **26**, 287.

VALENTINE, R. C. & ISAACS, A. (1957). The structure of viruses of the Newcastle disease-mumps-influenza (Myxovirus) group. *J. gen. Microbiol.* **16**, 680.

WECKER, E. (1957). Die Verteilung von ^{32}P im Virus der klassischen Geflügelpest bei verschiedenen Markierungsverfahren. *Z. Naturf.* **12***b*, 208.

WECKER, E. & SCHÄFER, W. (1956). Einbau von radioaktivem Phosphor in das Virus der klassischen Geflügelpest. *Z. Naturf.* **11***b*, 181.

WECKER, E. & SCHÄFER, W. (1957*a*). Studien mit ^{32}P-markiertem Virus der klassischen Geflügelpest. I. Untersuchungen über das Verhalten des Virus beim Eindringen in die Wirtszelle. *Z. Naturf.* **12***b*, 483.

WECKER, E. & SCHÄFER, W. (1957*b*). Eine infektiöse Komponente von Ribonuklein-säure-Charakter aus dem Virus der amerikanischen Pferde-Enzephalomyelitis (Typ Ost). *Z. Naturf.* **12***b*, 415.

WERNER, G. H. & SCHLESINGER, R. W. (1954). Morphological and quantitative comparison between infectious and non-infectious forms of influenza virus. *J. exp. Med.* **100**, 203.

ZILLIG, W., SCHÄFER, W. & ULLMANN, S. (1955). Über den Aufbau des Virus-Elementarteilchens der klassischen Geflügelpest. II. Chemische Eigenschaften des Elementarteilchens und seiner Spaltprodukte. *Z. Naturf.* **10***b*, 199.

EXPLANATION OF PLATES

PLATE 1

Fig. 1. Virus-specific units of KP. (*a*) KP-virus particles; (*b*) g-antigen; (*c*) haemagglutinin; (*d*) s-antigen; (*e*) filamentous form; (*f*) 'incomplete forms'.

PLATE 2

Fig. 2. Embryonic chicken cells. 3 hr. after infection; treated with fluorescent g-antigen-antiserum.

Fig. 3. Chicken macrophage giant cell. About 3 hr. after infection; treated with fluorescent g-antigen-antiserum.

Fig. 4. Embryonic chicken cell. 10 hr. after infection; treated with fluorescent g-antigen-antiserum.

Fig. 5. Chicken macrophage giant cell. About $5\frac{1}{2}$ hr. after infection; treated with fluorescent g-antigen-antiserum.

Fig. 6. Embryonic chicken cell. 14 hr. after infection; treated with fluorescent g-antigen-antiserum.

Fig. 7. Embryonic chicken cells. 4 hr. after infection; treated with fluorescent haemagglutinin-antiserum.

PLATE 3

Fig. 8. Embryonic chicken cell. 14 hr. after infection; treated with fluorescent haemagglutinin-antiserum.

Fig. 9. Chicken macrophage giant cell. About $3\frac{1}{2}$ hr. after infection; treated with fluorescent haemagglutinin-antiserum.

Fig. 10. Margin of allantoic chicken cell. (*a*) Not infected; (*b*) 4–5 hr. after infection; (*c*) 5 hr. after infection; (*d*) 12 hr. after infection; (*e*) 12 hr. after infection.

STUDIES OF MIXED INFECTIONS WITH NDV, POLIOVIRUS AND INFLUENZA*

GEORGE K. HIRST

Division of Infectious Diseases of The Public Health Research Institute of the City of New York, Inc.

The first report of recombination between animal viruses (Burnet & Lind, 1951 *a*) was followed by a period of activity which has now abated, possibly from an exhaustion of the early techniques and a delay in tooling-up with new ones. This may be a good time to take stock of the first phase of genetic studies with animal viruses in order to point out what substantial grounds exist for future development. This introductory review will be largely confined to RNA viruses of the influenza group. It will be assumed that many isolated observations and genetic models which are based on slender evidence are not of much interest or utility since the methods now exist to provide the kind of facts which can serve as a basis for solid development.

RECOMBINATION WITH INFLUENZA VIRUSES

Recombination of genetic markers has been obtained with a number of strains of influenza A (Burnet & Lind, 1951 *a*, 1956), between two strains of influenza B (Perry & Burnet, 1953), as well as with the presumably DNA viruses of herpes simplex (Wildy, 1955), vaccinia (Fenner & Comben, 1958), and psittacosis (Gordon & Mamay, 1957). With influenza A, recombination has been obtained from mixed infection carried out in mouse brain (Burnet & Lind, 1951 *a*), on the chorioallantoic membrane (Fraser & Burnet, 1952) and in de-embryonated eggs (Burnet & Lind, 1952). 'Pure' clones have been isolated from mixed yields by the use of limiting dilutions, a method which is very restrictive, since it is both difficult and time-consuming to use it in a manner rigid enough to rule out the occurrence of impure clones with near certainty. When several virus types are found in a clone, which has

* The original work reported in this paper was done under the support of several grants from the National Institute of Allergy and Infectious Diseases, Public Health Service, E-377, E-675 and E-2034.

A major portion of the new data in this paper was made available to the author in advance of publication elsewhere by his colleagues in the Division of Infectious Disease, Drs Allan Granoff, Nada Ledinko and Benjamin Mandel.

been common, it is difficult or impossible to differentiate between faulty purification and segregation of a recombinant.

Conversion to indicator state as a marker

A number of characters have been tested for recombination in mixed infection but the most convincing and convenient marker has been a change in indicator status on heating (Burnet & Lind, 1952). When some strains of influenza virus are heated at 56° (strain WSE) the haemagglutinin becomes extremely susceptible to inhibition by a mucoid from meconium. In other strains the haemagglutinin is not affected by heating so that even large amounts of mucoid do not inhibit it.

Recombination experiments were carried out between two strains which differed in serotype (W and M) as well as convertibility to the indicator state (+ and −) (Burnet & Lind, 1952). The rate of exchange of this marker was high and approximately equal numbers of the two recombinant types (W− and M+) were found in the yield. In a back-cross between W− and M+, however, the two wild types were found in a ratio of 7:1 (Lind & Burnet, 1953). The significance of this ratio is not clear, and this type of quantitative data is of very limited usefulness in arriving at satisfactory genetic models, partly because non-genetic factors, such as differences in growth rates, influence the yields.

Virulence as a marker

A second major marker in influenza recombination experiments has been virulence as measured either by ability to produce consolidation of the lungs, death after intracerebral inoculation or haemorrhagic death in chick embryos. The acquisition of pulmonary virulence through serial passage has been studied by Burnet & Lind (1954a) who found that the property was developed in multiple steps with many intermediate and often unstable stages, thus affirming the widely held view that virulence is a polygenic and complex character evolved by selection from numerous mutations.

After a mixed infection between highly virulent and completely avirulent strains of virus the progeny of both parent serotypes may exhibit varying degrees of intermediate grades of virulence, some clones being stable and others not. The tendency for virulence to shift, especially to decrease, on propagation of a clone greatly complicates the problem of separating, maintaining and identifying virus lines at specific virulence levels. In crossing distantly related strains there is also the problem that virulence markers will not have the same phenotypic effect in each (Lind & Burnet, 1957b). Hirst & Gotlieb (1955) found that virulence genes from WSN had no detectable phenotypic effect in strain Melbourne. Crosses between WSN and Melbourne are unique in that WSN virulence went from maximum to nothing on recombination and then returned to maximum on the back cross, and there were no detectable particles of intermediate virulence.

Virulence in most recombination studies behaves as if it were a complex polygenic character and has sometimes been the only marker in which reassortment could be detected. Burnet has laid great stress on the genetic interpretation of virulence and has postulated the existence of special virulence genes (Burnet, 1955) which he pictures as loosely attached multiple unit branches coming off various parts of the main genetic structure. These postulates are made to explain the rapidly changing, multiple and unstable intermediate steps encountered in the course of rising virulence, as well as the ease of adaptation to different hosts. The evidence for this view is certainly unconvincing. Even data suggesting the existence of a genetic backbone are lacking. Because of the polygenic character of virulence, and because of the practical difficulty of performing simple reproducible tests for such a marker, it is hard to imagine a character less suited to help solve the intricacies of animal virus genetics at the present stage.

Stability of recombinants

Some recombinants are stable after isolation while others appear to segregate into multiple types on passage. Because of the difficulties in isolating pure lines by limiting dilutions it is very hard to evaluate this evidence. One case of an unstable virus form arising from mixed infection has been thoroughly studied (Hirst & Gotlieb, 1953b; Gotlieb & Hirst, 1954) and it is now reasonably certain that the instability results from segregation of heterozygous diploids. An even better example will be given below.

Linkage

Information on linkage is of primary interest in formulating genetic models. With influenza strains the majority of markers tested do not change from one serotype to another with any considerable frequency. Two characters which do recombine with high frequency are conversion to the indicator state and virulence for the chick embryo and these two markers usually but not always recombine together (Burnet & Lind, 1952, 1956). This in essence is all that is known about linkage so far. It is obvious that those markers which appear to be linked to antigenic type may merely share some physiological barrier to transfer rather than a close physical connection between the corresponding genetic structures. Burnet's view that the genome of influenza virus is in two pieces is one of several possible interpretations of these very limited data.

Heterozygosis and diploidy

Gotlieb & Hirst (1954) provided the first evidence that an influenza particle might be diploid. A mixed infection of two influenza serotypes gives rise to single particles each alone able to segregate into both parent types. In some cases such a high proportion of heterozygous diploids was found that it appeared likely that all influenza particles were diploid, some homozygous and some heterozygous. This view was strengthened by the observation that the heterozygous condition could be serially propagated at limiting dilution in eggs (Hirst & Gotlieb, 1953 b). Granoff has recently found evidence that a similar diploid state occurs in NDV.

Another feature of heterozygous diploids in a Mel-WSN system (Hirst & Gotlieb, 1955) is that they were almost the sole source of recombinants, suggesting that the heterozygous state may favour or even be a prerequisite for recombination. Lind & Burnet (1957a), in repeating this work with other strains, found a heterozygous condition in only 12 % of particles from mixed infection, and although they could establish no connection between heterozygosis and recombination it is not clear from their description how rigidly the heterozygous state was excluded in most clones. In any case more examples will be required to know whether heterozygosis commonly precedes recombination.

The kind of relationship which exists between the paired genomes of a heterozygote is not known, but it now seems unlikely that the occurrence of double yielders is due to any mechanism of as trivial interest as aggregation of virus particles. However, the term 'doublet' might prove to be more descriptive of the actual condition than diploid. The high efficiency with which such forms produce recombinants may be the result of two genomes entering a large cell at the same spot rather than from some more intimate binuclear state. It is also conceivable that the number of genomes linked together may be more than two and quite variable.

Recombination with inactive virus

Markers can be readily recovered from virus that is either heat- or u.v.-inactivated (Burnet & Lind, 1954b; Baron & Jensen, 1955; Gotlieb & Hirst, 1956). Gotlieb & Hirst found some evidence indicating that u.v. irradiation may increase the rate of recombination, but such stimulation did not occur with the smallest amounts of inactivating irradiation used. One other interesting but unexplained feature of both types of inactivated virus is the fact that markers may still be efficiently recovered even when host cells are exposed to the inactive agent several days before the rescuing virus is added.

Phenotypic mixing

One of the main contributions of our laboratory to the study of mixed infections has been the elaboration of facts concerning phenotypic mixing. The phenomenon of mixed virus coats in influenza was independently described by Fraser (1953) and by Hirst & Gotlieb (1953a) and it consists of a condition in which individual particles carry surface antigenic material made in the cell under the direction of two different viruses. The corresponding antigenic substances may be fitted into the same particle even though the two viruses may be antigenically quite distinct as, for example, influenza A and B or even influenza A and NDV (Granoff & Hirst, 1954). Such mixed coats are not inherited. With fluorescent antibody (Watson & Coons, 1954; Breitenfeld & Schäfer, 1957) it has been shown that haemagglutinating antigen and the RNA-containing antigen are made in different parts of the same cell, thus providing morphological evidence for a mechanism of virus production which could promote phenotypic mixing.

In summary: (1) From studies with mixed infection of influenza viruses, several markers have been found which are transferable from one serotype to another. In the case of a few markers the recombination is reciprocal and the rate of exchange high, and one example has been found where two markers are frequently transferred together. (2) Virus particles containing two different genomes are so common after mixed infection as to suggest a normal diploid or polyploid condition of influenza virus. (3) Phenotypic mixing is very prominent in the progeny from a mixed infection, even when the two parent strains are very different viruses. (4) The character of the genetic apparatus in these RNA viruses is very poorly understood.

Our knowledge of mixed infection is principally qualitative in character and for some time it has been obvious that this deficiency could be overcome only through a more quantitative approach to the subject. For several years our laboratory has been largely devoted to the study of plaque-forming systems of NDV, influenza and poliomyelitis viruses with a view to selecting strains with suitable markers for examining genetic interaction. Progress has been slow and none of us has succeeded so far in extending the few quantitative recombination data garnered with older methods. This is due in part at least to the fact that unexpected phenomena have been encountered with the plaque technique and our interests have been temporarily diverted by findings which are very pertinent to any consideration of the problems of virus multiplication.

MIXED INFECTION WITH NDV

Recent experiments with NDV, which are the work of Dr Allan Granoff, will be outlined only briefly here because a full account will be published elsewhere. Although the original aim of this work was to study recombination, no such phenomenon has been found with the several markers tested. The importance of the experiments is in showing that there is a diploid state in NDV and in suggesting a way in which non-reproducing NDV particles may be physiologically active.

After investigating a large number of NDV strains, two were found which were very similar to each other but differed in three respects: plaque type, sensitivity to inactivation by heat and sensitivity to inactivation by antibody. One strain produces clear plaques on chick fibroblasts, suffers a very slow loss of infectivity and haemagglutinin at 56° and is completely resistant to prolonged exposure to an anti-NDV serum. The other strain produces turbid plaques because it fails to cause lysis of all the cells in the plaque area. The infectivity and haemagglutinin of this strain are highly sensitive to heat (56°) inactivation and the infectivity can be completely neutralized by moderate amounts of an absorbed NDV serum. Table 1 shows the behaviour of both strains towards heat and serum. The serum sensitivity of the turbid-plaque former may be due to the presence of an antigen that is absent from the clear strain. The antiserum was produced against the turbid strain and the cross-reacting elements were removed by absorption with the clear strain.

Table 1. *Characteristics of the two parent-type NDV strains*

Strain designation and plaque type	Percentage survival of infectivity after serum	Percentage survival of infectivity after heating 10 min. at 56°	Percentage survival of haemagglutinin after heating 30 min. at 56°
Clear (C)	100	3–4	100
Turbid (T)	0·1	0·005	0

Although the two strains were not derived in the laboratory from the same stock, they are very similar in general behaviour. Both lines multiply at similar rates in chick fibroblasts and the ratio of plaque-forming to egg-infective particles is very close to one. A study of the strains after propagation in chick embryos and in fibroblasts showed the marker characteristics to be stable. We shall refer to the two strains according to their plaque type or by the corresponding letters C (clear) and T (turbid).

Phenotypic mixing and diploidy with NDV

Chick fibroblasts in monolayers were infected with mixtures of the C and T strains in equal proportions and at high multiplicities, sometimes over 20. The yield from infection was harvested after 18–20 hr. and was plated out on monolayers so that the plaques were widely dispersed. Over 400 plaques were classified as clear or cloudy and were picked and subcultured in chick embryos. The virus haemagglutinin from the embryos was characterized for its sensitivity to heat and the plaque suspension for sensitivity to serum.

None of the clones investigated in this way was found to be of recombinant type; in other words, virus cultured from clear plaques was heat- and serum-resistant and that from cloudy plaques was heat- and serum-sensitive. One exception, to be described more fully below, was that some plaques yielded *both* parent types, but there is no exception to the statement that stable recombinations of these three characters were not found. It is important to remember that all these tests were done *after* plating. In order to characterize a clone, it was necessary to deal with the descendants of a single particle in the production of which a large number of cell-to-cell virus transfers was involved.

When the yields from mixed infections were treated with serum (or heat) *before* plating on a monolayer, it was expected that the turbid population would be wiped out, since the parental turbids are sensitive to both agents, and the serum especially is very efficient and selective in wiping out the parent-type turbids. It was surprising to find that 60–85 % of the turbid population from a mixed infection was able to survive serum treatment and the survival of turbids after heating was also much greater than expected. However, the virus in the surviving turbid plaques gave rise to clones which were parent-type turbids. On the other hand, the clear-plaque formers, which are ordinarily completely resistant to serum, were found to be partially inactivated (15–25 %) when the virus came from a mixed infection.

This temporary resistance to heat and serum is probably the result of phenotypic mixing. Sensitive and resistant coating materials are made in the same mixedly infected cell and the distribution of clear and turbid genotypes among sensitive and resistant phenotypes occurs in nearly random fashion. The absence of total randomness might be expected in a double infection of a large cell, where the coating products of each virus type are not evenly distributed throughout the cell.

When a mixture of virus types is heated at 56°, both the sensitive and resistant populations are inactivated, but at different rates, and therefore it is difficult to measure accurately the total yield of turbid heat-resistant particles. With an absorbed serum, however, it is possible to remove the serum-sensitive population completely (99·9 %) without detectably affecting the number of resistant particles. Very often the proportion of phenotypically mixed particles of either type (clear-sensitive and turbid-resistant) is about equal (see Table 5), but the occurrence of the turbid-resistants furnishes a much more accurate index of the degree of phenotypic mixing since this particle is normally absent after serum treatment. For this reason phenotypic mixing has been followed mostly in terms of the number of turbid serum-resistant particles present. The term 'turbid resistant', as used subsequently, refers to genetically turbid, phenotypically resistant particles. Particles which are genetically turbid and genetically resistant have not been found.

If the production of turbid resistant particles were due to phenotypic mixing alone, then infection of cells with turbid resistant virus at very low multiplicities, where double infection is nearly absent, should result in the virtual disappearance of this class in the first-cycle yield. The results of an experiment to test this assumption are given in Table 2.

Table 2. *Serial transmission of phenotypic mixing in NDV*

Test for production of phenotypic mixing

Virus preparation	Adsorption multiplicity		Calculated percentage of turbid infected cells that are also clear infected	Percentage of turbids in the yield that are serum-resistant	Heterozygotes found: expressed as percentage of total turbids
	Clear	Turbid			
1	0·04	0·01	4	27	20
2	0·0004	0·0002	0·04	8	6·5

Preparation 1 is the overnight yield from a mixed infection in which the multiplicity was over 20. 57 % of the turbids in this preparation were phenotypically serum-resistant. Preparation 2 was the yield from infection by 1 at the multiplicities shown in line 1.

The starting material for this experiment was the yield from fibroblasts that had been doubly infected at a very high multiplicity of both the C and T strains. The virus in this yield was about 20 % turbid and 57 % of these turbids were serum-resistant. This fluid was tested in two ways: first to determine the number of heterozygous diploid particles, and secondly to estimate the ability of the suspension to give turbid resistant particles from infections at low multiplicities.

The test for diploids, as has already been mentioned, consisted of plating the suspension, picking a large number of plaques at random and replating these plaques. Most plaques bred true by this test but about 7 % yielded virus of both types (clear and turbid) in nearly equal numbers. The plaques that yielded both parental types were sometimes clear, sometimes cloudy and fairly often mottled. This result, which is similar to the finding of diploid heterozygotes with influenza (Gotlieb & Hirst, 1954) is given in the extreme right-hand column of Table 2, where the frequency is expressed as a percentage of the turbid population. The total population from mixed infection at high multiplicities usually contains about 10 % of such double yielders.

In the test for capacity to produce resistant turbids, cells were infected with the virus at a fairly low multiplicity and a 6 hr. yield was tested to see what proportion of the turbid particles was serum resistant. About 4 % of resistant turbids might have been expected on the calculated frequency of doubly infected cells (line 1, Table 2), but the proportion of resistant turbids found was 27 %. This should not be true if resistant turbids occurred only as an expression of phenotypic mixing. This experiment was carried one step further by taking the virus yield from the first low multiplicity infection and testing it for diploids and ability to produce resistant turbids by infection. The heterozygous diploids made up 6·5 % of the turbid population. The second cycle of infection was carried out at extremely low multiplicities, so that the expected number of doubly infected cells was negligible, yet 8 % of the turbids in the yield were resistant.

Table 3. *Effect of multiplicity of infection on yield of mixed phenotypes*

	Adsorption multiplicities		Percentage of turbid infected cells expected to be mixedly infected	Percentage of turbids found to be phenotypically serum-resistant
Virus preparation	Clear	Turbid		
Yield from mixed C-T	0·021	0·012	2·1	25
infection of high multi-	0·0021	0·0012	0·21	25
plicity (line 1, Table 2)	0·00021	0·00012	0·021	24
In vitro mixture of clear	0·021	0·014	2·1	12
and turbid parental virus	0·0021	0·0014	0·21	4
	0·00021	0·00014	0·021	>0·6

In order to be certain that the turbid resistant particles found at low multiplicity were not the result of some occult double infection of cells (perhaps by non-plaque-forming particles), virus suspension 1 (Table 2) was used to infect cells at several multiplicities. If resistant turbids all came from two-particle-infection, then the first-cycle yield should change markedly with multiplicity. However, the proportion remained around

25 % (Table 3) regardless of multiplicity, indicating that single particles can give rise to resistant turbids.

These results indicate the occurrence of a phenotype which is transiently inheritable. The clue to the understanding of this effect probably lies in the close correspondence between the proportion of heterozygous diploids and the percentage of turbids which are resistant in each generation. If we subtract the 4 % mixedly infected cells in the first low multiplicity passage (a somewhat doubtful correction) we then find 20 % diploids and 23 % resistant turbids in one generation and 6·5 and 8 % in the next. Both types occur in similar proportion in each generation.

On this somewhat slender evidence, we postulate that NDV is a diploid virus, normally of a C-C or T-T variety. Under conditions of high multiplicity mixed infection, a large number of the new particles formed are by chance of the C-T variety. Infection of a cell with a C-T particle results in the production of both genomes and sufficient 'resistant' coating material so that most (possibly 75 %) of the particles produced will be serum-resistant. If both genomes reproduce in the cell at equal rates, and if there is a random assortment of genomes in making diploids, then half the progeny from a C-T-infected cell should be C-T and the proportion of C-T particles in the total population should decline by half with each cell generation. The decline which was found was from 20 to 6·5 %, and while these figures are preliminary and not very precise, they are consistent with such a mechanism. The results are not precise enough to rule out the occurrence of more than two genomes in some particles, a possibility which could be tested in a mixed triple infection. However, the striking similarity of these results to those with influenza suggests that a diploid or variable polyploid state may be quite general with haemagglutinating viruses and may be a result of the method of particle coating at the cell surface.

The foregoing data were obtained mainly by measuring phenotypic mixing in terms of serum sensitivity. The same general picture is found when heat resistance is followed except that the results are necessarily not quite so precise.

It was of interest to see with what frequency the two types of resistance occurred in the same turbid particle. One might expect that the incidence of double mixing (heat and serum) might be rather high since the opportunity exists in every C-T-infected cell. If the two types of resistance were randomly distributed among the progeny of a C-T-infected cell, one would not expect partial inactivation by heat to alter the proportion of serum-resistant turbids in the survivors. However, when 90 % of the turbid population was heat-killed, the proportion of serum-resistant turbids was reduced by half (Table 4). The results suggest that the distribution of the two forms of resistance is not random and that a heat-resistant particle has about half the average chance of being serum-resistant also. On the other hand, more than an average number of heat-sensitive particles must be resistant to serum. The problem may be further complicated by the existence of varying degrees of heat and

Table 4. *Survival of phenotypically serum-resistant turbid virus on heating*

| | | Turbids surviving heat and serum. Percentage of number surviving heat | |
Treatment of virus	Turbids surviving heat. Percentage of unheated number	Preparation 1	Preparation 2
Unheated control	100	57	28
56°, 5 min.	10	34	14
56°, 10 min.	0·7	34	—

Preparation 1 was made from cells doubly infected at a multiplicity over 20; 2 was made with a multiplicity of 7 for each virus.

serum sensitivity depending on the chance inclusion of variable amounts of resistant substances. At present we have no idea at what level this antagonism between the two forms of resistance operates. It is possible that it may be phenotypic in the sense that inclusion of heat-resistant material in a particle may tend to exclude serum-resistant material. In any case this is an interesting finding which will require more experimental study.

Phenotypic mixing with NDV at low multiplicities

From certain controls (see Table 3, part 2) it was noted that when the C and T viruses were mixed *in vitro* and then used to infect cells at low multiplicity, the yield of resistant turbids was sometimes considerably higher than would be expected from the probable proportion of infected cells which were mixedly infected. In Table 5 are shown the results of an experiment in which the two viruses, mixed *in vitro*, induced infections at multiplicities varying over a thousandfold range. The expected proportion of mixedly infected cells was calculated for each multiplicity. From the last column of Table 5 it may be seen that the proportion of phenotypic mixing found (resistant turbids/total turbids) was less than expected down to multiplicities of 0·25, but became much higher than expected at still lower multiplicities. In Table 6 are the results of another experiment of similar nature in which the multiplicity of the turbid line is kept constant and that of the clear line is varied. In each case the yield of resistant turbids was six to twelve times the expected number.

Table 5. *Amount of phenotypic mixing from mixed infections at low multiplicities*

(1) Adsorption multiplicities		(2) Percentage of turbids found to be serum-resistant	(3) Percentage of clears found to be serum-sensitive	(4) Calculated percentage of turbid infected cells that are mixedly infected	(5) Ratio of found/expected (col. 2/col. 4)
Clear	Turbid				
1·0	1·0	24	25	63	0·37
0·5	0·5	20	25	39	0·51
0·25	0·25	17	12	22	0·77
0·12	0·12	14	15	11	1·25
0·06	0·06	12	10	6	2·1
0·03	0·03	13	4	3	4·4
0·015	0·015	7·8	0	1·5	5·2
0·007	0·007	6·0	0	0·75	8·8
—	1·0	0·1	—	—	—
1·0	—	—	0	—	—

The C and T strains were mixed *in vitro* and then diluted in twofold steps for infecting cells. The 6 hr. yield was tested for phenotypic mixing.

Table 6. *Amount of phenotypic mixing with constant turbid and variable clear multiplicities*

(1) Adsorption multiplicities		(2) Percentage of turbids found to be serum-resistant	(3) Calculated percentage of turbid infected cells that are mixedly infected	(4) Ratio of found/expected (col. 2/col. 4)
Clear	Turbid			
0·017	0·008	10·2	1·7	6
0·008	0·008	10·8	0·8	10
0·004	0·008	4·9	0·4	12
0·002	0·008	1·4	0·2	7
0·001	0·008	1·0	0·1	10

The C and T strains were mixed *in vitro* and then monolayers were infected at various multiplicities. The 6 hr. yield was tested for phenotypic mixing.

The principal effect observed is that the proportion of particles showing phenotypic mixing is in excess of what can be accounted for in terms of the probable number of mixedly infected cells. In making these comparisons between expected mixed infections and yield of resistant turbids we are assuming that practically all the turbid virus from a mixedly infected cell will be resistant. Another assumption is that turbid resistant particles will be produced at the same rate as turbid sensitive virus in any cell. With these assumptions there are two main ways of explaining the results. One is to assume that the host cells do not all absorb virus equally well. If one-third or one-quarter of the cells did most of the absorbing then these cells would be infected at much higher multiplicities than the *average* figure would indicate, and the yield of mixed phenotypes could be correspondingly large. Not enough experiments have been done at the present time to rule out this possibility with assurance, but some of the data with poliomyelitis, given below, speak against this hypothesis. A second possibility is that both plaque-forming and non-plaque-forming particles in the NDV suspensions may be entering the same cells. The non-plaque formers may be stimulating the formation of virus substances that can become incorporated in new viable particles being made as a result of infection by a plaque former. Some estimates of the proportion of 'inactive' particles in NDV suspensions are as high as 90 % and hence are consistent with this explanation. At multiplicities around 1, there is considerable inhibition of the yield of phenotypically mixed particles but the basis of this inhibition is not clear.

DOUBLE NEUTRALIZATION WITH POLIOVIRUSES

Mixed poliovirus infections of HeLa cell monolayers have been studied by Dr Nada Ledinko. HeLa cells were simultaneously infected with equal multiplicities of types 1 and 2 poliovirus and the progeny, both early and late, were examined for the proportion of particles which carried both type 1 and 2 antigens. The occurrence of doubly neutraliz-able (phenotypically mixed) particles can be readily measured, even down to fairly low levels, by the plaque technique. The system is somewhat more limited than with NDV because observations are restricted to a single character, antigenic type.

Some of the results with this system are given in Fig. 1. The yield of doubly neutralizable virus is given in terms of the combined (1 plus 2) multiplicity. The amount of phenotypic mixing in yields taken at 20 hr. is somewhat less than might be expected from the calculated number of mixed infections involved, and when the total multiplicity was less than 1, the yield of doubly neutralizable types was too low to be measurable. With 4–6 hr. yields, the proportion of phenotypic mixing was very close to the expected at multiplicities above 1, though the maximum was about 85 %. At lower fractional multiplicities the yield was very much better than expected, in some cases by a factor of more than thirty. There is independent evidence that as many as 97 % of the particles in poliovirus preparations are non-plaque-forming and, to explain the high yield of phenotypic mixing, we may again invoke antigenic contributions from this class. Evidence will be presented below which indicates that an unequal distribution of virus among the cells is not a factor. However, another element is the observation (see below) that mixed phenotypes are excreted in highest concentration early in infection so that early yields may give an exaggerated impression of the number of double infections.

There are two significant respects in which the poliomyelitis results differ from those with NDV. Very few plaques from a mixed type 1– type 2 infection yield both parental types and there is no evidence for the temporary transmission of mixed serotypes. If the progeny of a mixed infection, containing 85 % of its particles in doubly neutralizable form, is used to infect cells at low multiplicities, no more doubly antigenic particles appear than in a suitable control.

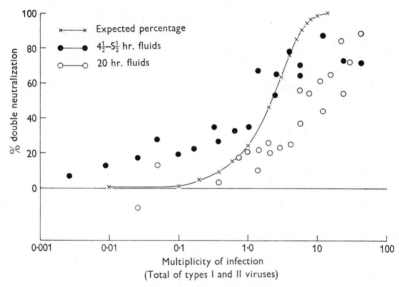

Fig. 1. The yield of doubly neutralizable poliovirus particles after infection of cells with types 1 and 2 at different multiplicities. The virus input of the two types does not differ by a factor greater than 3/2. ×—×, expected percentage of doubly neutralizable virus; ●, percentage found in $4\frac{1}{2}$ and $5\frac{1}{2}$ hr. fluids; ○, percentage found in 20 hr. fluids.

Another interesting, and thus far poorly explained, finding can be seen by comparing the early and late yields from mixedly infected cells as shown in Fig. 1. The late yields contain a much lower proportion of double forms than the corresponding early fluids. Preliminary experiments carried out at a multiplicity of about five showed that the peak of mixed antigenic virus concentration was reached very early in both supernatant and cells (3–4 hr.) and then declined rapidly from 70 to 20 % in several hours. It did not decline further overnight. It may also be seen from Fig. 1 that the proportional drop in percentage of mixed virus is less as the multiplicity goes above 1. There is a somewhat similar drop in the degree of phenotypic mixing seen with time in NDV-infected fibro-blasts. There is as yet no experimentally tested explanation for this marked shift with time in the type of virus produced. It seems possible, however, that double infection of HeLa cells (which are very large cells) may create cytoplasmic zones of virus production that frequently over-lap only partially, and since any overlap area would have a higher con-centration of virus precursor materials, virus may be finished and excreted from this area first. When the two overlapping zones are different with respect to the inciting virus, then the first virus completed would be largely made with mixed coats. This early surge of virus production may then deplete this area and tend to divide the singly infected zones. According to this view higher multiplicities of infection should increase the proportion of overlap area and decrease the amount of the early–late shift. This is in accord with the findings.

If the phenotypic mixing seen after infection with poliovirus at low multiplicities is considered to be due to phenotypic contributions from non-plaque formers, then these imperfect particles must be able to enter cells, to stimulate the production of virus substances but not to repro-duce. Since the nature of the defect in non-plaque formers is unknown, tests for multiplicity reactivation between these non-viable forms might be interesting. The high proportion of non-plaque formers would permit experiments in which multiple non-plaque-forming particles could pene-trate cells, usually without accompanying plaque formers.

Some preliminary experiments have been carried out on these lines by Dr Benjamin Mandel. HeLa cells in suspension were infected with poliovirus type 1. Infection was carried out at a number of multiplicities. The cells were then plated for infectious centres on HeLa monolayers and the results (Fig. 2) are expressed as a proportion (found/expected or F/E) in which the numerator is the number of infectious centres found and the denominator is the number of cells infected based on the number of plaque-forming units absorbed and corrected for Poisson distribution.

At a multiplicity of 1 the yield was the same as the expected; this is evidence against the occurrence of big differences in the amounts of virus adsorbed to different cells. Since the expected number of cells was in-fected at a multiplicity of one, the distribution was most probably random. This type of virus distribution could not explain therefore the large excess of doubly neutralizable particles which was found at low multiplicities of mixed infection.

At multiplicities between 1 and 10 the yield was less than expected, possibly due to auto-interference effects. At multiplicities below 0·6 the yield rose to twice the expected until at multiplicities around 0·002 the yield returned to the expected level. It is conceivable that the excess of infectious centres over input results from a reactivation process between two non-plaque formers.

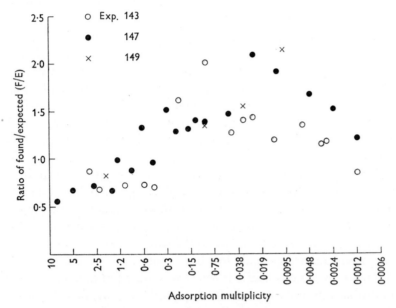

Fig. 2. The yield of infectious centres in terms of input with poliovirus 1 and suspended HeLa cells. The cells were infected at different multiplicities, in terms of plaque-forming units. The amount of virus adsorbed was used to calculate the expected yield of infectious centres, taking into account the Poisson distribution.

INFLUENZA VIRUS PLAQUE FORMATION

Interest in influenza virus genetics is high because this is the only RNA virus in which recombination has been demonstrated. It is somewhat ironic that it is also a virus which offers great practical obstacles to the use of the plaque technique.

We have found that chick fibroblast monolayers give good plaques with certain influenza strains. Cells from 12-day-old chick embryos are allowed to attach to glass in the presence of 20 % horse serum and lact-albumin hydrolysate. After 24 hr. the plates are washed, infected and overlaid with a mixture of lactalbumin hydrolysate, yeast extract, gelatin and agar. It has proved to be very important to incubate the plates, both before and after infection, in an atmosphere of 10 % carbon dioxide. In 5 % carbon dioxide the number of plaques formed is drastically reduced. On this type of monolayer the neurotropic strain of WS isolated by Francis and Moore (WSN) gives good distinct plaques after

7

3 to 4 days' incubation. The plaques are much larger than those of NDV and they are perfectly round. The number is proportional to input, indicating that a single particle can give rise to a plaque. The ratio of plaque-forming to egg-infective units is about one. Adsorption of virus to fibroblasts is rapid and virtually complete in about 30 min.

Other strains of influenza strain WS also give plaques but with a much lower efficiency in our experience. A Melbourne strain which was rescued from a u.v.-inactivated state by mixed infection with WSN, was found to be somewhat virulent for mice (Gotlieb & Hirst, 1956) and it also produces very turbid plaques on chick fibroblasts with an efficiency of about 1–10 %, based on egg infectivity. Our regular strain of Melbourne and a number of other strains have been tested but produce no pathogenic effect.

Recombination has been accomplished with the WSN strain in chick fibroblasts *in vitro* as is shown by the following: a small plaque mutant with a slow growth rate was isolated from WSN stock by picking small plaques. Most small plaques give either plaques of normal size or small plaques with a high reversion rate to the wild type size. The small plaque former used had an unusually low back mutation rate to large. Virus of the PR8 strain (a non-plaque former) was added in high concentration to a fibroblast monolayer and after a period of adsorption the plate was washed and seeded with a small number of plaque-forming units of the small WSN plaque former. About one-third of the resultant plaques (WSN serotype) were large in size and were large on subculture. This was probably the result of recombination between a plaque-forming and a non-plaque-forming virus.

In the following experiment the efficiency of fibroblasts in forming infectious centres with WSN was measured in a test essentially like that shown with polio-virus (Fig. 2). Fibroblasts were prepared from monolayers by trypsinization and the washed cells were mixed with various concentrations of virus at a final level of 5×10^6 cells/ml. Adsorption of 60 % of the virus was complete in 30 min. The supernatant fluids were tested for unadsorbed plaque-forming units and the cells were plated for infectious centres. The results are shown in Table 7 in which the yield is calculated in relation to the amount of virus adsorbed or the yield expected, after correcting for virus distribution. For the first three multiplicities the yield was 25–30 % of expected and thereafter the yield rose sharply to about twice the input and remained at this level to the lowest multiplicity tested.

Thus there appears to be something in the inoculum which, at higher multiplicities, interferes with virus production in most of the cells.

Table 7. *Efficiency of plating infectious centres at various adsorption multiplicities of influenza strain WSN*

Adsorption multiplicity	Actual yield of infectious centres / Expected yield of infectious centres
1·1	0·25
0·18	0·30
0·06	0·29
0·009	0·97
0·0026	2·49
0·001	1·82

Preliminary studies indicate that the interfering substance has a sedimentability of the same order as plaque-forming virus. Treatment of cells that had been infected with virus at low multiplicity with a WSN antiserum had no effect on the number of infectious centres. All of the adsorbed virus became unavailable to serum. On the other hand, cells that had adsorbed virus at a multiplicity of 0·3 plaque-forming units/cell gave a poor yield of infectious centres, but this low yield was completely abolished by treating the cells with antiserum. Furthermore, the serum-treated cells behaved after washing like new ones at either high or low multiplicity.

From this preliminary evidence it appears possible that non-plaque-forming virus may be interfering with cell infection by plaque formers. It is odd that no particles appear to have entered cells exposed to multiplicities of about 1. Interference appears to be established very rapidly and this fact and the ease of serum reversal suggest that this may be a kindred phenomenon to that found by Baluda (1957) with u.v.-irradiated NDV.

In summary, our recent experience with NDV and poliovirus shows that phenotypic mixing occurs readily with these viruses and that, with NDV, there is a diploid state which provides for a transient transmission of a state of phenotypic mixing. It seems likely that this diploid state may be common to all myxoviruses, but apparently not to polioviruses. Phenotypic mixing also occurs following mixed infection at low multiplicities, conceivably by virus antigen contributions generated by non-plaque-forming virus particles.

Recombination has been found with influenza but not so far with NDV or polioviruses. These negative results may merely mean that recombination rates with the latter agents are very low, possibly because the genetic pieces are small; or they may only mean that insufficient numbers of markers have been tested. But they may finally prove to reflect a fundamental difference between influenza and the other viruses.

REFERENCES

BALUDA, M. (1957). Homologous interference by ultraviolet-inactivated Newcastle disease virus. *Virology*, **4**, 72.

BARON, S. & JENSEN, K. E. (1955). Evidence for genetic interaction between noninfectious and infectious influenza A viruses. *J. exp. Med.* **162**, 677.

BREITENFELD, P. M. & SCHÄFER, W. (1957). The formation of fowl plague virus antigens in infected cells, as studied with fluorescent antibodies. *Virology*, **4**, 328.

BURNET, F. M. (1955). *Principles of Animal Virology*. New York: Academic Press.

BURNET, F. M. & LIND, P. E. (1951a). A genetic approach to variation in influenza viruses. 3. Recombination of characters in influenza strains used in mixed infections. *J. gen. Microbiol.* **5**, 59.

BURNET, F. M. & LIND, P. E. (1951b). A genetic approach to variation in influenza viruses. 4. Recombination of characters between the influenza virus A strain NWS and strains of different serological subtypes. *J. gen. Microbiol.* **5**, 68.

BURNET, F. M. & LIND, P. E. (1952). Studies on recombination with influenza viruses in the chick embryo. III. Reciprocal genetic interaction between two influenza virus strains. *Aust. J. exp. Biol. med. Sci.* **30**, 469.

BURNET, F. M. & LIND, P. E. (1954a). An analysis of the adaptation of an influenza virus to produce lesions in the mouse lung. *Aust. J. exp. Biol. med. Sci.* **32**, 711.

BURNET, F. M. & LIND, P. E. (1954b). Reactivation of heat inactivated virus by recombination. *Aust. J. exp. Biol. med. Sci.* **32**, 133.

BURNET, F. M. & LIND, P. E. (1956). Comparative study of recombinants of different types of influenza A virus with the strain WSE. *Aust. J. exp. Biol. med. Sci.* **34**, 1.

FENNER, F. & COMBEN, B. M. (1958). Genetic studies with mammalian poxviruses. 1. Demonstration of recombination between two strains of vaccinia virus. *Virology*, **5**, 530.

FRASER, K. B. (1953). Genetic interaction and interference between the Mel and NWS strains of influenza A virus. *Brit. J. exp. Path.* **34**, 319.

FRASER, K. B. & BURNET, F. M. (1952). Studies on recombination with influenza viruses in the chick embryo. II. Genetic interaction between influenza virus strains in the chick embryo. *Aust. J. exp. Biol. med. Sci.* **30**, 459.

GORDON, F. B. & MAMAY, H. K. (1957). Combination of characters (drug resistance) in a single strain of psittacosis virus. *Science*, **126**, 354.

GOTLIEB, T. & HIRST, G. K. (1954). The experimental production of combination forms of virus. III. The formation of doubly antigenic particles from influenza A and B virus and a study of the ability of individual particles of X virus to yield two separate strains. *J. exp. Med.* **99**, 307.

GOTLIEB, T. & HIRST, G. K. (1956). The experimental production of combination forms of virus. VI. Reactivation of influenza viruses after inactivation by ultraviolet light. *Virology*, **2**, 235.

GRANOFF, A. & HIRST, G. K. (1954). Experimental production of combination forms of virus. IV. Mixed influenza A Newcastle disease virus infections. *Proc. Soc. exp. Biol., N.Y.* **86**, 84.

HIRST, G. K. & GOTLIEB, T. (1953a). The experimental production of combination forms of virus. I. Occurrence of combination forms after simultaneous inoculation of the allantoic sac with two distinct strains of influenza virus. *J. exp. Med.* **98**, 41.

HIRST, G. K. & GOTLIEB, T. (1953b). The experimental production of combination forms of virus. II. A study of serial passage in the allantoic sac of agents that combine the antigens of two distinct influenza A strains. *J. exp. Med.* **98**, 53.

HIRST, G. K. & GOTLIEB, T. (1955). The experimental production of combination forms of virus. V. Alterations in the virulence of neurotropic influenza virus as a result of mixed infection. *Virology*, **1**, 221.

LIND, P. E. & BURNET, F. M. (1953). Back-recombination of influenza A strains obtained in recombination experiments. *Aust. J. exp. Biol. med. Sci.* **31**, 361.

LIND, P. E. & BURNET, F. M. (1957a). Recombination between virulent and non-virulent strains of influenza virus. 1. The significance of heterozygosis. *Aust. J. exp. Biol. med. Sci.* **35**, 57.

LIND, P. E. & BURNET, F. M. (1957b). Recombination between virulent and non-virulent strains of influenza virus. 2. The behaviour of virulence markers on recombination. *Aust. J. exp. Biol. med. Sci.* **35**, 67.

PERRY, B. & BURNET, F. M. (1953). Recombination with two influenza virus B strains. *Aust. J. exp. Biol. Med. Sci.* **31**, 519.

WILDY, P. (1955). Recombination with herpes simplex virus. *J. gen. Microbiol.* **13** 346.

WATSON, B. K. & COONS, A. H. (1954). Studies on influenza virus infection in the chick embryo using fluorescent antibody. *J. exp. Med.* **99**, 419.

VIRAL INTERFERENCE

ALICK ISAACS

National Institute for Medical Research, Mill Hill, London

Interference describes the action of a virus, either live or inactivated, on cells, as a result of which the cells are rendered unable to support fully the growth of immunologically related and unrelated viruses. Interference is, therefore, characteristically a phenomenon at the *cellular* level, and it does not include specific immunological protection or factors such as increased phagocytosis which might give rise to non-specific protective effects. Nevertheless, the above definition is a very broad one which could still embrace those instances where one virus, as a result of its destructive behaviour, renders cells uninhabitable for other viruses. But the field of interest was narrowed when Henle and Henle showed in 1943 that inactivated virus, which was incapable of multiplying, retained its ability to interfere with the growth of other viruses, and the Henles' experimental model, that is, interference by inactivated influenza virus with the growth of other viruses in the allantoic cavity of the chick embryo, has been used extensively by them and by other workers.

However, even this experimental system includes at least three distinct mechanisms. In the first, influenza or related virus which has been inactivated, for example, by ultraviolet (u.v.) light, in such a way that it retains its enzymatic (neuraminidase) activity, is able to remove virus receptors from susceptible cells by its enzymatic action. Interference therefore results from the fact that the challenge virus cannot adsorb to the cells, and this appears to be the explanation (Baluda, personal communication) for the interference produced by u.v.-irradiated Newcastle disease virus in chick embryo fibroblasts in the system described by Baluda (1957).

A second type of interference was described by Henle & Rosenberg (1949). In this case, u.v.-irradiated influenza virus could interfere with the growth of *homotypic* influenza virus in the chick embryo even when it was inoculated after the live virus. This phenomenon was found to have two important characteristics which differentiate it from other forms of viral interference. First, the interference is strictly homotypic, i.e. u.v.-irradiated influenza A viruses interfere with the growth of influenza A virus but not influenza B virus, and vice versa. This indicates that this form of interference may be directed against the production of a type-specific component of the virus. Secondly, the fact that homotypic interference was still effective when the u.v.-inactivated virus was inoculated 3 hr. after the live virus (Henle, 1949), that is, when the growth cycle of the live virus was well under way, differentiates it clearly from the third form of interference, in which some hours are required before interference by inactivated virus becomes established. Presumably the synthesis of this particular type-specific component is not completed until at least 3 hr. after infection is initiated, and can still be interrupted during the first 3 hr. of the virus cycle. Unfortunately, this interesting phenomenon does not seem to have been further studied and most research on viral interference has been concentrated on the third type.

In this third type interference is effective not only against the virus used to initiate the interference but also against quite unrelated viruses. Thus inactivated influenza (a ribonucleic acid- or RNA-containing) virus can interfere not only with influenza viruses but also with DNA (deoxyribonucleic acid) viruses like vaccinia. There is some evidence that this form of interference, which we might call heterologous interference (a name used by Fazekas de St Groth & Edney, 1952), is mediated through an intermediate substance, to which the name 'interferon' has been given (Isaacs & Lindenmann, 1957). Heterologous interference induced by inactivated virus, as well as being the most carefully investigated variety of viral interference, is also the phenomenon which at the moment throws most light on the processes of virus multiplication. We shall consider now the important characteristics of heterologous interference and of the action of interferon, with particular reference to their bearing on the processes of virus multiplication.

HETEROLOGOUS INTERFERENCE BY INACTIVE VIRUS

In most studies on heterologous interference one of the myxoviruses, inactivated in one or other way, was used as interfering agent, and a number of different viruses have been tested as challenge viruses. The degree of interference which results depends on a number of factors such as the method used for inactivating the virus, the multiplicity of the inactive virus, the time interval between interfering and challenge viruses and the strains of virus used. These factors will now be considered.

The significance of the method of virus inactivation

Interfering virus has been prepared by inactivating virus in a number of different ways, for example, by treatment with u.v. light, heat, formaldehyde or nitrogen mustard (Henle, 1950). Probably the most effective method is the use of u.v. light. Henle & Henle (1947) made a careful study of the effect of varying doses of u.v. light on different properties of influenza viruses. The most sensitive property was the infectivity, and after that, in order of decreasing sensitivity, came the toxic, interfering, haemagglutinating and complement-fixing properties of the virus. Powell & Setlow (1956) showed that the rapid loss of influenza virus infectivity on u.v. irradiation results primarily from damage of the viral RNA. The haemagglutinating, enzymatic and complement-fixing properties, being functions of the virus protein, are more resistant to u.v. irradiation at 2537 Å. The fact that the interfering activity of influenza virus is much more sensitive to u.v. light than the serological properties of the virus suggests that interference depends on the use of virus in which the nucleic acid has not been heavily damaged. Some evidence will be presented (p. 109) to show that optimal interferon production also requires the use of lightly irradiated virus.

Recently, Paucker & Henle (1958) have compared the interfering activity of u.v.-irradiated preparations of standard influenza virus with those of irradiated incomplete virus. The two showed comparable interfering activity on a haemagglutinin (that is, virus particle) basis except when incomplete virus with a very low infectivity/haemagglutinin (ID_{50}/HA) ratio was used. Under these conditions the virus has been shown to have a low content of soluble antigen (nucleoprotein) extractable by ether from the elementary bodies and a low RNA content (Ada & Perry, 1956). In addition, a preparation of haemagglutinin from influenza virus grown in HeLa cells contained no extractable soluble antigen and was devoid of interfering activity. These findings led Paucker and Henle to conclude that the soluble antigen of the irradiated virus or its RNA component may be the actual interfering agent. Direct experimental proof of this is unfortunately lacking, since the soluble antigen extracted from irradiated virus by ether treatment showed no interfering activity, a result which Dr Burke and I found independently. Nevertheless, the indirect evidence strongly favours the hypothesis that interfering activity depends on a particular degree of damage to the viral nucleic acid.

The fact that interference can result from an exclusion effect (Baluda, 1957) might be taken as support for an early theory of viral interference, that it resulted from a cell-blocking action of the interfering virus which prevented the challenge virus from being adsorbed to the cells. However, the experiments of Henle & Henle (1947) show that after u.v. irradiation the interfering activity of a virus preparation can be lost while it retains its full haemagglutinating and enzymatic activity, that is, its full ability to exclude the challenge virus, and this provides indirect evidence that interference occurs at an intracellular site. The fact that enzymatic activity of the virus is not required for interference was shown by Isaacs & Edney (1950) who found that virus heated at 56° for 1 hr. had lost all detectable enzymatic activity but was still able to induce interference. Virus heated at 56° is a less efficient interfering agent than virus inactivated by u.v. light, but heating at lower temperatures, for example incubation for many hours at 37 or 42°, was found to be better (Tyrrell & Tamm, 1955). Presumably, at these lower temperatures, less damage to the virus nucleic acid occurs than at 56°.

The interfering activity is therefore a function of the virus particle independent of its infective, haemagglutinating and enzymatic properties, and seems to depend on a particular degree of damage to the viral nucleic acid. The damaged virus particle is unable to complete the process of virus multiplication, but it can enter the susceptible cell and set up a reaction which leads to a block at an intracellular site of virus synthesis.

Multiplicity of interfering virus

Many interference experiments have been carried out using inactivated virus at a multiplicity (that is, number of virus particles per cell) of many thousands. But a high multiplicity is not essential for inducing interference.

According to Henle & Henle (1947) a dose of 3×10^7 ID_{50} of influenza virus was capable after irradiation with u.v. light of suppressing completely haemagglutinin production by influenza virus in the chick allantoic cavity, that is, of a more than 99·9 % inhibition of virus growth. More recently Henle & Paucker (1958) reported that significant interference in the allantoic sac was induced by seven agglutinating doses of irradiated virus, corresponding to about $1·5 \times 10^7$ ID_{50}. The number of allantoic cells is in the same range, that is, between 2 and 5×10^7 and measurable interference therefore occurs when the equivalent of one ID_{50} is present per cell. However, under these experimental conditions one ID_{50} corresponds to about ten virus particles as seen in the electron microscope (Donald & Isaacs, 1954), and a similar relationship might hold for interference, that is, when a multiplicity of ten virus particles per cell is needed to induce interference only one out of ten particles may be actually effective. On the other hand, it is interesting that incomplete virus with an ID_{50}/HA ratio of less than one hundredth that of standard virus has an unimpaired ability to induce interference (Paucker & Henle, 1958); this suggests that the total number of virus particles rather than the number of infective doses may be the significant figure in the degree of interference induced. Hence on present experimental evidence minimal interference is found at a multiplicity of 5–10.

With influenza virus inactivated by heating at 56° a much higher multiplicity (of some hundreds) is required for inducing interference, although Fazekas de St Groth & Edney (1952) have presented statistical evidence that a single 'effective' heated virus particle per cell completely prevents multiplication of challenge virus in that cell. It may be that one heated virus particle out of some hundreds inoculated is capable of inducing interference while the remainder have lost this property. Alternatively one heated virus particle may be required to induce interference in one *site* and each cell may contain a number of sites at which interference with viral synthesis can be induced. If this were so, one would have to assume that each particle of u.v.-inactivated virus was capable of blocking a number of sites.

Interval of time between interfering and challenge viruses

In early studies on heterologous interference it was not always appreciated that interference took some hours to be established. However, Fazekas de St Groth, Isaacs & Edney (1952) showed, by studying growth curves of influenza virus in eggs in which interference had been induced by heated influenza virus, that some hours were required before interference was established. In addition Fazekas de St Groth & Edney (1952) found that if a 24 hr. interval was allowed between interfering and challenge viruses, the final yield of virus was independent of the dose of challenge virus, quite a different result from that obtained when insufficient time was allowed for interference to be established (Isaacs & Edney, 1950).

Tyrrell & Tamm (1955) observed that if heated influenza virus was inoculated 23 hr. before the challenge virus, interference was established, but with a 2 hr. interval it was not established. Also, if a 23 hr. interval was allowed, but the interfering virus and tissue were incubated together at 4° instead of the usual 37°, no interference was established. The time and temperature required for establishment of interference might be due to the necessity for the interfering virus to be taken up by cells or for some other intracellular action of the interfering virus. However, Isaacs & Lindenmann (1957) showed that if a short period of incubation at 37° was allowed for the uptake of heated influenza virus and the tissues were then washed, incubation for between 4 and 20 hr. at 37° was still required to establish interference, and that incubation at 2° for the same time was ineffective. This suggested that some other metabolic activity was necessary and investigations revealed that some of this time could be accounted for by the time required to produce an intermediate in the interference reaction which we have called 'interferon' (see below). However, this may not fully explain the time required because some hours' incubation at 37° are still required before interference by interferon is established (Lindenmann, Burke & Isaacs, 1957).

In a more precise evaluation of the time required before interference by u.v.-irradiated influenza virus became established, Henle & Paucker (1958) found that interference was complete 9 hr. after inoculating large doses of irradiated virus (850 HA* units per egg). When smaller doses (20–100 HA units per egg) of irradiated virus were used, interference was marked though not complete after 24 hr. Thus, the rate of development of resistance varied directly with the multiplicity.

Lack of specificity of heterologous interference

In an excellent review on interference Henle (1950) gave numerous examples to show that one inactivated virus could interfere with the growth of many unrelated viruses. Cross-interference has been described among the myxoviruses—influenza A and B, mumps and Newcastle disease viruses. But inactivated influenza virus interferes not only with other myxoviruses but also with viruses of different families, for example western equine encephalomyelitis virus (Henle & Henle, 1945). Perhaps even more surprising is the fact that inactivated influenza interferes with vaccinia virus (Depoux & Isaacs, 1954) since there is firm chemical evidence that the former is a RNA virus and the latter a DNA virus. This argues that interference probably results from blocking of an early common pathway rather than a later stage in virus synthesis. In support of this argument, interference has been found to affect the synthesis of complete virus particles and also of what are believed to be viral building blocks; for example, in interference with the growth of influenza virus, no piling up of soluble antigen or haemagglutinin occurs in the cells.

Henle & Henle (1945) drew attention to the fact that interference of approximately the same degree was found with the different strains of challenge virus which they used. However, Isaacs & Edney (1951) found that some strains of virus were significantly more sensitive to interference than others and in recent work it was noted that the Sendai virus is unusually sensitive to interference and makes a good indicator of small doses of interfering virus or interferon (see below). At present we do not know what determines this sensitivity to interference, although this might afford a useful hint about the nature of interference.

* One HA (or haemagglutinating) unit as measured in a pattern test with 1 % chick red blood cells.

We may summarize the picture of heterologous interference by inactive virus as a cellular inhibition produced by a small number of virus particles per cell, this inhibition resulting in a block at some intracellular and probably early stage in virus reproduction. To produce this block the interfering virus must have sustained a certain moderate degree of damage to its nucleic acid, and have been allowed to interact with the cell for some hours at 37°. When interference is established, the inhibition extends to the multiplication of many different viruses.

We shall consider now experiments on interferon, and their bearing on our understanding of the interference phenomenon.

INTERFERON

Dr J. Lindenmann and I became interested in investigating the pheno-menon described by Mooser & Lindenmann (1957), in which heated influenza virus adsorbed on chick red blood cells was found to be a good interfering agent. There seemed to be two reasonable explanations of this finding—first, the virus might have become detached from its site on the red cells and entered the allantoic cells. Secondly, the virus haem-agglutinin might have remained attached to the red blood cell, to which it is known to be firmly adsorbed, while part of the virus entered the allan-toic cells—by analogy with phage infection, where the protein coat remains outside while the DNA enters the bacterium (Hershey & Chase, 1952). We decided to test this second possibility by biological methods and, with Dr R. C. Valentine, by electron microscopy. It was found that if heated influenza virus adsorbed to chick red cells was incubated with normal red cells (in test-tubes in a roller-drum) some virus became attached to the normal red cells, a result which favoured the first hypo-thesis. However, in the course of testing different materials for inter-fering activity, more activity was found after incubating virus-coated cells with tissue for 24 hr. than would have been anticipated. The experi-mental system seemed unduly complex, however, and a simpler one was adopted. In this, heated influenza virus was mixed with pieces of chick-chorio-allantoic membrane *in vitro* and sampled to see how much inter-fering activity remained at the end of a 24 hr. incubation period. More activity was found than we expected from the amount of virus haem-agglutinin which was taken up and the amount of inactivation of interfer-ing activity which would have occurred in this time. The possibility was therefore considered that new interfering activity was being produced, and, when heated virus was incubated with tissue and the tissue then washed, it was indeed possible to show that new interfering activity was produced in the chorio-allantoic membrane and secreted into the medium. The new interfering material was quite distinct in its physicochemical and other properties from the original heated virus and it was called 'interferon' (Isaacs & Lindenmann, 1957). Its interest in relation to virus interference lies in its constant association with heterologous interference by inactive virus, and the fact that its interfering behaviour is very like that of the inactive virus used to initiate the interference. It therefore seems reasonable to postulate that heterologous interference by inactive virus is mediated through interferon.

FACTORS AFFECTING THE PRODUCTION OF INTERFERON

The different factors which affect the production of interferon can be grouped for convenience under the headings of the virus, the cells and the conditions of incubation.

Strain of virus

A number of different myxoviruses have been tested after irradiation with u.v. light for their ability to produce interferon when incubated with whole chick chorio-allantoic membranes. The viruses include the PR8 and MEL strains of influenza A, the LEE strain of influenza B and strains of fowl plague and Newcastle disease virus of fowls. All these viruses produced interferon of comparable activity. In this case the term interferon is used to describe material with some of the physicochemical properties and interfering activity of interferon, but since it has not been possible to make an antiserum to interferon, one cannot say whether the materials prepared with different viruses are identical. This same reservation applies to materials prepared with virus inactivated in different ways.

Method of inactivating virus

Influenza virus (strain MEL) was inactivated by different methods and tested for its ability to produce interferon (Burke & Isaacs, 1958b). The methods used were: irradiation by u.v. light, heating at 37° for prolonged periods, heating at 56°, and treatment with 0·02 % formaldehyde. This order is that of decreasing interfering activity and it was also the order of decreasing production of interferon. It was found, too, that virus heated at 60° for 1 hr. had lost its interfering activity and its ability to produce interferon, whereas virus heated at 56° had both properties (Isaacs & Lindenmann, 1957); and essentially the same type of correspondence was noted after irradiation by u.v. light for different periods of time. Thus, irradiation of influenza virus eluates for 30 sec. at a dose of 9.5×10^5 ergs/sq.cm./min. with a lamp giving maximal emission at 2537 Å caused inactivation of the virus which then produced good yields of interferon. Irradiation for up to 4 min. led to a reduction in the ability to produce interferon, and after 8 or 16 min. irradiation the yields were negligibly small and interfering activity was greatly reduced. This correspondence forms an essential part of the argument that heterologous interference by inactive virus is mediated through interferon.

Dose of virus

About 160 agglutinating doses of u.v.-irradiated MEL virus for one whole chorio-allantoic membrane were found to give optimal yields of interferon. This would correspond to a multiplicity of about 10–20 if we assume that the total number of chorionic and allantoic cells exposed is about 10^8. Significant amounts of interferon (as tested on small pieces of chorio-allantoic membrane) could be detected with an inoculum of 1·6 agglutinating doses, but not with 0·16 agglutinating doses, although this figure must obviously depend on the sensitivity of the method for detecting small amounts of interferon. With a dose of 1·6 agglutinating doses for the whole chorio-allantoic membrane there is a multiplicity of less than one.

The yield of interferon rises with increasing multiplicity of u.v.-irradiated influenza virus to a plateau at a dose of about 2400 agglutinating doses per membrane (multiplicity of 150–300) (Burke & Isaacs, 1958a). This plateau could be due to saturation of the cells with virus particles or to an inability of the cells to produce more interferon. In an attempt to distinguish these two possibilities a similar experiment was carried out with the same virus heated at 56°. At comparable doses this produces much less interferon than u.v.-irradiated virus, but its yield of interferon was still increasing when the dose was raised considerably beyond 2400 agglutinating doses per membrane. This supports the hypothesis that the plateau occurred when the cells had reached the limit of their ability to synthesize interferon.

Incomplete virus

Von Magnus (1954) showed that incomplete influenza virus, as prepared by serial allantoic passage of high concentrations of virus, was able to induce interference with the growth of influenza virus in the chick embryo, provided that sufficient time was allowed for interference to be established. As mentioned earlier, Paucker & Henle (1958) found that similar preparations of incomplete virus, after irradiation with u.v. light, were good interfering agents. Burke & Isaacs (1958a) found that un-irradiated incomplete virus produced good yields of interferon when cultivated on the chick chorion; this site was chosen for study because only limited multiplication of live virus can occur in the chorionic cells and the behaviour of incomplete virus could therefore be observed free from much growth of live virus.

Live virus

The same cells infected with standard influenza virus (that is, with high ID_{50}/HA ratio) did not produce interferon, and this was also found to be true of influenza virus grown in whole chorio-allantoic membranes for a 24 hr. period. Taken together these findings suggest that interferon is not normally produced by live virus or by heavily damaged virus, but by virus in which a light degree of damage has been induced in the viral nucleic acid or by incomplete virus which is known to be deficient in nucleic acid (Ada & Perry, 1956).

Tyrrell (personal communication) studied the growth of influenza viruses in bovine kidney cultures. He found that during the first 24 hr. incubation, virus production was active but no interferon could be detected. Later, as virus production was tailing off, interferon was liberated into the medium. We have confirmed these findings in the case of influenza virus grown for 3 days in whole chorio-allantoic membranes (Burke & Isaacs, 1958 b). Interferon was found on the second and third days of incubation, i.e. at a time when virus production was decreasing. In the later stages of infection the cells are exposed to a very high multiplicity of virus, much of which may have become spontaneously inactivated at 37°, and this may produce incomplete virus. Virus inactivated by incubation at 37° and incomplete virus are both able to produce interferon, and it seems reasonable to postulate that the 24 hr. delay in appearance of interferon represents the time needed for inactive and incomplete virus to accumulate before inducing interferon production in cells previously liberating active virus. To assume that some cells produce virus and others interferon would leave the delay still unexplained, but another reasonable possibility is that interferon production normally follows the ending of active virus production in any cell. Interferon might then be a factor in the so-called tissue immunity, as distinct from humoral immunity.

Use of different cells

Most of our studies have been carried out with whole chick chorio-allantoic membranes as a convenient source of cells. It was of great interest to find that interferon production occurred to a similar extent in both the chorionic and allantoic cells, although they differed greatly in their ability to support a full virus multiplication cycle (Lindenmann *et al.* 1957). One possible interpretation is that interferon production corresponds to the production of a viral intermediate which appears early in the virus life-cycle. This interpretation is in line with the suggestion that interference represents a block at an early intracellular stage of viral synthesis.

Interferon production has been observed by us in monkey kidney and HeLa cells and by Tyrrell in bovine kidney cells. At the moment there is no reason to believe that it is restricted to any particular type of cell.

Time of production

In early experiments with influenza virus inactivated at 56° and incubated with chick chorio-allantoic membranes interferon was detected in suspensions of the membrane 3 hr. after a preliminary period of virus adsorption. The concentration of interferon was at first higher in the membrane than in the surrounding medium, but within a few hours the position was reversed, that is, liberation of interferon into the medium was rapid. By 24 hr. no further liberation of interferon could be detected (Isaacs & Lindenmann, 1957). With influenza virus inactivated by u.v. light, production of interferon continued for 3 or 4 days after a single inoculation of virus (Burke & Isaacs, 1958*b*). In an experiment in which interferon production was measured after incubating chorio-allantoic membranes with u.v.-irradiated virus at an estimated multiplicity of 20, the interfering activity of the u.v.-irradiated virus used as inoculum was about the same as that of the interferon produced. This is what one would expect if the interfering activity of the virus is mediated through interferon.

In passing, it is interesting to speculate why interferon is liberated from the cells. Completed virus particles may, of course, be liberated from cells which retain their integrity, while on the other hand virus building blocks (such as the influenzal soluble antigen and S haemagglutinin) tend to be retained within cells. It is almost as if the cell were able to recognize that interferon is not required for virus synthesis! The liberation of interferon is not confined to the exposed surface of the cells, for if the chorionic surface of the membrane is inoculated with u.v.-irradiated virus, interferon, produced in the chorionic cells, diffuses through to the allantoic cells where it induces interference (Isaacs, Burke & Fadeeva, 1958).

Conditions of incubation

We have not investigated in detail the influence of conditions of incubation, but a few points are well established. A temperature of 35–37° has been used routinely; at 2° no significant production of interferon occurs.

Good aeration seems to be an important factor and can be achieved by incubation in shallow layers with gentle agitation; incubation in deep layers of medium kept stationary led to poor yields. As a suspending medium for cells Earle's buffered salt solution or Parker's 199 medium led to satisfactory yields, and Tyrrell's results suggest that more complex media do not prevent production of interferon.

Effect of metabolic inhibitors

Proflavine is thought to inhibit cytoplasmic protein synthesis and Dr R. M. Franklin (personal communication) has shown that it inhibits the formation of fowl plague virus haemagglutinin without affecting the formation of the nucleoprotein soluble antigen. At comparable doses proflavine had no effect on the production of interferon (Burke & Isaacs, 1958 b).

Tyrrell (personal communication) has found in some recent preliminary experiments that dichlororibofuranosylbenzimidazole (DRB), a known inhibitor of the growth of influenza virus (Tamm, Folkers, Shunk & Horsfall, 1954), inhibits at higher concentrations the production of interferon.

PHYSICO-CHEMICAL PROPERTIES OF INTERFERON

Size. With present preparations of interferon it has not yet been possible to define the size except in broad terms. It does not diffuse from dialysis sacs and can be filtered through collodion membranes with an average pore diameter of 0.048μ. On centrifuging it was not significantly sedimented at $100,000\,g$. for 4 hr. On centrifuging overnight at $100,000\,g$. no activity was recovered from the deposit, the supernatant, or the top layer, and it is possible that activity was adsorbed on the walls of the tube. Clearly further experiments are required with more concentrated and purified materials. The limited results available suggest that it is macro-molecular, but of considerably smaller size than the virus used to prepare it.

Temperature stability. Interferon is stable for many weeks at 2°. Its behaviour on freezing has been erratic. It appears to be stable for many hours at 37° but at pH 7 it is inactivated by heating at 60° for 1 hr. or 100° for 5 min.

pH *stability.* pH stability was tested by suspending preparations of interferon in dialysis sacs at 2° and dialysing overnight against large volumes of buffer of the required pH. This was then followed by dialysis back to pH 7·4. Under these conditions interferon was stable over the entire pH range 1–11.

8

Serological tests. Attempts were made to neutralize the interfering activity of interferon by mixing it with various sera, but no significant neutralization has been found. The sera used were ferret antiserum to the strain of influenza virus A used to make the interferon, a human convalescent influenza A serum pool, an antiserum to normal chick chorioallantoic membrane (prepared by Dr A. Harboe) and sera prepared in rabbits and a chicken by repeated injection, over a period of 4 weeks, of unconcentrated and 10-fold concentrated interferon. It is likely that the total amount of antigen was extremely small and this may account for the failure to induce any neutralizing antibody.

Effect of enzymes on interfering activity of interferon. The stability of interferon at low pH allowed us to test its sensitivity to pepsin under optimal pH conditions. It was found to be completely inactivated by incubation for 1 hr. at 37° with 0·001 % pepsin. It was also sensitive to trypsin at pH 8·0 but some activity remained even after prolonged digestion. On the other hand, interferon was insensitive to similar treatment with deoxyribonuclease or ribonuclease, and the latter enzyme did not affect the residue of activity which remained after trypsin digestion. The receptor-destroying enzyme (RDE) of *Vibrio cholerae* had no effect.

Miscellaneous. Interferon was inactivated by shaking with ether or with a mixture of amyl alcohol and chloroform (1:2). It can be precipitated by saturation with ammonium sulphate, but less saturated solutions have not given clear-cut separations. Under the conditions used, 6 M urea, sodium metaperiodate and sodium iodoacetate have had no effect. Interferon was not unduly sensitive to treatment with u.v. light with a maximal emission at 2537 Å.

In summary, it seems reasonable to assume for the moment that interferon is a protein and not associated with either nucleic acid or carbohydrates. More precise identification of its chemical nature must await its purification.

MODE OF PRODUCTION AND ACTION OF INTERFERON

Mode of production. Interferon could theoretically be part of the virus or a product of the cell, and at the moment it is not possible to make a categorical decision between these alternatives. But indirect evidence strongly supports the latter. The fact that it is produced continually by cells over a period of three or four days in response to a single inoculum of u.v.-inactivated virus suggests that it is being synthesized in the cells, and further reasons for holding this view are detailed below.

When influenza virus heated at 56° was incubated with chorio-allantoic membranes it was found that interferon was produced for a period of about 24 hr. During a second 24 hr. period no further significant production occurred, but live virus would not grow in the membranes, that is, interference was induced. Nevertheless, in response to a second dose of heated influenza virus, a second 'crop' of interferon was produced (Lindenmann *et al.* 1957). Clearly therefore the establishment of interference in these cells was compatible with the entry of heated influenza virus and the synthesis of a new crop of interferon.

It was interesting therefore to see what would happen if live virus were inoculated instead of heated virus for the second crop. In previously untreated membranes live virus does not normally produce interferon during a 24 hr. incubation period and the problem was to see what would happen in membranes in which interference was induced. Interferon is readily measured in the presence of live virus by adjusting the fluid to pH 2 for 24 hr. then readjusting to pH 7. Interferon is stable at pH 2, but live virus is completely inactivated. The results of two experiments are shown in Table 1.

Table 1. *Production of interferon by live influenza virus grown in cells previously treated with heated influenza virus*

Whole chorio-allantoic membranes were incubated for 3 hr. at 35° with heat-inactivated influenza virus (MEL strain) or buffer. After washing, the membranes were incubated overnight at 35° with buffer. Next day the interferon was removed, the membranes washed and incubated for 3 hr. at 35° with live influenza virus or buffer. The membranes were then washed and again incubated overnight at 35° with buffer. By titrating the fluids for haemagglutinin it was shown that interference had been induced in the membranes previously incubated with heated influenza virus. The fluids were then dialysed at pH 2 overnight to destroy live virus, dialysed back to pH 7·4 and finally titrated for interferon. The table shows the degree of inhibition expressed as the geometric mean ($\log_2$) difference (d) between the yield in the experimental and control groups. A difference of two is significant at the 1 % level.

		Interferon yield ($\log_2 d$)	
First inoculum	Second inoculum	Experiment 1	Experiment 2
Heated influenza virus	Buffer	0·6	0
Heated influenza virus	Live influenza virus	3·5	2·3
Buffer	Live influenza virus	0·5	0·1

In previously untreated control membranes live virus by itself did not produce interferon. It seems therefore that the heated influenza virus induced the cells of the chorio-allantoic membrane to take a different metabolic pathway, that is, one leading to the synthesis of interferon rather than to the synthesis of some normal virus intermediate. Once the cell has taken the alternative metabolic pathway, live virus inoculated subsequently seems to continue in the same direction and the end result of the cells' synthesis is interferon instead of live virus.

This experiment led to the question—would interferon behave in the same way as heated influenza virus? There is one important difference: interferon does not by itself lead to the synthesis of more interferon. However, it was most interesting to find that interferon had the same effect as heated influenza virus in inducing the cells to produce more interferon when they were inoculated with live influenza virus. The results of illustrative experiments are shown in Table 2.

Table 2. *Production of interferon by live influenza virus grown in cells previously treated with interferon*

The experiments were carried out with conditions similar to those described in Table 1, except that the first inoculum was interferon instead of heated influenza virus.

First inoculum	Second inoculum	Interferon yield ($\log_2 d$)	
		Experiment 1	Experiment 2
Interferon	Buffer	0	0
Interferon	Live influenza virus	3·5	2·2
Buffer	Live influenza virus	0·7	0·1

In control experiments it was shown that membranes which had been treated with interferon did not produce interferon when stimulated with irradiated virus which had been heated at 60° for 1 hr.

The following provisional generalization may therefore be justified: Heated influenza virus induces cells to produce interferon, which in turn blocks the multiplication of subsequently added live virus by making it form more interferon instead of new virus.

This concept of alternative metabolic pathways (leading to production of interferon or virus intermediate) finds support in some experiments of Lindenmann (personal communication). He has found that cells do not produce interferon if infected with live influenza virus shortly before, or at the same time as, the application of a large dose of inactivated virus. Besides furnishing another example of the fact that establishment of interference is accompanied by production of interferon, these experiments suggest some form of competition for metabolic pathways. Interference takes some hours to be established, and before this has occurred live virus is presumably able to establish its own metabolic pathway. Once this metabolic pathway is established, interferon production cannot occur. But this concept needs qualification for two reasons. First, later in infection production of virus appears to be replaced by production of interferon, and secondly, it is known that interference lasts a few days only. These two findings suggest that the use of one alternative metabolic pathway does not permanently exclude another. In recent experiments carried out in collaboration with Dr H. G. Pereira, interferon, in the doses tested so far, has not been found to exert any observable toxic effect, or to inhibit cell division in HeLa cells. This finding is not incompatible with the postulated action of interferon in diverting virus synthesis.

Site of action of interferon. The hypothesis described above requires that interferon should act at an intracellular site. We have in fact found that interferon has no direct viricidal action on extracellular virus, and in addition it has shown optimal activity when it is incubated with cells for some hours before the challenge virus. This period of incubation before interference was established could be shown to be due to the need for some metabolic activity to occur, since after a period for interferon to be adsorbed, some hours' incubation at 37° was still required; similar incubation at 2° did not suffice for interference to be established (Lindenmann *et al.* 1957).

Further evidence for an intracellular site of action of interferon was provided by my colleague Dr A. C. Allison who found that isotope labelled fowl plague and vaccinia viruses were adsorbed equally well to interferon-treated and control tissues. It appears then that interferon acts at an intracellular site, but at the moment it is not known where in the cells this is.

Range of action of interferon. Interferon has been found to have the same wide range of interfering activity as inactivated virus. *In vitro* it inhibits the growth of a number of different myxoviruses and in the chorion of fertile hen's eggs it inhibits pock production by vaccinia, cowpox and herpes simplex viruses (Isaacs *et al.* 1958). Inhibition was shown by a reduction in the number of pocks, but not in the average pock size. Pocks are produced by excessive proliferation of initially infected cells, and the fact that pocks are not reduced in size in interferon-treated membranes suggests that the proliferating cells which produce the pock do not contain interferon. We may assume that when the pock count has been reduced by say 90 %, one out of ten of the challenge virus infective units reaches a cell which contains insufficient interferon to prevent it from multiplying. This cell is then induced to proliferate and the newly formed cells presumably would not contain interferon; as a result, local multiplication of this virus is not restricted and a pock of normal size is produced.

Some viruses were found to be more sensitive than others to the interfering action of interferon (as had been noted with inactive virus as an interfering agent). Herpes simplex virus was more resistant to interferon than vaccinia and cowpox viruses grown on the chick chorion, and

Sendai virus was more sensitive to interferon when tested *in vitro* than the other myxoviruses tested. There is as yet no hint of what factors might be involved in these differences.

Attempted preparation of competitor. The hypothesis has been advanced that interferon may be an analogue of a normal intermediate in virus synthesis (Burke & Isaacs, 1958*a*). In a search for such an intermediate a number of experiments have been carried out, but with uniformly negative results. In one set of experiments the chick chorion was inoculated with live influenza virus (which does not undergo a complete cycle of virus growth in this site) and an extract tested for its ability to inhibit interferon. A second set of experiments was based on the fact that when u.v.-inactivated influenza virus is inoculated on the chick chorion it produces interferon which diffuses through to the allantoic cells (Isaacs *et al.* 1958). Live influenza virus did not induce interference in a similar experiment and an attempt was made to see whether live virus produced an intermediate product which might diffuse through to the allantois and prevent the action of subsequently inoculated interferon; but no such effect was found.

These negative results do not disprove the hypothesis that interferon is an analogue of a normal virus intermediate. This still seems to explain best the difference between the effects produced by normal virus and virus with slightly damaged nucleic acid. However, if such an intermediate exists it is presumably used up very rapidly and does not diffuse from cells under the conditions studied so far.

CONCLUSIONS

The term virus interference is generally used to describe inhibition by one virus of the growth of another at the cellular level. It includes a number of distinct mechanisms, of which only one, interference by inactive virus with the growth of heterologous viruses, has been selected for discussion. In this phenomenon the following course of events occurs.

To induce interference it appears necessary to use virus whose nucleic acid has been slightly damaged. Influenza and related viruses which have been damaged by irradiation with u.v. light are able to induce interference at a multiplicity of 5–10 virus particles per cell. Interference is not induced at once, but requires some hours of incubation at 37° to become established. During this period of incubation the cells are synthesizing interferon.

There is suggestive evidence that the interference is mediated through interferon. The evidence is based on a close correspondence between the ability of different virus preparations to induce interference and to produce interferon, on the fact that the amount of interferon produced is just about sufficient to account for the degree of interference induced, and on the overall similarity between interference induced by inactive virus and by interferon. Interferon appears to be a product of an abnormal virus synthesis, perhaps an analogue of some normal virus intermediate which acts by deflecting virus synthesis towards the production of more interferon; that is, by inducing the cell to take a different metabolic pathway.

Any further idea of how interferon acts is hampered, at the moment, by our ignorance of its chemical nature. The available evidence suggests that it is a protein without any associated nucleic acid, and if this should prove to be so, there might well be an analogy in the field of bacteriophages. Burton (1957) has reviewed the evidence that following the initiation of phage infection there is a considerable synthesis of protein which does not possess antigens characteristic of the phage and which is not a precursor of the phage proteins. This non-viral protein is formed most rapidly during the first ten minutes of infection and some of it appears to be involved in the synthesis of phage DNA; for example, if a tryptophan-requiring mutant of *Escherichia coli* is used as a host cell and is infected in the absence of tryptophan, no phage DNA synthesis occurs and no hydroxymethylcytosine (the pyrimidine which is found in T-even phage but not bacterial DNA) is formed. However, this protein is only required for the initiation of the synthesis of new DNA, and once initiated the synthesis of DNA is largely, if not completely, independent of protein synthesis. This protein may therefore function as a template in the formation of new nucleic acid. Stent (1958) has proposed a very similar hypothesis to explain the decrease in sensitivity of T2 phage to irradiation and to ^{32}P decay early in the vegetative phase of virus replication. To account for this he proposed that information is transferred from phage DNA to a protein or ribonucleoprotein template which would be insensitive to irradiation, and from which fresh DNA would then be synthesized.

It is conceivable that in the synthesis of a new nucleic acid during viral infection of animal cells a similar protein synthesis occurs. Interferon could then be considered as an analogue of this protein. It would be necessary to assume that cells are able to form only one kind of protein template at a time, and there is some evidence in regard to the synthesis of interferon and virus that this may be so. Recently, Nossal & Lederberg (1958) have described most interesting experiments from which it appears that isolated cells prepared from an animal stimulated with two antigens synthesize antibody to one or other antigen, but not both. It is tempting to speculate whether the synthesis by cells of an abnormal protein, such as occurs during the formation of virus, antibody or interferon, is a process which occurs at a single site within the cell and tends to exclude the formation of other abnormal proteins by the same cell.

As one further and final speculation, it would be in line with present theorizing to suggest that interferon does not contain enough 'information' to permit the synthesis of viral nucleic acid, and it is not inappropriate that a molecule which cannot be further used in the cell's economy—that is, an end-product of a synthetic process—should be liberated from the cells. This would define interference as an inhibition of the formation of viral nucleic acid, and one (and perhaps the only) excuse for these speculations is that they may be capable of being tested experimentally.

REFERENCES

ADA, G. L. & PERRY, B. T. (1956). Influenza virus nucleic acid: relationship between biological characteristics of the virus particle and properties of the nucleic acid. *J. gen. Microbiol.* **14**, 623.

BALUDA, M. (1957). Homologous interference by ultraviolet-inactivated Newcastle disease virus. *Virology*, **4**, 72.

BURKE, D. C. & ISAACS, A. (1958*a*). Further studies on interferon. *Brit. J. exp. Path.* **39**, 78.

BURKE, D. C. & ISAACS, A. (1958*b*). Some factors affecting the production of interferon. *Brit. J. exp. Path.* **39**, 452.

BURTON, K. (1957). Interrelationships of nucleic acid and protein in the multiplication of bacteriophage. *Symp. biochem. Soc.* **14**, 60.

DEPOUX, R. & ISAACS, A. (1954). Interference between influenza and vaccinia viruses. *Brit. J. exp. Path.* **35**, 415.

DONALD, H. B. & ISAACS, A. (1954). Counts of influenza virus particles. *J. gen. Microbiol.* **10**, 457.

FAZEKAS DE ST GROTH, S. & EDNEY, M. (1952). Quantitative aspects of influenza virus multiplication. II. Heterologous interference. *J. Immunol.* **69**, 160.

FAZEKAS DE ST GROTH, S., ISAACS, A. & EDNEY, M. (1952). Multiplication of influenza virus under conditions of interference. *Nature, Lond.* **170**, 573.

HENLE, W. (1949). Studies on host-virus interactions in the chick embryo influenza virus system. II. The propagation of virus in conjunction with the host cells. *J. exp. Med.* **90**, 13.

HENLE, W. (1950). Interference phenomena between animal viruses: a review. *J. Immunol.* **64**, 203.

HENLE, W. & HENLE, G. (1943). Interference of inactive virus with the propagation of virus of influenza. *Science*, **98**, 87.

HENLE, W. & HENLE, G. (1945). Interference between inactive and active viruses of influenza. III. Cross-interference between various related and unrelated viruses. *Amer. J. med. Sci.* **210**, 362.

HENLE, W. & HENLE, G. (1947). The effect of ultraviolet irradiation on various properties of influenza viruses. *J. exp. Med.* **85**, 347.

HENLE, W. & PAUCKER, K. (1958). Interference between inactivated and active influenza viruses in the chick embryo. I. A re-evaluation of factors of dosage and timing using infectivity titrations for assay. *Virology*, **6**, 181.

HENLE, W. & ROSENBERG, E. B. (1949). One-step growth curves of various strains of influenza A and B viruses and their inhibition by inactivated virus of the homologous type. *J. exp. Med.* **89**, 279.

HERSHEY, A. D. & CHASE, M. (1952). Independent functions of viral protein and nucleic acid in growth of bacteriophage. *J. gen. Physiol.* **36**, 39.

ISAACS, A., BURKE, D. C. & FADEEVA, L. (1958). Effect of interferon on the growth of viruses on the chick chorion. *Brit. J. exp. Path.* **39**, 447.

ISAACS, A. & EDNEY, M. (1950). Interference between inactive and active influenza viruses in the chick embryo. I. Quantitative aspects of interference. *Aust. J. exp. Biol. med. Sci.* **28**, 219.

ISAACS, A. & EDNEY, M. (1951). Interference between inactive and active influenza viruses in the chick embryo. V. The behaviour of different strains of challenge virus. *Aust. J. exp. Biol. med. Sci.* **29**, 169.

ISAACS, A. & LINDENMANN, J. (1957). Virus interference. I. The interferon. *Proc. roy. Soc.* B, **147**, 258.

LINDENMANN, J., BURKE, D. C. & ISAACS, A. (1957). Studies on the production, mode of action and properties of interferon. *Brit. J. exp. Path.* **38**, 551.

MAGNUS, P. VON (1954). Incomplete forms of influenza virus. *Advanc. Virus Res.* **2**, 59.

MOOSER, H. & LINDENMANN, J. (1957). Homologe Interferenz durch hitzein-aktiviertes, an Erythrozyten adsorbiertes Influenza-B-Virus. *Experientia*, **13**, 147.

NOSSAL, G. J. V. & LEDERBERG, J. (1958). Antibody production by single cells. *Nature, Lond.* **181**, 1419.

PAUCKER, K. & HENLE, W. (1958). Interference between inactivated and active influenza viruses in the chick embryo. II. Interference by incomplete forms of influenza virus. *Virology* **6**, 198.

POWELL, W. F. & SETLOW, R. B. (1956). The effect of monochromatic ultraviolet radiation on the interfering property of influenza virus. *Virology*, **2**, 337.

STENT, G. S. (1958). Mating in the reproduction of bacterial viruses. *Advanc. Virus Res.* **5**, 95.

TAMM, I., FOLKERS, K., SHUNK, C. H. & HORSFALL, JUN., F. L. (1954). Inhibition of influenza virus multiplication by N-glycosides of benzimidazoles. *J. exp. Med.* **99**, 227.

TYRRELL, D. A. J. & TAMM, I. (1955). Prevention of virus interference by 2,5-dimethyl benzimidazole. *J. Immunol.* **75**, 43.

HOST-CONTROLLED VARIATION IN
ANIMAL VIRUSES

J. M. HOSKINS

Department of Bacteriology, University of Manchester

The properties we measure when we study viruses quantitatively are generally those of populations rather than individual particles. These properties are generally heritable. Nevertheless, viruses do vary in their characteristics, and variants can arise in at least two ways. One of these is by the appearance of a mutant—a spontaneous change in the genetic material of one individual—which is converted into a change in the whole population by selection. A second way is by host-controlled variation, in which the properties of such populations are directly influenced by the host cell in which they grow. In contrast to variation of the mutational kind, host-controlled variation does not originate as a change in a single virus particle, but is reflected as a sudden transformation of the whole population, taking place during the course of one growth cycle. It does not, therefore, require selection in order to express itself at the population level. Furthermore, the change is stable only so long as the variant replicates within the host causing the change, and host-controlled variants may become altered following growth in other host systems (Luria, 1953; see also following section).

In animal viruses variation has usually been attributed to mutation and selection, and this is almost certainly the way in which a great many variants do arise. The kind of variation most often seen is a change in host range; the new host being either a different animal species, as in the adaptation of a chick embryo strain of influenza to the mouse lung (Burnet & Lind, 1954), or a different cell type within a single host (Hoskins & Sanders, to be published). Such variation is often associated with loss of virulence for the original host (Enders, Weller & Robbins, 1952; Li & Schaeffer, 1953; Edney, 1957); less frequently, the change is from an attenuated to a more virulent form (Dane *et al.* 1957). Variations in respect of antigenicity (Burnet, 1955), heat resistance (Stanley, Dorman, Ponsford & Larkin, 1956), plaque size (Sanders, Huppert & Hoskins, 1958), cold adaptation (Dubes & Chapin, 1956), pH sensitivity (Vogt, Dulbecco & Wenner, 1957) and resistance to naturally occurring inhibitors (Takemori *et al.* 1958) are also known.

Since precise knowledge of mutation frequency is usually lacking, evidence for the assumption that changes of this kind owe their origin to mutation is commonly based on the fact that a certain number of passages of the virus in a new host is required before any change is observed to take place in the population; under these conditions time is available for the selection of mutant forms. But if the selection pressure operating in favour of a mutant is sufficiently intense, the appearance of a variant virus population may be apparent after a single passage—nevertheless representing several growth cycles—in a new host (Burnet & Bull, 1943; Sabin, 1955; Dane *et al.* 1957). Thus, Burnet & Bull (1943) found that a single passage of influenza virus A of human origin in the cells lining the chick amniotic cavity resulted in the emergence of a variant which, unlike the original material, was able to grow in the allantois and agglutinate chick erythrocytes. The evidence that this change in the virus population from the original (O) to the derivative (D) form was due to selection of a variant and not to a modifying effect of the host was the demonstration that passage at high dilution resulted in retention of the O form, the D form emerging only when passage was made at low dilution.

Similar considerations to these apply also to many instances of variation in bacterial viruses, although some variation under conditions of single passage has been shown to be under the direct control of the host. In all cases of the latter kind which have been reported, variation appears to affect host range only, and, since the earliest demonstration of the phenomenon by Luria & Human (1952), many clear-cut instances have been described (Luria, 1953; Zelle, 1955; Anderson, 1955). The variation may of course be towards either an extension or a restriction of the virus host range. For example, bacteriophage λ, which normally destroys a population of *Escherichia coli* S cells, is unable to do so after a single growth cycle in cells of *E. coli*, strain C. After growth in *E. coli* C cells the phage, now called λC, can be modified again by single cycle growth in a few exceptional cells in a strain S population (one in 5×10^3) so that it reverts to the λ form and is once more able to grow in all strain S cells (Bertani & Weigle, 1953).

Now in many animal viruses the carrier of genetic information seems to be ribonucleic acid (RNA) (Dulbecco, 1957), and not, as in the bacterial viruses, deoxyribonucleic acid (DNA) (Cohen, 1955). However, the nature of the carrier in most animal viruses is not fully established, and various reports that this is in some instances constituted of both types of nucleic acid may sometimes be a reflection of the technical difficulties of obtaining virus material uncontaminated with host components (Markham, 1953; Cohen, 1955). This is illustrated by the contradictory findings for influenza virus. Taylor (1944) found only DNA in the virus. Knight (1947) and Graham (1950) found both DNA and RNA. More recently Ada & Perry (1954, 1956) found only RNA in influenza, while Miller (1956) has since reported that the virus contains both types of nucleic acid. In their most recent communication, Ada & Perry (1958) now state that small amounts of DNA may be present. Cunha *et al.* (1947) have reported the occurrence of both RNA and DNA in Newcastle disease virus. There is no reason for believing that both nucleic acids may not exist together in animal viruses, and the participation of DNA even when present as a small proportion of the total nucleic acid cannot be excluded from a significant genetic role. With encephalo-myocarditis (EMC) virus Huppert & Sanders (1958) found that the infectivity of RNA preparations obtained from infected tissues was not derived from the sedimentable virus component, and that they could not extract infective RNA from purified preparations of the virus. However, the true significance of this observation must await further study, since it is not even known whether EMC virus contains any DNA.

The presumptive occurrence of both DNA and RNA in an animal virus suggests that virus genetics may involve more complex processes than would be required for a virus possessing only one type of nucleic acid. The role of nucleic acid and the processes of heredity in RNA organisms are still largely unexplored in comparison with those of DNA organisms. The study of the mechanisms involved in host-controlled variation, in which the host can modify the virus phenotype, may provide a clue to the processes involved.

HOST-CONTROLLED VARIATION IN ENCEPHALO-MYOCARDITIS (EMC) VIRUS

Murine encephalomyocarditis (EMC) virus was used in these experiments. It is a small (25–30 mμ), probably RNA virus, which is highly infective for mice by all routes of inoculation (Warren, 1952). At least three distinct genotypes of EMC are known, each of which can be identified by two properties not shared with the others (see Table 1); in this instance we are interested in that of host-controlled variation (Table 1).

Cells of the S 180 mouse sarcoma maintained *in vitro* are not normally susceptible to EMC virus of mouse brain origin. However, starting with an infected brain suspension from the 63rd intracerebral mouse passage of the original virus isolated by Helwig & Schmidt (1945) a variant capable of growing in and destroying S 180 sarcoma cultures was isolated. This variant, which itself presumably arose by mutation and selection, is referred to as S180 virus (Hoskins & Sanders, to be published). Although it was isolated by infecting cultures of S180 cells with the mouse brain strain of EMC (Table 1), S180 virus can also be obtained by plating on agar cell suspensions and picking the mutant virus plaques that appear (Hoskins & Sanders, to be published). The single pool of stock S180 virus used in the experiments described in this section contained $2 \cdot 0 \times 10^7$ plaque-forming units (PFU)/ml.

Considered as a mutant which is highly destructive for monolayer cultures of S180 sarcoma cells, it was supposed that S180 virus would still destroy the tumour cells after growth in various host systems. However, when a small inoculum of the virus (containing 10^2 PFU) was injected intracerebrally into mice, the suspension subsequently prepared from the brains of these animals when they became moribund a week later was no longer able to multiply in or destroy tumour cultures. Three explanations of this appear to be worth considering.

(a) An infected mouse brain suspension contains a substance capable of inhibiting infection of the tumour cells by S180 virus. This would explain both the failure of EMC virus of mouse brain origin normally to destroy S180 cells, and the inability of S180 virus to infect the cells after growth in the mouse brain.

(b) S180 virus is modified as a whole by growth in the mouse brain in vivo, to a form no longer infective for the tumour cells.

(c) S180 virus mutates, either in the mouse brain or in the tumour cells in vitro, to a form which is not infective for S180 cells; this mutant then overgrows and suppresses the action of S180 virus, in a way analogous to the O–D change in influenza virus (Burnet & Bull, 1943).

The presence of an inhibitor seemed to be unlikely since high dilutions of a stock suspension of mouse brain-propagated virus failed to destroy cultures of S180 cells. Similarly, a preparation of the same virus, purified by protamine precipitation and subsequent high-speed centrifuging (Weil et al. 1952), also failed to destroy the cells. And, furthermore, a mixture in equal proportions of a 20 % normal mouse brain suspension and undiluted S180 virus was fully destructive for similar cultures. If, therefore, an inhibitor were present, it would be a substance appearing only in infected brains, sedimenting with the virus during purification, and active at a dilution comparable with the virus infectivity endpoint.

Possibilities (b) and (c), above, were distinguished in the following way. Two supposed clones of S180 virus were prepared by:

(i) Three limiting infective dilution passages in S180 cells in vitro;

such a procedure would be expected to isolate the predominant component—in this case tumour-infective—in a heterogeneous virus population (Isaacs & Edney, 1950a). The virus suspension from the third passage contained 1.5×10^6 PFU/ml.

(ii) Two successive single plaque isolations from limiting infective dilutions; the second plaque, suspended in phosphate-buffered saline (Dulbecco & Vogt, 1954a), contained 2.9×10^5 PFU/ml.

0.03 ml. volumes of each virus clone were inoculated intracerebrally into mice, whose brains were removed at the end of one virus growth cycle (12 hr.). 0.15 ml. volumes of a 10 % suspension of these brains had no destructive action on S180 cultures, although samples of the virus clone preparations with which the mice had been inoculated were fully infective for control tumour cells (see Table 2). At the same time, control assays showed that the virus had multiplied normally in the mouse brain, so that failure to multiply was not the reason for failure of the brain-propagated virus to infect the tumour cells (Table 2).

It follows from this that a single growth cycle of S180 virus in the mouse brain in vivo is sufficient to render a clonal preparation of the virus—normally destructive for S180 cultures—non-destructive for these cells. In fact, whereas a single particle (PFU) of S180 virus is able to initiate a spreading wave of destruction in S180 cultures (Hoskins, unpublished), the above experiment shows that less than one particle in 10^5–10^6 is able to do so after growth in the mouse brain. Since the virus population as a whole appears to be changed during the course of one growth cycle only, the phenomenon is not likely to be explicable as the emergence and selection during this period of a mutant which overgrows and suppresses the action of S180 virus. We can therefore rule out possibility (c), above, and regard the phenomenon as a modification of the virus directly induced through growth in the mouse brain.

Though the S180 virus phenotype is changed by growth in the mouse brain, one cannot say to what extent there is a corresponding change in the virus genome. However, the following evidence suggests that at least a part of the genetic integrity may be maintained during the modification. Cell suspension cultures (Sanders, 1957a) of Krebs-2 ascites cells were inoculated with 10^3–10^4 PFU of mouse brain-modified S180 virus prepared from each of the clones described in the previous experiment. After incubation at 37° for 12 hr., portions of the centrifuged suspensions, containing 10^4–10^5 PFU, were inoculated into fresh Krebs-2 cell suspensions and incubation carried out for a further growth cycle. Control assays (see Table 2) showed that virus multiplication had

Table 1. *Characteristics of encephalomyocarditis (EMC) virus strains*

	Mouse brain virus	K-2 virus	S180 virus
Growth in S180 sarcoma	−	+	+
Growth in Krebs-2 carcinoma	+	+	+
Growth in B.P. epithelioma	−	+	+
Growth in Ehrlich carcinoma	−	+	+
Host-controlled modification by mouse brain		−	+
Cytopathic effect on S180 cells after growth of mouse brain phenotype in Krebs-2 cells	−		
Plaque size on Krebs-2 cells	Small	Large	Small

Table 2. *Effect of growth in mouse brain on properties of S180 virus*

Virus	Effect on S180 cells *before* growth in mouse brain	Virus content* of mouse brain after		Effect on S180 cells *after* growth in mouse brain	Virus content† of Krebs-2 cell cultures infected with mouse brain phenotype			Effect on S180 cells after growth of mouse brain phenotype in Krebs-2 cells	
		1 hr.	12 hr.		At infection	After 1 cycle	After 2 cycles	After 1 cycle	After 2 cycles
Plaque-isolated clone	C.P.E.	$1 \cdot 0 \times 10^2$	$1 \cdot 1 \times 10^6$	Nil	$2 \cdot 5 \times 10^3$	$9 \cdot 6 \times 10^4$	$2 \cdot 6 \times 10^6$	C.P.E.	C.P.E.
Tissue culture clone	C.P.E.	$1 \cdot 1 \times 10^3$	$8 \cdot 4 \times 10^6$	Nil	$2 \cdot 1 \times 10^4$	$1 \cdot 1 \times 10^6$	$1 \cdot 4 \times 10^7$	C.P.E.	C.P.E.

C.P.E. = Cytopathic effect.
* = PFU/ml. of 10% brain suspension.
† = PFU/ml. of cell suspension supernatant fluid.

occurred during each period of incubation. Table 2 also shows that, following growth of modified S180 virus in suspensions of Krebs-2 cells, the undiluted culture fluid subsequently contained virus which was once more destructive for monolayer cultures of S180 cells. Moreover, this re-acquired cytopathic property was inherited through a second growth cycle in Krebs-2 cells.

This phenomenon is analogous to the bacteriophage modification described by Bertani & Weigle (1953), in which phage P2B, which normally destroys a population of *Escherichia coli* B cells, is unable to do so after a single cycle of growth in cells of *Shigella dysenteriae*, strain Sh. But modified P2B virus can also have this restriction removed; it grows in one cell in 10^4 of an *Escherichia coli* B population, the progeny from the latter cell-virus interaction then being fully infective for the entire population. It is also possible that modified S180 virus may behave in the same way as modified P2B phage, and that a similar small proportion of S180 cells can support the multiplication of the modified virus. Nevertheless, the effects of such virus growth in the tumour cultures would presumably not be detected because the spread of cytopathic destruction would be limited by interference from the excess brain-modified virus always present.

MECHANISMS IN HOST-CONTROLLED VARIATION

While there is a formal analogy between the S180 virus–mouse brain and P2B–*Shigella* systems described above, we do not know how far the similarities go; in all probability they do not extend very far. We must remember that the whole P2B system is a DNA one, as indeed is every other known bacteriophage system, whereas at least the smaller (15–30 mμ) animal viruses may contain only RNA. Furthermore, the phage is responsible for a gross disruption of the cells' metabolism which sets in immediately after infection. Thus, enzyme synthesis stops (Cohen, 1949; Pardee & Williams, 1953), and synthesis of phage DNA completely replaces, synthesis of bacterial DNA and RNA (Cohen, 1947). Experiments with radioactive materials indicate that much of the bacterial nucleic acid becomes incorporated into the phage DNA. For example, all the phosphorus and much of the DNA purine and pyrimidine carbon appears in the bacteriophage DNA (Siddiqi, Kozloff, Putnam & Evans, 1952; Hershey, 1953; Hershey, Garen, Fraser & Hudis, 1954). Unfortunately, we do not know how this conversion of bacterial DNA to phage nucleic acid takes place; that is, whether the nucleic acid is degraded to the level of single nucleotides, or further, before resynthesis starts. Nevertheless, since no microbiologist would now dispute the fact that genetic information is carried by the nucleic acid it is conceivable that, if bacterial DNA breakdown does not proceed too far, the bacterial host may be provided with an opportunity to insert bacterial genetic information into the phage genome.

With animal viruses the metabolic consequences of infection are much less clear. However, they often appear to exert a much less profound disruption of the cell metabolism so that, until cytopathic changes begin to take place, many of the metabolic processes go on as usual. For example, animal viruses may multiply in and be liberated from cells before any cytological changes appear (Bang & Gey, 1952; Dulbecco & Vogt, 1954b). When the chick chorio-allantois is infected with influenza virus there is a latent period of about 3 hr. Infective virus is then released from the cells at a more or less constant rate for about 30 hr., and cell degeneration does not appear until 48 hr. after infection (Henle, Liu & Finter, 1954). Ackermann, Rabson & Kurtz (1954) found that although HeLa cells infected with the Saukett strain of poliomyelitis showed some cell deterioration before new virus was produced, the majority of the cells retained much of their integrity for several hours after most of the virus was released. The cells also retained some metabolic functions, since they were able to utilize oxygen and reduce tetrazolium salts. Cells may even have their metabolic processes speeded up, so that active cell proliferation may occur; resulting, for example, in the formation of pocks when the chick chorio-allantois is infected with vaccinia and herpes simplex viruses (Burnet, 1955). Since animal cells are able to produce virus over considerable periods of time after infection, it is obvious that they have not been destroyed and that, in fact, some cell metabolism must be able to proceed, as Ackermann showed experimentally. But whether the host is able to insert its own genetic information into the viral nucleic acid during this cell-virus interaction we are unable to say. We can, however, attempt to resolve the problem by studying the virus genome independently of its phenotype. And this can be done by the use of infective ribonucleic acid preparations. No one has yet succeeded in isolating an infective nucleic acid from a bacterial virus, but it has been accomplished with many animal viruses and one RNA plant virus.

Gierer & Schramm (1956) were able to demonstrate the ability of RNA preparations from tobacco mosaic virus to initiate the production of new, infective virus. Similarly, Colter, Bird & Brown (1957) claimed that RNA prepared from cells of the mouse Ehrlich ascites carcinoma infected with Mengo virus was infective; and similar claims have been made in respect of the viruses of Eastern Equine encephalitis (Wecker & Schäfer, 1957), West Nile (Colter, Bird, Moyer & Brown, 1957), poliomyelitis (Alexander *et al.* 1958), Semliki Forest (Cheng, 1958), and foot and mouth disease (Brown, Sellers & Stewart, 1958). More recently, and of special interest in the present context, is the demonstration by Huppert & Sanders (1958) that infective RNA preparations can be extracted from mouse tissues infected with EMC virus, a virus which, as we have seen, shows host-controlled variation.

The following evidence suggests that the study of such infective RNA preparations may give informative results. If we take the K2 strain of EMC virus (Sanders, Huppert & Hoskins, 1958), grow it in different types of mouse tumour cell *in vitro* under single growth cycle conditions, and then study the product, we find that, whereas the virus has the same host range irrespective of the cell in which it is grown, infective RNA preparations made from the same materials differ widely in their host range (see Table 3) (Sanders, personal communication). Furthermore,

Table 3. *Host range of RNA preparations made from different types of host cell infected with K2 encephalomyocarditis (EMC) virus*

	Titre of RNA* when tested in			
Virus grown in	Krebs-2 carcinoma	Sarcoma 37	Ehrlich carcinoma	Sarcoma 180
Krebs-2 carcinoma	6×10^3	$\geqslant 4 \times 10^4$	9×10^2	$\geqslant 5 \times 10^4$
Sarcoma 37	Trace	1×10^3	7×10^1	0†
Ehrlich carcinoma	2×10^3	$< 4 \times 10^1$	9×10^2	4×10^2
Sarcoma 180	1×10^3	6×10^2	3×10^3	6×10^2

* RNA was prepared by a phenol extraction procedure (Schuster, Schramm & Zillig, 1956) from the supernatant fluids of infected ascites tumour cell suspensions (see Sanders, 1957*a*) harvested after a single growth cycle (12 hr.). The initial infection was at a calculated multiplicity of 3 PFU/cell. Assays of RNA were made by preparing a mixture in equal proportions of RNA dilutions and a suspension of washed tumour cells (10^8/ml.); after 30 min. interaction at room temperature 0·1 ml. volumes were inoculated intraperitoneally into albino mice, using five mice/dilution. Mice developing specific signs of infection (absence of ascites, subsequent death) were scored as positive; those developing ascites were scored as negative. The results are expressed as 50 % mouse infective doses/ml.

† No deaths when five mice were inoculated with undiluted RNA.

if we take viruses with different host ranges (see Table 1) we discover that infective RNA preparations derived from them are both host determined and virus determined in their host range (Table 4) (Sanders, personal communication). These instances of changes in host range are undoubtedly changes which are host-controlled in origin; and it therefore appears that animal virus variation controlled by the host may be the result of processes going on at the level of the viral nucleic acid. It is possible that this may also be the case for the bacterial viruses, since, following adsorption to the (modifying) host, DNA is injected into the cell, leaving the empty protein shell outside (Hershey & Chase, 1952). It would seem unlikely that the host can act upon anything other than the phage genetic material, but the possibility cannot be excluded since, as Hershey (1957) points out, up to 3 % of the phage protein enters the bacterium during the injection process. It may well be that some virus protein is also present in infective ribonucleic acid preparations derived from animal viruses.

Table 4. *Host range of RNA preparations made from two types of host cell infected with different encephalomyocarditis (EMC) virus strains*

Host cell	Virus strain	Titre of RNA* when tested in			
		Krebs-2 carcinoma	Sarcoma 37	Ehrlich carcinoma	Sarcoma 180
Krebs-2 carcinoma	EMC (mouse brain)	$\geqslant 1 \times 10^4$	$\geqslant 2 \times 10^4$	Trace	Trace
	S180	$\geqslant 3 \times 10^4$	$\geqslant 3 \times 10^4$	Trace	Trace
	K2	6×10^3	$\geqslant 4 \times 10^4$	9×10^2	$\geqslant 5 \times 10^4$
Sarcoma 37	EMC (mouse brain)	Trace	6×10^1	6×10^3	5×10^2
	S180	0†	0†	6×10^3	Trace
	K2	Trace	1×10^3	7×10^1	0†

* See footnote to Table 3.
† No deaths when five mice were inoculated with undiluted RNA.

Crick & Watson (1957) have proposed a model for animal viruses consisting of a central packet of nucleic acid, surrounded by protein subunits. It seems certain that the nucleic acid is somehow wrapped up since, in the intact virus, it is inaccessible to the action of ribonuclease (Crick & Watson, 1957; Valentine & Isaacs, 1957). If we do regard the virus as being composed of these two basic parts, we cannot then exclude the possibility that biochemical structures other than the nucleic acid are involved in host-controlled variation, either alone, or in conjunction with the genetic material. It then also seems reasonable to suppose that the protein shell is the first part of the virus to make contact with the host cell during infection, and that this structure plays some role in the initial stages of infection. Whatever the nature of the first stages of infection, the protein coat would certainly provide a material basis upon which a potentially modifying host could act. There is some evidence that it may be involved. Bawden (1956) has described an instance of a legume-infective strain of tobacco mosaic virus which is modified following growth in a variety of French bean. The change is not reported to take place under single cycle conditions, but it is reversible. The point is that since it is the serological nature of the virus which is affected we can assume that the virus protein is altered in some way. In a more recent paper, Bawden (1958) concludes that host-controlled modification is unlikely to be the mechanism responsible for the sudden changes observed, and that the change from one form of the virus to another is explicable only by the hosts selecting variants which originate in them as a result of events equivalent to reversible mutations. His conclusion rests upon observed changes in the virus nucleic acid. However, there is no reason for assuming that the genetic material of tobacco mosaic virus may not be changed by the host—as was indeed suggested for EMC virus (see above)—and host-controlled modification cannot therefore be excluded from being responsible for Bawden's observations. A change in the virus nucleic acid does not invalidate the importance of the altered protein in the present argument. We do not know whether this happens with other viruses. Nevertheless, it seems that host range modification of a virus does not necessarily affect its initial adsorption. Both modified and unmodified forms of the same phage adsorb equally well (Luria, 1953), and preliminary studies have shown that adsorption of host-modified S 180 virus to S 180 tumour cells can take place *in vitro* (Hoskins, unpublished). Adsorption of the phage does not lead to death of the bacterium (Bertani & Weigle, 1953). The block in virus production therefore occurs at some stage between adsorption and release of infective virus. The actual stage is unknown. Zinder (1953) found that phage PLT-22—the transducing agent in *Salmonella*—although modified by growth in *Salmonella gallinarum* to a form with restricted ability to grow in *Salmonella typhimurium*, is nevertheless still able after growth in *S. gallinarum* to transduce genetic properties from *S. gallinarum* to *S. typhimurium* with about the normal frequency. This suggests that at least some part of the modified virus is able to enter the cell in which it does not grow.

THE RELATION BETWEEN ABORTIVE MULTIPLICATION CYCLES AND HOST-CONTROLLED VARIATION

It would appear from the foregoing that host-modified viruses are able to take part in at least some of the initial stages in the process of infection without giving rise to new infective virus, and that their development bears a certain resemblance to those phenomena which are often loosely termed abortive multiplication cycles. A closer comparison of these processes would therefore be of interest.

The PR 8 and Lee strains of influenza virus are normally fully infective for cells of the chick allantois. But Schlesinger (1950, 1953) found that when inoculated intracerebrally into mice they undergo a single cycle of multiplication that results in the formation of new haemagglutinin and complement-fixing antigen which are not infective for the chick embryo and cannot be passaged in further mice. Similarly, Fulton & Isaacs (1953) infected the chorionic surface of the chick chorio-allantoic membrane *in ovo* and *in vitro* with influenza A strains, and found that a considerable increase in soluble antigen might accompany only a slight rise in infectivity. Most recently, Henle, Girardi & Henle (1955) have shown that HeLa cells inoculated with any of several strains of influenza virus yield only non-infectious haemagglutinin and complement-fixing antigen. In all three instances the virus-cell interaction leads to the formation of a product non-infective for the host cell, and therefore exclusively derived from the cells originally infected. Henle and his co-workers indeed showed that the cytopathic change which developed following infection did not spread throughout the cultures and that the degree of cytopathic destruction was directly related to the initial infecting dose of virus. Similarly, Fulton & Isaacs found that the yield of soluble antigen was directly related to the initial virus inoculum. Neither of these observations would be expected if secondary infection occurred. In this respect the 'modified' influenza viruses behave differently from the modified bacteriophages and S 180 virus described earlier since, in the latter cases, the changed virus replicates within the modifying host and can continue to do so as long as fresh cells are available for infection. Thus, the change which was apparent after a single cycle of growth was also demonstrable when S 180 virus had been growing in the mouse brain for a week (see above). Nevertheless, these do represent instances of modification of the virus by the host, and, since no new infective virus is produced to initiate a second cycle, are, by definition, changes brought about under single growth cycle conditions.

There is no *a priori* reason for assuming that a cell-virus interaction in which the virus is modified should proceed to the development of a fully infectious virus particle. Like any other complex biological entity, a virus probably develops in a series of recognizable steps. Certain phases that can be formally recognized during phage replication illustrate this point (Hershey, 1956). Thus, adsorption of phage is followed by penetration of the bacterium. Then follows a period, representing the so-called vegetative phase, during which the phage cannot be detected within the cell. Later, on completion of maturation, new phage particles appear in the cell and the total yield is liberated from it in a single burst. In animal viruses the chain of events following infection may be divided

into a number of analogous phases (Sanders, 1957b): adsorption, penetration, an eclipse period during which virus cannot be detected intracellularly, maturation and, finally, virus release. The situation is less
well-defined than in the bacterial viruses, although it should perhaps be
emphasized that in both cases these stages represent little more than
formal divisions; they provide no information about the mechanisms
involved. However, various virus activities can be recovered from cells
at different times after infection, and, in addition, various morphological structures can be found in infected cells. Von Magnus (1951)
showed that serial passage of high dilutions of stock influenza virus
preparations in the chick embryo resulted in the production of progeny
virus with a certain infectivity/haemagglutinin ratio; but when passage
was made using large inocula this ratio fell to about 1/10,000 of the
former. This is interpreted as a failure of virus maturation, resulting in
the formation of non-infectious haemagglutinin. Von Magnus considers
that the non-infective component interferes with the completion of
immature particles newly produced from infective virus present in any
stock suspension. This certainly nicely accounts for the observed correlation between the infectivity/haemagglutinin ratio and dilution on serial
passage. Similarly, Henle's (1953) finding that when chick embryos are
infected with influenza the liberated virus reveals a higher infectivity/
haemagglutinin ratio than the infected tissues suggests that haemagglutinin is formed as a by-product in infective virus production.
Hoyle's (1953) studies with influenza virus likewise suggest that soluble
complement-fixing antigen may be recovered from infected chorio-
allantoic membranes before the appearance of fully infective virus even
though they have been criticized (Cairns, 1953) on the ground that
increases with time in different virus activities have generally been
referred to base lines of different levels.

A second type of non-infectious haemagglutinin, produced by heating
infective virus or by u.v. irradiation, is also capable of causing interference (Isaacs & Edney, 1950b). Furthermore, a recently described
component, interferon, is produced following infection of chick embryos
with heat- and u.v.-inactivated influenza virus, and induces interference
in the chorio-allantoic membrane challenged with the viruses of influenza
A, Sendai, Newcastle disease and vaccinia (Isaacs & Lindenmann,
1957; Isaacs, Lindenmann & Valentine, 1957; Lindenmann, Burke &
Isaacs, 1957; Burke & Isaacs, 1958). Interferon is not produced following infection with fresh virus. However, the ability of heat- and u.v.-
inactivated virus particles to infect cells without yielding new infective
virus may well have a different basis from that of fully infective virus

to undergo abortive development following infection since the inactivated bodies are not natural products of infection.

The non-infectious haemagglutinin of Von Magnus is characterized by a sedimentation constant which is smaller than that of infectious virus (Hanig & Bernkopf, 1950; Gard, Von Magnus, Svedmyr & Birch-Andersen, 1952), and, when adsorbed to laked fowl erythrocytes it appears in electronmicrographs to consist of flattened 'ghost-like' structures whose average diameter is larger than that of active particles (Schlesinger & Werner, 1952; Werner & Schlesinger, 1954). Kipps *et al.* (1957) obtained three different particle-size fractions from the brains of baby mice infected with MEF1 poliovirus; the smallest (8–12 mμ) fixed complement but was not infective, while 24 and 30 mμ components corresponded to infective virus. Kipps and his co-workers also obtained several fractions from the brains of baby mice infected with the virus of horse sickness; a soluble antigen of about 8–12 mμ was separated from infective particles 24, 30 and 50 mμ in diameter. The work reported by Brooksby (1958) indicated that several virus components with diverse activities may occur in tissues infected with the virus of foot and mouth disease.

The nucleic acid content varies in different particles of the same virus, and may be negligible in non-infective particles. Thus, immature phage 'heads' which can be isolated from infected bacteria, contain little or nothing of the DNA present in mature phage (Hershey, 1956). Similarly, Markham has described two types of particle in plants infected with turnip yellow mosaic virus, one of which appears to be the infective virus without its nucleic acid (Markham, 1951). And the occurrence in tobacco seedlings infected with tobacco mosaic virus of a crystallizable antigen devoid of RNA may be a further example (Jeener & Lemoine, 1953). Influenza virus preparations of low infectivity possess less nucleic acid than ones of higher infectivity; for example, Ada & Perry (1955) showed that PR8 virus with a high haemagglutinin/infectivity ratio contains less nucleic acid than standard virus preparations. However, there does not appear to be a simple relationship between the two, and a 99-fold decrease in infectivity may be accompanied by only a twofold decrease in the nucleic acid content (Ada & Perry, 1956). These findings also suggest the existence of particles of differing nucleic acid content, and it may be, as Ada & Perry point out, that only those virus particles with a nucleic acid content above a certain value can elicit the production of new, infective virus.

Findings such as these clearly do not establish the occurrence of well-defined stages in virus growth, and there is indeed some evidence to the contrary. Matthews (1958) showed that in cabbage plants infected with turnip yellow mosaic virus the ratio of nucleoprotein to protein particles remained constant throughout the growth cycle. This suggests that the protein is not a precursor of the nucleoprotein particle. Although non-infectious haemagglutinin is probably a by-product of virus replication, complement-fixing antigens may well be precursors in the development of fully infectious virus, and comparable with the 'doughnuts', apparently produced as precursors in *Escherichia coli* B cells infected with a T series phage whose subsequent development is blocked by pro-flavine (deMars, Luria, Fisher & Levinthal, 1953). In a series of elegant studies Kellenberger and his co-workers (Kellenberger & Kellenberger, 1957; Kellenberger & Séchaud, 1957) have recently demonstrated the occurrence of rods as well as empty heads and intact phages in infected cells; the rods appeared similar in shape and size to the tail cores of T2 and T4 phages isolated by the oxidation procedure of Kellenberger & Arber (1955).

The artificial blocking of phage development by the use of proflavine may then be analogous to the natural failure of viral synthesis in abortive multiplication cycles or after the adsorption to non-susceptible cells of host-induced variants. It seems reasonable to suppose that virus metabolism could be blocked at any developmental stage, and that although normal development would then be frustrated, interaction with the cells' metabolism might still proceed and even lead to death of the cell. Ackermann et al. (1954) indeed showed that fluorophenylalanine would prevent the multiplication of type III poliovirus in HeLa cells yet allow the cytopathic changes to appear in the usual way. Furthermore, Prince & Ginsberg (1957a, 1957b, 1957c) found that Newcastle disease virus adsorbed to and killed cells of the Ehrlich mouse ascites tumour, even though it did not lead to the production of either infective, haem-agglutinating or complement-fixing particles. However, by the use of the fluorescent antibody technique of Coons & Kaplan (1950) these workers demonstrated that a specific virus antigen is nevertheless formed. Although its composition and function remain unknown, the apparent absence of any other demonstrable biological activity suggests that in the formation of this antigen we have an abortive multiplication cycle of a simplicity not hitherto recognized in the replication of animal viruses.

REFERENCES

ACKERMANN, W. W., RABSON, A. & KURTZ, H. (1954). Growth characteristics of poliomyelitis virus in HeLa cell cultures: lack of parallelism in cellular injury and virus increase. *J. exp. Med.* **100**, 437.

ADA, G. L. & PERRY, B. T. (1954). The nucleic acid content of influenza virus. *Aust. J. exp. Biol. med. Sci.* **32**, 453.

ADA, G. L. & PERRY, B. T. (1955). Infectivity and nucleic acid content of influenza virus. *Nature, Lond.* **175**, 209.

ADA, G. L. & PERRY, B. T. (1956). Influenza virus nucleic acid: relationship between biological characteristics of the virus particle and properties of the nucleic acid. *J. gen. Microbiol.* **14**, 623.

ADA, G. L. & PERRY, B. T. (1958). Properties of the nucleic acid of the Ryan strain of filamentous influenza virus. *J. gen. Microbiol.* **19**, 40.

ALEXANDER, H. E., KOCH, G., MOUNTAIN, I. M., SPRUNT, K. & VAN DAMME, O. (1958). Infectivity of ribonucleic acid of poliovirus on HeLa cell monolayers. *Virology*, **5**, 172.

ANDERSON, E. S. (1955). Consideration of the Vi-phage types of *Salmonella typhi* on a structural basis. *Nature, Lond.* **175**, 171.

BANG, F. B. & GEY, G. O. (1952). Comparative susceptibility of cultured cell strains to the virus of Eastern Equine encephalomyelitis. *Johns Hopk. Hosp. Bull.* **91**, 427.

BAWDEN, F. C. (1956). Reversible, host induced changes in a strain of tobacco mosaic virus. *Nature, Lond.* **177**, 302.

BAWDEN, F. C. (1958). Reversible changes in strains of tobacco mosaic virus from leguminous plants. *J. gen. Microbiol.* **18**, 751.

BERTANI, G. & WEIGLE, J. J. (1953). Host controlled variation in bacterial viruses. *J. Bact.* **65**, 113.

BROOKSBY, J. B. (1958). The virus of foot-and-mouth disease. *Advanc. Virus Res.* **5**, 1.

BROWN, F., SELLERS, R. F. & STEWART, D. L. (1958). Infectivity of ribonucleic acid from mice and tissue culture infected with the virus of foot-and-mouth disease. *Nature, Lond.* **182**, 535.

BURKE, D. C. & ISAACS, A. (1958). Further studies on interferon. *Brit. J. exp. Path.* **39**, 78.

BURNET, F. M. (1955). *Principles of Animal Virology.* New York: Academic Press.

BURNET, F. M. & BULL, D. R. (1943). Changes in influenza virus associated with adaptation to passage in chick embryos. *Aust. J. exp. Biol. med. Sci.* **21**, 55.

BURNET, F. M. & LIND, P. E. (1954). An analysis of the adaptation of an influenza virus to produce lesions in the mouse lung. *Aust. J. exp. Biol. med. Sci.* **32**, 711.

CAIRNS, H. J. F. (1953). In discussion of paper by HOYLE, L. (1953): The multiplication of the influenza virus considered in relation to the general problem of biological multiplication. *Symp. Soc. gen. Microbiol.* **2**, 225.

CHENG, PING-YAO (1958). Infectivity of ribonucleic acid from mouse brains infected with Semliki Forest virus. *Nature, Lond.* **181**, 1800.

COHEN, S. S. (1947). The synthesis of bacterial viruses in infected cells. *Cold Spr. Harb. Symp. quant. Biol.* **12**, 35.

COHEN, S. S. (1949). Growth requirements of bacterial viruses. *Bact. Rev.* **13**, 1.

COHEN, S. S. (1955). Comparative biochemistry and virology. *Advanc. Virus Res.* **3**, 1.

COLTER, J. S., BIRD, H. H. & BROWN, R. A. (1957). Infectivity of ribonucleic acid from Ehrlich ascites tumour cells infected with Mengo encephalitis. *Nature, Lond.* **179**, 859.

COLTER, J. S., BIRD, H. H., MOYER, A. W. & BROWN, R. A. (1957). Infectivity of ribonucleic acid isolated from virus-infected tissues. *Virology*, **4**, 522.

COONS, A. H. & KAPLAN, M. H. (1950). Localization of antigen in tissue cells. II. Improvements in a method for the detection of antigen by means of fluorescent antibody. *J. exp. Med.* **91**, 1.

CRICK, F. H. C. & WATSON, J. D. (1957). Virus structure: general principles. In *Ciba Foundation Symposium on The Nature of Viruses*, p. 5. Edited by G. E. W. Wolstenholme and E. C. P. Millar. London: Churchill.

CUNHA, R., WEIL, M. C., BEARD, D., TAYLOR, A. R., SHARP, D. G. & BEARD, J. W. (1947). Purification and characters of the Newcastle disease virus (California strain). *J. Immunol.* **55**, 69.

DANE, D. S., DICK, G. W. A., CONNOLLY, J. H., FISHER, O. D., McKEOWN, F., BRIGGS, M., NELSON, R. & WILSON, D. (1957). Vaccination against poliomyelitis with live virus vaccines. I. A trial of TN type II vaccine. *Brit. Med. J.* i, 59.

DUBES, G. R. & CHAPIN, M. (1956). Cold-adapted genetic variants of polioviruses. *Science*, **124**, 586.

DULBECCO, R. (1957). Quantitative aspects of virus growth in cultivated animal cells. In *Ciba Foundation Symposium on The Nature of Viruses*, p. 147. Edited by G. E. W. Wolstenholme and E. C. P. Millar. London: Churchill.

DULBECCO, R. & VOGT, M. (1954a). Plaque formation and isolation of pure lines with poliomyelitis viruses. *J. exp. Med.* **99**, 167.

DULBECCO, R. & VOGT, M. (1954b). One-step growth curves of western equine encephalitis virus on chick embryo cells grown *in vitro* and analysis of virus yields from single cells. *J. exp. Med.* **99**, 183.

EDNEY, M. (1957). Variations in animal viruses. *Annu. Rev. Microbiol.* **11**, 23.

ENDERS, J. F., WELLER, T. H. & ROBBINS, F. C. (1952). Alteration in pathogenicity for monkeys of Brunhilde strain of poliomyelitis virus following cultivation in human tissues. *Fed. Proc.* **11**, 467.

FULTON, F. & ISAACS, A. (1953). Influenza virus multiplication in the chick chorio-allantoic membrane. *J. gen. Microbiol.* **9**, 119.

GARD, S., VON MAGNUS, P., SVEDMYR, A. & BIRCH-ANDERSEN, A. (1952). Studies on the sedimentation of influenza virus. *Arch. ges. Virusforsch.* **4**, 591.

GIERER, A. & SCHRAMM, G. (1956). Infectivity of ribonucleic acid from tobacco mosaic virus. *Nature, Lond.* **177**, 702.

GRAHAM, A. F. (1950). The chemical analysis of purified influenza virus (PR 8) strain containing radioactive phosphorus. *Canad. J. Res.* E **28**, 186.

HANIG, M. & BERNKOPF, H. (1950). The sedimentable components of influenza virus propagated in de-embryonated eggs. *J. Immunol.* **65**, 585.

HELWIG, F. C. & SCHMIDT, E. C. H. (1945). A filter-passing agent producing interstitial myocarditis in anthropoid apes and small animals. *Science*, **102**, 31.

HENLE, W. (1953). Developmental cycles in animal viruses. *Cold Spr. Harb. Symp. quant. Biol.* **18**, 35.

HENLE, G., GIRARDI, A. & HENLE, W. (1955). A non-transmissable cytopathogenic effect of influenza virus in tissue culture accompanied by formation of non-infectious haemagglutinins. *J. exp. Med.* **101**, 25.

HENLE, W., LIU, O. C. & FINTER, N. B. (1954). Studies on host-virus interactions in the chick embryo-influenza virus system. IX. The period of liberation of virus from infected cells. *J. exp. Med.* **100**, 53.

HERSHEY, A. D. (1953). Nucleic acid economy in bacteria infected with bacterio-phage T2. II. Phage precursor nucleic acid. *J. gen. Physiol.* **37**, 1.

HERSHEY, A. D. (1956). Chemistry and viral growth. In *Currents in Biochemical Research*, p. 1. Edited by D. Green. New York: Interscience.

HERSHEY, A. D. (1957). Bacteriophages as genetic and biochemical systems. *Advanc. Virus Res.* **4**, 25.

HERSHEY, A. D. & CHASE, M. (1952). Independent functions of viral protein and nucleic acid in growth of bacteriophage. *J. gen. Physiol.* **36**, 39.

HERSHEY, A. D., GAREN, A., FRASER, D. K. & HUDIS, J. D. (1954). In Growth and inheritance in bacteriophage. *Carnegie Inst. Washington Year Book*, no. **53**, 210.

HOYLE, L. (1953). The multiplication of the influenza virus considered in relation to the general problem of biological multiplication. *Symp. Soc. gen. Microbiol.* **2**, 225.

HUPPERT, J. & SANDERS, F. K. (1958). An infective 'ribonucleic acid' component from tumour cells infected with encephalomyocarditis virus. *Nature, Lond.* **182**, 515.

ISAACS, A. & EDNEY, M. (1950a). Variation in laboratory stocks of influenza viruses: genetic aspects of variations. *Brit. J. exp. Path.* **31**, 209.

ISAACS, A. & EDNEY, M. (1950b). Interference between inactive and active influenza viruses in the chick embryo. I. Quantitative aspects of interference. *Aust. J. exp. Biol. med. Sci.* **28**, 219.

ISAACS, A. & LINDENMANN, J. (1957). Virus interference. I. The interferon. *Proc. roy. Soc.* B, **147**, 258.

ISAACS, A., LINDENMANN, J. & VALENTINE, R. C. (1957). Virus interference. II. Some properties of interferon. *Proc. Roy. Soc.* B, **147**, 268.

JEENER, R. & LEMOINE, P. (1953). Occurrence in plants infected with tobacco mosaic virus of a crystallizable antigen devoid of ribonucleic acid. *Nature, Lond.* **171**, 935.

KELLENBERGER, E. & ARBER, W. (1955). Die Struktur des Schwanzes der Phagen T2 und T4 und der Mechanismus der irreversiblen Adsorption. *Z. Naturf.* **10b**, 698.

KELLENBERGER, G. & KELLENBERGER, E. (1957). Electron microscopical studies of phage multiplication. III. Observation of single cell bursts. *Virology*, **3**, 275.

KELLENBERGER, E. & SÉCHAUD, J. (1957). Electron microscopical studies of phage multiplication. II. Production of phage-related structures during multiplication of phages T2 and T4. *Virology*, **3**, 256.

KIPPS, A., NAUDÉ, W. DU T., POLSON, A., SELZER, G. & VAN DEN ENDE, M. (1957). The size distribution of specific antigens in virus-infected tissues and their significance. In *Ciba Foundation Symposium on The Nature of Viruses*, p. 224. Edited by G. E. W. Wolstenholme and E. C. P. Millar. London: Churchill.

KNIGHT, C. A. (1947). The nucleic acid and carbohydrate of influenza virus. *J. exp. Med.* **85**, 99.

LI, C. P. & SCHAEFFER, M. (1953). Further modification of the mouse adapted Type III poliomyelitis virus. *Proc. Soc. exp. Biol., N.Y.* **83**, 706.

LINDENMANN, J., BURKE, D. C. & ISAACS, A. (1957). Studies on the production, mode of action and properties of interferon. *Brit. J. exp. Path.* **38**, 551.

LURIA, S. E. (1953). Host induced modifications of viruses. *Cold Spr. Harb. Symp. quant. Biol.* **18**, 237.

LURIA, S. E. & HUMAN, M. L. (1952). A nonhereditary, host-induced variation of bacterial viruses. *J. Bact.* **64**, 557.

MAGNUS, P. VON (1951). Propagation of the PR8 strain of influenza A virus in chick embryos. II. The formation of 'incomplete' virus following inoculation of large doses of seed virus. *Acta path. microbiol. scand.* **28**, 278.

MARKHAM, R. (1951). Physicochemical properties of the turnip yellow mosaic virus. *Disc. Faraday Soc.* **11**, 221.

MARKHAM, R. (1953). Virus nucleic acids. *Advanc. Virus Res.* **1**, 315.

DEMARS, R. I., LURIA, S. E., FISHER, H. & LEVINTHAL, C. (1953). The production of incomplete bacteriophage particles by the action of proflavine and the properties of the incomplete particles. *Ann. Inst. Pasteur*, **84**, 113.

MATTHEWS, R. E. F. (1958). Studies on the relation between protein and nucleo-protein particles in Turnip Yellow Mosaic virus infection. *Virology*, **5**, 192.

MILLER, H. K. (1956). The nucleic acid content of influenza virus. *Virology*, **2**, 312.

PARDEE, A. B. & WILLIAMS, I. (1953). Enzymatic activity and bacteriophage infection. III. Increase of deoxyribonuclease. *Ann. Inst. Pasteur*, **84**, 147.

PRINCE, A. M. & GINSBERG, H. S. (1957*a*). Studies on the cytotoxic effect of Newcastle disease virus (NDV) on Ehrlich ascites tumour cells. I. Characteristics of the virus-cell interaction. *J. Immunol.* **79**, 94.

PRINCE, A. M. & GINSBERG, H. S. (1957*b*). Studies on the cytotoxic effect of Newcastle disease virus (NDV) on Ehrlich ascites tumour cells. II. The mechanism and significance of *in vitro* recovery from the effect of NDV. *J. Immunol.* **79**, 107.

PRINCE, A. M. & GINSBERG, H. S. (1957*c*). Immunohistochemical studies on the interaction between Ehrlich ascites tumour cells and Newcastle Disease virus. *J. exp. Med.* **105**, 177.

SABIN, A. B. (1955). Characteristics and genetic potentialities of experimentally produced and naturally occurring variants of poliomyelitis virus. *Ann. N.Y. Acad. Sci.* **61**, 924.

SANDERS, F. K. (1957*a*). Virus titration in cell suspension cultures. *Proc. R. Soc. Med.* **50**, 911.

SANDERS, F. K. (1957*b*). The multiplication of animal viruses. In *Ciba Foundation Symposium on The Nature of Viruses*, p. 158. Edited by G. E. W. Wolstenholme and E. C. P. Millar. London: Churchill.

SANDERS, F. K., HUPPERT, J. & HOSKINS, J. M. (1958). Replication of an animal virus. *Symp. Soc. exp. Biol.* **12**, 123.

SCHLESINGER, R. W. (1950). Incomplete growth cycle of influenza virus in mouse brain. *Proc. Soc. exp. Biol., N.Y.* **74**, 541.

SCHLESINGER, R. W. (1953). The relation of functionally deficient forms of influenza virus to viral development. *Cold Spr. Harb. Symp. quant. Biol.* **18**, 55.

SCHLESINGER, R. W. & WERNER, G. H. (1952). Quantitative and morphological aspects of 'incomplete' growth cycle of influenza virus in mouse brain. *Fed. Proc.* **11**, 480.

SCHUSTER, H. VON, SCHRAMM, G. & ZILLIG, W. (1956). Die Struktur der Ribonuclein-säure aus Tabakmosaikvirus. *Z. Naturf.* **11***b*, 339.

SIDDIQI, M., KOZLOFF, L. M., PUTNAM, F. W. & EVANS, E. A. (1952). Biochemical studies of virus reproduction. IX. Nature of the host cell contributions. *J. biol. Chem.* **199**, 165.

STANLEY, N. T., DORMAN, D. C., PONSFORD, J. & LARKIN, M. (1956). Isolation of a heat-resistant variant of poliovirus. *Nature, Lond.* **178**, 413.

TAKEMORI, N., NOMURA, S., NAKANO, M., MORIOKA, Y., HENMI, M. & KITAOKA, M. (1958). Mutation of polioviruses to resistance to neutralizing substances in normal bovine sera. *Virology*, **5**, 30.

TAYLOR, A. R. (1944). Chemical analysis of the influenza viruses A and B and the swine influenza virus. *J. biol. Chem.* **153**, 675.

VALENTINE, R. C. & ISAACS, A. (1957). The structure of influenza virus filaments and spheres. *J. gen. Microbiol.* **16**, 195.

VOGT, M., DULBECCO, R. & WENNER, H. A. (1957). Mutants of poliomyelitis viruses with reduced efficiency of plating in acid medium and reduced neuropatho-genicity. *Virology*, **4**, 141.

WARREN, J. (1952). Encephalomyocarditis. In *Viral and Rickettsial Infections of Man*, p. 675. 2nd ed., edited by T. M. Rivers. Philadelphia: Lippincott.

WECKER, E. VON & SCHÄFER, W. (1957). Eine infektiöse Komponente von Ribo-nucleinsäure-Charakter aus dem Virus der amerikanischen Pferde-Enzephalo-myelitis (Typ Ost). *Z. Naturf.* **12** *b*, 415.

WERNER, G. H. & SCHLESINGER, R. W. (1954). Morphological and quantitative comparison between infectious and non-infectious forms of influenza virus. *J. exp. Med.* **100**, 203.

WEIL, M. L., WARREN, J., BREESE, S. S., RUSS, S. B. & JEFFRIES, H. (1952). Separation of encephalomyocarditis virus from tissue components by means of pro-tamine precipitation and enzymic digestion. *J. Bact.* **63**, 99.

ZELLE, M. R. (1955). Genetics of Microorganisms. *Annu. Rev. Microbiol.* **9**, 45.

ZINDER, N. D. (1953). Quoted by S. E. Luria (1953). In Host-induced modifications of viruses. *Cold Spr. Harb. Symp. quant. Biol.* **18**, 237.

GROWTH STUDIES WITH HERPES VIRUS

M. G. P. STOKER*

Department of Pathology, University of Cambridge

INTRODUCTION

Herpes virus is of particular interest among the animal viruses because deoxyribonucleic acid (DNA) accumulates in the nucleus of the infected cells during virus growth, and this has led to the supposition that the virus itself contains DNA. If so it resembles rabbit papilloma virus, vaccinia virus and possibly the adenoviruses, the insect viruses and, of course, bacteriophage, but differs from the other animal viruses which have been examined, and found to contain ribonucleic acid (RNA) alone. At the time of writing, however, no chemical studies on purified herpes virus have been reported, and there is thus no evidence at all to show whether the virus particle contains DNA or RNA or both.

Whatever the type of nucleic acid, the new virus particles are assembled in the nucleus, and not in the cytoplasm or at the cell surface, like the pox and influenza virus groups. Herpes virus also differs from many other viruses in its effect on cells in culture. For example, HeLa cells infected with herpes virus do not undergo early lysis but continue to produce excess acid, probably due to increased glycolysis. Finally, amongst animal viruses, herpes virus is a classical cause of latent infection, a problem of very general interest.

It may be noted that the features which distinguish herpes virus, and the related herpes B virus of monkeys, are shared by the adenoviruses, and possibly the salivary gland viruses, which also give rise to long-standing latent infections. Though adenovirus has some advantages for study, because it is more heat stable and perhaps easier to purify, we chose herpes because it has a wider host range, because it grows faster and might, therefore, form plaques, and because the pock-counting technique was already available for reasonably accurate quantitative work. Virus growth has been studied in a continuously propagated cell line (strain HeLa, Gey) in which it might be possible to investigate latent infection.

This communication describes attempts to gain some basic information about virus growth in HeLa cells before attempting to study latent infection in these cells.

* Present address: Department of Virology, University of Glasgow.

PREVIOUS STUDIES ON GROWTH OF HERPES VIRUS

Several workers have studied the growth of herpes virus in the chorio-allantois of the developing chick embryo (Schaffer & Enders, 1939; Scott, Coriell, Blank & Gray, 1953; Wildy, 1954; Modi & Tobin, 1954; Yoshino & Taniguchi, 1956). Using various ingenious techniques, such as rotation of the egg (Wildy, 1954), inversion during harvesting (Modi & Tobin, 1954), and insertion of the inoculum smeared on coverslips (Yoshino & Taniguchi, 1956), all have shown a rapid attachment of the virus to the ectodermal cells. The combined results suggest that 50–80 % of the virus particles become attached in 15 min., and 80–99 % in 1 hr. By addition of antiserum at successive intervals after inoculation, Scott, Coriell *et al.* (1953) found that most of the virus had entered the cells in 10–15 min., but Wildy's (1954) results suggested a slower penetration rate. These authors all report the disappearance or 'eclipse' of the major part of the adsorbed virus for a latent period of 7–12 hr., depending on the inoculum size. The infectivity then rose in the membrane for about 10 hr., either exponentially, or, according to Modi & Tobin (1954), in a series of steps. Some of the results suffer from the disadvantage that only the supernatant from the emulsified membranes was assayed and it is not known how much virus was lost through attachment to particles of cell debris, particularly in the latent period (see Cartwright, Pay & Henderson, 1957). Wildy, however, assayed completely ground-up pieces of chorioallantois and found very little virus compared with unground fragments of the same membranes.

More recently Yoshino (1956) and Yoshino & Taniguchi (1957) have reported growth studies in the blastoderm of one-day chick embryos, where cell numbers can be estimated. They claim that the blastodermal cells proliferated after infection and continued to release virus for several weeks. This system has the disadvantage, however, that, because the blastoderm is not a monolayer, it is only possible to produce simultaneous infection of the cells on one (entodermal) side, so that subsequent events are difficult to interpret.

The use of relatively homogeneous monolayers or suspensions of cells offers such obvious advantages for quantitative studies of virus-cell relationships, that most recent work has been on virus growth in tissue culture.

Herpes virus grows and causes a cytopathic effect on many different types of cultured cells, including rabbit corneal cells (Scott, Burgoon, Coriell & Blank, 1953), human fibroblasts (Enders, 1953), a pure line of mouse fibroblasts (Scherer, 1953), chick embryo cells (mainly fibroblasts) (Stulberg & Schapira, 1953; Gostling & Bedson, 1956), rabbit kidney cells (Sosa-Martinez, Gutierrez-Villegas & Sosa, 1955; Barski, Lamy & Lépine, 1955; Kaplan, 1957), monkey kidney cells (Barski *et al.* 1955), and various lines of continuously cultured cells such as HeLa cells (Scherer & Syverton, 1954), KB cells (Eagle, Habel, Rowe & Huebner, 1956) and others (Lebrun, 1956).

Gostling & Bedson (1956) studied virus growth in trypsinized suspensions of chick embryo cells. They allowed virus adsorption to occur for 18 hr. at 4° in order to measure the virus content of the cells before multiplication commenced. After treatment with antiserum to remove superficially attached virus, they found that about 1 % of the inoculum had been taken up and was detectable in the cell fraction before incubation at 37° commenced. On incubation, some 90 % of this virus in the cell fraction disappeared but, if the original inoculum was sufficiently large, 10 % was still detectable in the latent period of more than 6 hr. The method of cell disintegration did not disrupt the nucleus, but Gostling (1956) subsequently showed that the lost virus had not entered the nucleus, and the residual infectious virus was in the cytoplasm. The authors claim that there is no evidence for an eclipse phase, because the new virus might have developed from the 10 % infectious virus remaining in the latent period. From Gostling's results this would imply that virus multiplication commenced in the cytoplasm, which (for reasons stated below) seems unlikely.

With the introduction of the plaque technique to animal virology by Dulbecco (1952) it has become possible to study virus growth more accurately and especially to measure the input dose of virus in relation to the number of cells. It had previously been found by Black & Melnick (1955) that the related herpes B virus could cause plaques to form in monkey kidney cells. Kaplan (1957) has shown that herpes virus causes plaques in monolayers of rabbit kidney cells under agar, and has used this technique for studies of virus growth. The virus attaches slowly to the rabbit kidney cells, 50 % of the inoculum adsorbing to the monolayers in 90 min. 85 % of this was firmly adsorbed and could not be removed by washing. With an inoculum sufficient to infect 99 % of the cells, virus appeared in the medium after 8 hr., and rose exponentially until there were 280 plaque-forming units per cell. When the cells were suspended and diluted in the latent period to prevent readsorption and second cycles of multiplication, virus first appeared in the cell fraction 5 hr. after infection and in the medium after 6–8 hr., but the latent period was affected by the input dose per cell suggesting that more than one particle could initiate infection in each cell. After plating on uninfected monolayers in the latent period, only about 10 % of the intact cells yielded virus and formed plaques, which was considerably less than the number expected from the exposure of each cell to several infectious units. In view of the probability that herpes multiplication involves synthesis of DNA, Kaplan investigated the effect of previous X irradiation of the cells on virus growth and found that virus production was not diminished even 3 days after as high a dose as 40,000 r. This is in contrast to X irradiated *Escherichia coli* which rapidly loses the capacity to yield certain T phages (Labaw, Mosley & Wyckoff, 1953).

Much interest has naturally been focused on the site of development of herpes virus, particularly in relation to the nuclear changes in the infected cell. Lépine & Sautter (1946) claimed that the nuclear inclusion was Feulgen negative, and Francis & Kurtz (1950) and Ackermann & Kurtz (1952) found that the bulk of the infectivity was in the cytoplasmic rather than the nuclear fraction of chick embryo liver cells. This discovery led to the conclusion that virus multiplication did not take place in the nucleus. Scott, Burgoon, Coriell & Blank (1953), however, showed that the virus multiplication in rabbit corneal cells occurred before the typical eosinophilic Feulgen-negative inclusion developed, and was accompanied by an increase in basophilic material in the nucleus, previously described by Crouse, Coriell, Blank & Scott (1950). Gray & Scott (1954) also showed that, in fractionated chick embryo liver cells, virus was associated with the nucleus at an earlier stage in the infection than that examined by Francis & Kurtz (1950) or by Ackermann & Kurtz (1952). Subsequently the electron-microscope studies of Morgan, Ellison, Rose & Moore (1954) confirmed that virus particles appeared first in the nucleus of infected chorio-allantoic cells. They found round dense objects 30–40 mμ in diameter, then particles 70–100 mμ in diameter with dense central material surrounded by a single membrane, and later, outside the nucleus, particles 120–130 mμ in diameter with double membranes.

Lebrun (1956) has studied the appearance of herpes virus antigen in mouse brain, chorio-allantois, and cultures of human carcinoma cells, using fluorescent antibody staining. She showed that antigen first appeared in the nucleus in foci which corresponded well to the clusters of single-ringed particles shown by electron microscopy. Subsequently O'Dea & Dineen (1957) also described the development of herpetic antigen in unfixed baby rabbit kidney and human amnion cells.

Because of the latent infection caused by the virus in man it is important to know if infected cells can themselves continue to divide, and Gray, Tokumaru & Scott (1958) have studied the response of HeLa cells to infection with one freshly isolated strain of herpes virus. They described three types of response, proliferative, non-proliferative and giant cell, which were produced consistently with seeds prepared at different times from the same line. The temporary acceleration of cell growth occurring after infection in the proliferative type of response was certainly more than that of the uninfected controls, but the latter appeared to be growing at suboptimal rate, and the proportion of cells infected was not known. It is difficult therefore to exclude the possibility that the inoculum contained, beside the virus, a nutritional factor which stimulated growth of uninfected cells. This question of cell division after infection is an important one which will be considered again in relation to our own studies on infection in HeLa cells.

GROWTH OF HERPES VIRUS IN HeLa CELLS

The work to be described was carried out at Cambridge, with colleagues whose major contribution will be apparent from the frequent references to their work, both published and unpublished. As already stated, HeLa cells were chosen because of the need for continued cultivation in the study of latent infection. Single HeLa cells also form colonies with relatively high efficiency, and it is thus easy to isolate cell clones or to measure the cell-killing effect of virus.

Most of our experiments to date have been done with the wild strain of cells, grown in human serum or rabbit serum, with lactalbumin hydrolysate or synthetic medium (Puck, Cieciura & Fisher, 1957), but HeLa clone S3 (Puck & Fisher, 1956) has also been investigated.

Virus assay

The Melbourne variant of the classical HF strain of herpes virus (HFEM) which was used, forms large and easily counted pocks on the chorio-allantoic membrane of embryonated eggs. With a modified inoculation technique, we found a linear dose-response relationship with a standard error between 10 and 20% of the mean (Stoker & Ross, 1958).

Dr A. P. Waterson has shown that the HFEM strain also produces plaques on monolayers of trypsinized chick embryo cells. As with the original plaque technique described by Dulbecco (1952), the plaques may be seen macroscopically as circular areas where cells are unstained by neutral red. Plaques may also be seen in cell suspensions in agar as described by Cooper (1955), but this method is less sensitive than the monolayer method, probably because of the slow adsorption to the cells in suspension. When first developed the plaque technique in chick cells was about one-fifth as sensitive as the pock-counting technique, and it was not used routinely for assay in the experiments reported here. However, improvements in culture media such as the introduction of synthetic medium in place of embryo extract, and calf serum in place of bovine serum, the use of smaller volumes of inoculum and adsorption at 31° to reduce thermal inactivation, have recently increased the sensitivity of the plaque method in chick cells and it is now equal to that of the pock counts.

Rabbit kidney cells, which have been shown by Kaplan (1957) to be 10–1000 times more sensitive than the chorio-allantois to his selected H4 strain, have not yet been used by us for plaque assay, but the 50 % endpoint in tube titrations suggests that the rabbit kidney cells are no more sensitive to the HFEM strain than the chorio-allantois, or trypsinized chick cells (Dr A. P. Waterson, to be published).

It was obviously important to determine infectivity accurately in HeLa cells, whatever the sensitivity, in order to measure virus adsorption and multiplicity of infection. In tube titrations it was observed that, at high dilutions of virus, microscopic focal lesions were formed which remained localized, and these foci developed even in the presence of antiserum, as did those produced by B virus in monkey kidney cells (Black & Melnick, 1955). These foci stained with neutral red, however, and enlarged very slowly, and it has not yet been possible to keep HeLa cells under agar long enough for plaques to become visible to the naked eye. Nevertheless, Miss A. E. Farnham has evolved a satisfactory method of assay by enumeration of microscopic plaques in monolayers under fluid medium. These plaques first become visible 2 days after infection and, if antiserum has been added to prevent secondary spread, they do not increase in number after 3 days. Adding antiserum at successive intervals also showed that secondaries were not seeded until after the second day, and were not visible until the fourth day after the original inoculation. The primary plaques can, therefore, be counted at the third day without antiserum. This method without antiserum is in current use, and Miss Farnham has demonstrated a linear dose-response relationship, and a good agreement between observed plaque counts and the theoretical Poisson distribution expected of independently distributed particles (Farnham, 1958). The absence of late-developing primary plaques is an important factor in this technique and has been confirmed in cultures maintained for 19 days. In this respect herpes infection differs from adenovirus infection in HeLa cells, in which Pereira & Kelly (1957) have shown that the cytopathic effect may be delayed.

Pl. 1, figs. 1, 2 and 3, shows pocks on the chorio-allantois, plaques in chick cells and a microscopic plaque in HeLa cells, produced by the HFEM strain.

Relative sensitivity. The results of titrating representative virus seeds by these assay techniques are shown in Table 1. The original HFEM

Table 1. *Comparison of methods for titrating four strains of herpes virus*

		Infectivity determined in				
Virus strain	Source of virus	Chorio-allantois. Log_{10} pock units/ml.	Chick cells. Log_{10} plaque units/ml.	HeLa cells. Log_{10} plaque units/ml.	Rabbit kidney cells. Log_{10} 50 % cyto-pathic dose/ml.	Ratio pock units/ HeLa plaque units
HFEM-egg	Allantoic fluid (after many passages in eggs, none in HeLa cells)	7·53	7·32	6·68	7·04	7·08
HFEM-HeLa	Culture fluid from HeLa cells (after 34 consecutive passages in HeLa cells)	7·45	7·45	6·26	7·04	15·5
MS-egg	Allantoic fluid (after 3 consecutive passages in eggs, none in HeLa cells)	5·98	<2·7	4·48	6·14	31·6
MS-HeLa	Culture fluid from HeLa cells (after 12 consecutive passages in HeLa cells, none in eggs)	6·18	<2·7	5·92	6·56	1·82

strain (HFEM-egg) had not been passaged on HeLa cells. Seeds prepared from unconcentrated allantoic fluid generally contained more than 10^7 pock units per ml. and about the same number of chick plaque units. The number of HeLa plaque units was lower and indicated that seven pock units were needed to initiate plaque formation in the HeLa cells (pock/HeLa plaque ratio = 7). Once infection had occurred, the virus apparently grew well, however. 10^6 cells inoculated with 10^3 or more HeLa plaque units showed confluent cytopathic changes in 2–4 days, by which time the medium usually contained about 10^7 pock units per ml. This still showed the lower infectivity for HeLa cells, however, and the virus was therefore passaged in HeLa cells in an attempt to produce a variant with a higher relative infectivity for these cells. Results on a typical seed prepared after thirty-four passages (HFEM-HeLa) are shown in Table 1, and it is apparent that the infectivity for HeLa cells fell, rather than rose, relative to the infectivity for the chorio-allantois (pock/HeLa plaque ratio = 16). Virus produced in HeLa cells, even in the first passage, had in fact a lower infectivity for these cells, but not for the chorio-allantois, than the original egg-grown virus (Miss A. E. Farnham, to be published). Addition of chick embryo extract to the

HeLa cell-grown virus did not increase its infectivity, so that the difference is probably not due to traces of some non-specific enhancing factor from the eggs.

By contrast, a strain of virus freshly isolated from a patient with a herpetic vesicle and passaged twelve times in HeLa cells (MS-HeLa) with no egg passage, was almost as infectious for HeLa cells as for the chorio-allantois (pock/HeLa ratio = 1·8) but the same strain isolated and passed three times in eggs with no HeLa cell passage (MS-egg) had a very low infectivity for HeLa cells (pock/HeLa plaque ratio = 32) with approximately the same number of pock-forming particles. The pocks produced by the MS strain were much smaller (less than 0·5 mm. diameter) than those produced by the HFEM strain (approx. 1·0 mm. diameter), and it is interesting to note that the MS strain produced no cytopathic effect in chick fibroblast monolayers, even after egg passage (Dr A. P. Waterson, unpublished).

The linear relationship between HeLa plaque numbers and dose of virus shows that one particle can initiate infection in these cells. We must, therefore, conclude that the HFEM strain, whether produced in HeLa cells or eggs, is composed mostly of particles which do not infect HeLa cells, but which can be detected by their pock-forming ability.

On the evidence so far, it cannot be assumed that such particles are any different from those that successfully infect the HeLa cells. They may all be identical, but the probability of one particle infecting a chorio-allantoic cell may be higher than that for a HeLa cell, due, for example, to smaller numbers of receptor sites, or a high rate of virus destruction by HeLa cells. On the other hand, the population of virus particles may be heterogeneous, with some unable to infect HeLa cells and capable of infecting chorio-allantoic cells only.

At first sight it may appear unwise to use the HFEM strain, because of its low efficiency of infection in HeLa cells. On the other hand, HeLa cells themselves produce the unsuccessful particles as well as the successful ones and fortunately we can detect and measure both. The ideal system may be like the T phages, with every physical particle infectious for, and detectable by, the type of cell which produced it. Many animal viruses, however, give rise to physical particles which are predominantly non-infectious and detectable so far only by electron microscopy. The pock-forming virus produced by HeLa cells may not constitute the total physical population of virus particles, but it is at least nearer the total than that detected by HeLa cell infectivity tests, and thus additional information may be obtained about virus growth and formation of incomplete virus.

Thermal inactivation

Anyone working with herpes virus must be aware of its high thermo-lability. There have been many conflicting reports on the rate of inactivation at 37° which presumably arise from the use of differing strains, suspending media, or methods of assay of infectivity. (Compare, for example, those of Gostling & Bedson, 1956; Yoshino & Taniguchi, 1956; and Kaplan, 1957.)

Miss A. E. Farnham (unpublished) has studied the heat sensitivity of the HFEM strain in maintenance medium with 5 % rabbit serum. Her results show that at pH 7·2–7·4 pock-forming ability declines as a first-order reaction at temperatures between 30 and 44° with a half-life of 0·77 hr. at 44°, 5·0 hr. at 37°, and 24 hr. at 30°. This means that at 37° only a tenth of the infectivity survives 16 hr.

Between pH 7·4 and 8·0 the inactivation rate is little altered, but it increases considerably below pH 6·8. The HeLa plaque-forming titre is reduced at about the same rate as pock-forming titre.

Adsorption to HeLa cells

When HeLa cells are exposed to a layer of fluid about 1·0 mm. deep, containing the HFEM-HeLa strain, about half the pock-forming virus disappears from the fluid and becomes adsorbed to the cells in 1 hr. Thereafter adsorption becomes difficult to measure accurately because it becomes slower and approaches the rate of thermal inactivation (Stoker & Ross, 1958).

At least ten pock-forming particles can adsorb per cell and the union is a firm one because only a quarter of the virus can be removed by repeated washing, and most of this appears in the first wash.

This may be compared to the rate of attachment of HeLa plaque-forming virus found by Farnham (1958), who exposed monolayers to about 70 HeLa plaque units and washed off unadsorbed virus at successive time-intervals. She found that 50 % of the plaque-forming virus became attached in 50 min. and 80 % in 2 hr.

Furthermore, the relative infectivity of the residual unadsorbed virus for the chorio-allantois and HeLa cells was unchanged (Miss A. E. Farnham, unpublished). This similarity in rate of adsorption of pock-forming and HeLa plaque-forming virus shows that all particles attach slowly and it is not possible to account for the low infectivity of the virus for HeLa cells by failure of the majority of particles to adsorb at all.

Virus penetration

Though pock-forming virus attaches firmly to the HeLa cells and little is removed by washing, over half this adsorbed virus may subsequently be recovered from the cell debris after cycles of freezing and thawing as shown in Fig. 1 (Stoker & Ross, 1958). If the cells are treated with antiserum during the latent period, and then washed before disintegration, very little of the virus is found. We therefore assume that the bulk of it remains extracellular and is antiserum-sensitive. The small amount of pock-forming virus which is found in the cell debris after antiserum treatment constitutes only about 0·01 % of the virus which originally adsorbed to the cells. This could be intracellular, but the same amount may be released without damaging the cells by suspending them in the chelating agent, sodium ethylenediamine tetra-acetate (EDTA). We have postulated that this virus is also extracellular, but deep in crypts of the HeLa cell surface which are revealed by electron microscopy (Stoker, Smith & Ross, 1958) and inaccessible to antiserum but released by EDTA. (EDTA was used for cell suspension in preference to trypsin, because the latter rapidly inactivates the virus.) After allowing for thermal inactivation the amount of pock-forming virus which is lost without trace is small but difficult to determine because of the lack of accuracy in estimation of total virus originally attached to the cells.

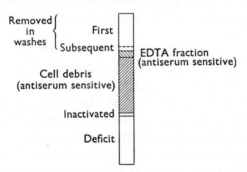

Fig. 1. Distribution of residual pock-forming virus in HeLa cell monolayer after infection with herpes virus.

The pock-forming virus, which adsorbs to HeLa cells and fails to initiate infection, does not produce a lasting interference with the subsequent cytopathic effect of HeLa infectious virus. This may be seen in a culture infected with about 0·1 HeLa plaque-forming units per cell. In such a culture, about a tenth of the cells will be infected and most of the remainder will have adsorbed pock-forming particles. The cytopathic effect nevertheless spreads from the original cells to involve the whole monolayer.

Penetration of HeLa infectious virus may be estimated by the reduction in HeLa plaque count which follows addition of antiserum after virus attachment. When antiserum was added 1 hr. after the HFEM-HeLa strain the plaque count was reduced to about half. Two hours after addition of virus, however, the plaque count was little affected by addition of antiserum. Virus adsorption was unaffected by temperature but penetration was markedly reduced at temperatures below 37° (Miss A. E. Farnham, unpublished).

Another estimate of virus penetration may be made by experiments to show the effect of virus on cell division, which will be described later in this article. It will be shown that all HeLa-infective, but not all pock-forming particles, inhibit mitosis. By using synchronously dividing HeLa cells (Wildy & Newton, 1958), Dr Alison Newton and I have found that this effect on cell division is produced in most cells 1 hr. after exposure to the virus.

It thus appears that most of the detectable (that is, pock-forming and plaque-forming) virus will attach slowly but firmly to the cell surface, but that only a small proportion enters the cells to initiate infection within two hours. In the rest of this article the term 'input' will be used to refer to the estimated number of HeLa-infectious particles initiating infection under given conditions of adsorption and antiserum treatment. 'Multiplicity' refers to the mean number of such infectious particles per cell.

Proportion of cells infected

In early experiments, in collaboration with Dr Ross, attempts were made to determine the proportion of HeLa cells yielding virus by inoculating known numbers of intact cells on to the chorio-allantois during the latent period of virus growth, and determining the number which formed pocks. The cells had been treated with antiserum to remove contaminating extracellular virus and we assumed that pocks would be formed by cells yielding new virus, as in the infective-centre counts with phage-infected bacteria. At that time, the number of pock-forming particles in the inoculum was known but, not having the HeLa plaque technique, the actual input of HeLa infectious virus was not known, though it was deduced retrospectively and in most experiments was thought to be more than one HeLa plaque unit per cell. The resulting estimate of pock-forming cells varied considerably, was not related to the multiplicity of infection, and was much lower than would be theoretically expected.

Since the chorio-allantois may not be an ideal environment for HeLa cells, it seemed possible that they were destroyed during the latent period before they produced virus. Consequently, with Dr P. Wildy, we took cells previously exposed in a monolayer to virus, and isolated single cells in individual microdrops under oil by a modification of De Fonbrune's (1949) technique. We could then sample the medium in the microdrop at intervals for pock-forming virus and so determine which cells were productive. This method had the additional advantage that it was unnecessary to treat the cells previously with antiserum, because superficially adsorbed virus was destroyed by thermal inactivation before the cells yielded new virus. The results showed that a higher proportion of cells released virus than was detected by infective centre counts on the membrane, but the number was still less than that expected from the estimated multiplicity of infection. With between 16 and 79 pock-forming units per cell (estimated 0·7–3·3 HeLa plaque units per cell), the proportion of single cells that yielded virus lay between 19 and 35 %, but there was no direct relationship with the multiplicity over this range. The proportion releasing and the number released per cell was not affected by previous antiserum treatment of the cells, so residual attached antibody did not account for the low proportion of pock-forming cells found on the chorio-allantoic membrane in the earlier experiments (Wildy, Stoker & Ross, 1958).

It was possible that a larger proportion of isolated single cells produced virus but failed to release it into the medium. When single cells were disrupted by freezing and thawing, however, the number releasing virus was no higher.

In subsequent experiments with the HFEM-egg strain, where the multiplicity of infection has been known to be about one HeLa plaque unit per cell, 4 % of cells produced pocks when inoculated on to the chorio-allantois, and 5 % of isolated single cells released virus, against an expected infection of about 63 % of cells according to Poissonian distribution.

The isolated cells have also been sampled to see if they contain or release HeLa-infectious virus not detected by pock formation, but such virus has been found in less than 2 % of cells.

HeLa cells may be a very heterogeneous population with varying ability to produce virus. Dr Waterson and I therefore studied the infection in HeLa clone S3 cells (Puck & Fisher, 1956), but the proportion yielding pocks on the membrane was as low as that of the wild strain.

An attempt to estimate the proportion of virus-yielding cells by their ability to form plaques in uninfected HeLa cell monolayers has only recently been made, partly because the system was known to be less sensitive to free virus than the chorio-allantois, and partly because of difficulties inherent in working without an agar overlay. Preliminary experiments have shown that intact cells, added to HeLa cell monolayers during the latent period, do give rise to discrete plaques and that the number is related directly to the number of cells. Despite the disadvantage of tending to form areas of confluent cytopathic effect, HeLa cells appear to be a fairly reliable indicator of other infected whole cells, and a sensitive one considering their lack of susceptibility to free virus released by such cells. With a multiplicity of 0·7 HeLa plaque units per cell, 4·5 % of HeLa cells formed pocks when inoculated directly on to the chorio-allantois. In isolated cell cultures, 5 % released pock-forming virus, and none (out of thirty) released HeLa plaque-forming virus. In direct contact with HeLa cell monolayers, however, 35 % of the cells formed plaques, against a theoretical expectation of 50 %.

The reason for this discrepancy is not known, and will be considered again when discussing spread from cell to cell. Meanwhile, we can conclude that no accurate determination of the number of HeLa cells releasing virus has been made, though we can deduce from the input the number of cells which could give rise to infection of neighbouring uninfected cells and form a plaque.

Virus growth and concurrent changes in the cells

Virus growth is best studied when it is confined to one cycle, either by addition of antiserum during the preliminary lag phase, or by dilution of the cells to diminish reattachment of released virus. Antiserum does not prevent spread of herpes virus between contiguous HeLa cells, however, and removal of cells from the glass for dilution may, as already stated, interfere with the release of infective virus. Virus growth has, therefore, been studied in intact monolayer cultures exposed to undiluted seed virus, in an attempt to infect most of the cells initially. In our earlier experiments (Stoker & Ross, 1958) the cells were exposed to inocula containing up to 740 pock units per cell of the HFEM-HeLa strain, but the actual input of HeLa-infectious virus was not known, and our estimations of it may have been inaccurate, based, as they were, on Farnham's (1958) results with different seed preparations of the same strain, which were not titrated under identical experimental conditions.

In more recent experiments the input has been known and the HFEM-egg strain has been used as well as HFEM-HeLa because the former has a higher infectivity for HeLa cells. Appearance of infective virus has been assayed largely by pock counts, because the chorio-allantois is more sensitive to free virus at all stages of virus growth.

Virus growth in monolayer cultures. Fig. 2 shows the appearance of virus after exposure of monolayers to thirteen pock units, or 1·8 HeLa plaque units of the HFEM-egg strain per cell. Adsorption was for 2 hr. followed by 2 hr. under antiserum to remove the extracellular virus. This gave an input of 0·78 HeLa plaque units per cell, and should have caused infection of 55 % of the cells. Inoculation of intact cells on to the membrane showed 21 % pock-forming cells, higher than usual but still less than was to be expected.

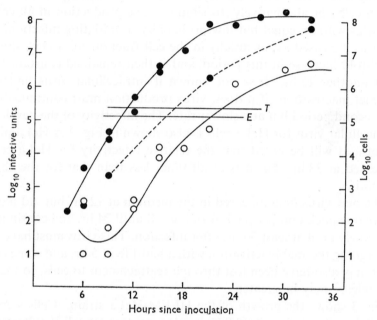

Fig. 2. Growth and release of HFEM-egg strain of herpes virus in undisturbed monolayer cultures of HeLa cells. $10^{5\cdot41}$ cells exposed to 13 pock units (or 1·8 HeLa plaque units) per cell for 2 hr. followed by 2 hr. under antiserum. Resulting input was 0·78 HeLa plaque-forming units per cell. T, total cells; E, expected number with one or more infectious unit. ●——●, pock-forming virus in cell debris; ●- - - -●, HeLa plaque-forming virus in cell debris; ○——○, pock-forming virus in medium.

Four hours after inoculation only 0·08 % of the input virus was found in the cell fraction. This constitutes one infectious particle per 324 pockforming cells, or 848 theoretically infected cells. Previous experiments have shown that virus cannot be detected by more thorough methods of cell disintegration and that none of these methods or the presence of any resulting debris affects the infectivity of free virus. The virus is therefore eclipsed in that no infective material is demonstrable during the latent period in most of the cells which ultimately yield virus.

The infectivity of the cell fraction rose between the fourth and sixth hours and no lag phase was observed, but it did not reach an average of one infectious particle per cell until 12 hr. after inoculation. It is possible that the early rise was due to dissociation of contaminating surface virus from residual antiserum, but, since no increase was found in the medium, or in the fraction released by treating the cells with EDTA, it seems more likely to indicate truly intracellular virus. If this be so, the initial increase in pock-forming virus may be attributed to multiplication in only a few cells, implying asynchronous virus multiplication in different cells, or alternatively, to simultaneous production in all cells of particles with an equal but low probability of initiating infection.

Virus increased exponentially in the cell fraction for 15 hr., showing a 10^5-fold increase in this period, and it then remained constant for at least another 15 hr. It is not known if intracellular virus undergoes thermal inactivation; if it does, virus production must continue during this second period but at a slower rate. The infectivity of the developing intracellular virus for HeLa cells is also shown in Fig. 2 as HeLa plaque counts. It will be noted that the relative infectivity for HeLa cells is increased at 33 hr., but it is at all times less than that for the chorio-allantois.

The new virus first appeared in the medium at 12 hr. but did not rise above one pock unit per pock-forming cell until 24 hr. and continued to rise slowly until at least 36 hr. after infection. This virus must have been undergoing thermal inactivation with a half-life of 5 hr. and some of the virus may also have been lost through reattachment to cells, so that the true release may be greater.

Fig. 3 shows the growth of the HFEM-HeLa strain. Cells were exposed to seven pock units (0·8 HeLa plaque units) per cell, resulting in an input of 0·21 HeLa plaque units per cell. There was a lag period up to 9 hr. before virus increased exponentially in the cells, followed by a rise in the fluid at 15 hr. For comparison, the results of another experiment are given with HFEM-HeLa seed concentrated to give an input of 1·0 HeLa plaque units per cell. A lag was not detected and the growth of intracellular virus resembled that of the HFEM-egg strain. Thus the lag phase seems to depend on input of virus, as found by Kaplan (1957) with herpes virus in rabbit kidney cells. The rate of increase over the exponential phase of growth was also somewhat less with the lower input of HFEM-HeLa strain. In our earlier experiments with the HFEM-HeLa strain there was a 9 hr. lag even though we deduced the input to be considerably more than one HeLa plaque unit per cell (Stoker & Ross, 1958). These earlier experiments involved a long and complicated washing procedure, however, which may previously have delayed virus growth and which has since been shortened and simplified.

Dr Ross and I also found that pock-forming virus appeared in the fraction released from the cells by EDTA before it appeared in the medium. This was not due to specific removal of calcium and magnesium ions, because the virus could also be released in buffered salt solution containing calcium and magnesium. Though it was not possible to exclude intracellular virus released by cell damage, we suggested that the EDTA fraction might have come from virus particles attached to the cell surface, which are visible in large numbers in electron micrographs of the infected cells.

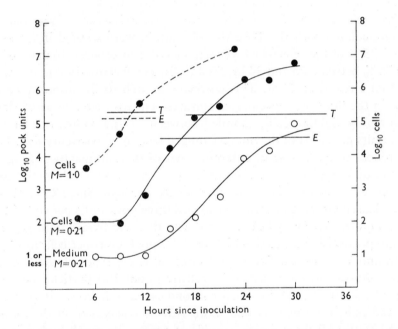

Fig. 3. Growth and release of HFEM-HeLa strain of herpes virus in undisturbed mono-layer cultures of HeLa cells. $10^{5 \cdot 22}$ cells exposed to 7 pock units or 0·8 HeLa plaque units per cell for 2 hr., followed by 2 hr. under antiserum; resulting input was 0·21 HeLa plaque units per cell. Second experiment also shown with input of 1·0 HeLa plaque units per cell. *T*, total cells; *E*, expected number with one or more infective units. ●——●, pock-forming virus in cell debris; ●----●, pock-forming virus in cell debris; ○——○, pock-forming virus in medium.

Electron-microscopy of infected monolayer cultures. Morgan *et al.* (1954) had shown that herpes virus could be recognized in infected cells as a characteristic single or double-ringed particle with dense central dot. In our experiments, monolayers of HeLa cells infected with HFEM

HeLa strain were fixed at intervals during the growth cycle, sectioned by Dr Kenneth Smith and examined by electron microscopy for these characteristic ringed particles, while unfixed cells were assayed for infective virus (Stoker, Smith & Ross, 1958). The first particles were seen at 12 hr. after infection in the nuclei of two of twenty-five cells, and this corresponded to the first rise in infective virus in the cell fraction. At 26 hr. and later, large numbers of typical particles were seen, single-ringed or occasionally double-ringed in the nucleus, and double-ringed in the cytoplasm and at the cell surface. Since these cells were removed from the glass with EDTA, this process clearly does not release all the surface particles, which were present in large numbers. A typical collection of such surface particles is shown in Pl. 2, fig. 4.

Virus release from single cells and diluted cell suspensions. When single cells inoculated with the HFEM-HeLa strain were studied in isolated drops, 25 % of the cells which yielded virus did so between 16 and 26 hr. and 75 % between 26 and 34 hr. (Wildy, Stoker & Ross, 1958). No cells released virus after 34 hr. This corresponds well to the appearance of virus in the fluid over monolayer cultures. The average release of virus from eighty yielding cells, sampled between 27 and 33 hr., was twelve pock units per cell, but the number ranged from one to seventy-five. The differences could be due to different times of thermal inactivation after release, different times of sampling during a continuing release, or real differences in the amount of virus produced per cell. Since 25 % of the cells released virus, the average yield was three pock units per cell of the whole culture. This may be compared with the yield from a diluted mass culture previously reported, which gave 1·7 pock units per cell (total) at 26 hr. and 3·4 pock units at 50 hr. (Stoker & Ross, 1958). Intact monolayer cultures, however, generally release about 100 particles per cell (total) by 50 hr. Even allowing for second cycles of infection in perhaps half the cells, this suggests that more virus is released from the undisturbed cells. All these yields, would, of course, be much higher if we allowed for thermal inactivation.

Inhibition of mitosis. The effect of herpes virus upon cell division is obviously important where there is a possibility of latent infection, and Gray *et al.* (1958) have reported proliferation of HeLa cells after infection with a freshly isolated strain of virus under certain conditions. During our earlier studies on single cells, a few were seen to divide after infection and subsequently to release virus (Wildy *et al.* 1958), and virus has frequently been obtained from healthy looking, well spread cells. These cells were in maintenance medium, however, in which uninfected control cells rarely divided, so further experiments were carried out with the isolated cells in a medium which allowed a high proportion of uninfected cells to multiply (Wildy & Stoker, 1958).

The HFEM-egg strain was used because of its higher infectivity for HeLa cells. Monolayers were infected with different multiplicities of HeLa plaque units per cell and, after washing without antiserum treatment, were suspended in EDTA (1/5000 w/v in buffered saline). The cells were then isolated in microdrops of medium containing non-immune serum and synthetic growth mixture. The state of the cells was recorded 24–72 hr. after isolation. Representative cells in their drops were frozen 30 hr. after infection, stored at $-70°$ and later thawed for assay of pock-forming virus.

The combined results of several experiments are shown in Fig. 4. By 24 hr., 40–50 % of control cells had divided, 30–40 % were spread on the glass, and the remaining 20 % had mostly disappeared. By 3 days 76 % had divided once, twice, or three times.

When the input was 0·1 HeLa plaque units per cell, there was an increase in the proportion of degenerate cells at 24 hr. ($P < 0·01$) but not at 72 hr. ($P > 0·2$). With 1·0 and 2·7 HeLa plaque units per cell, however, there was a marked reduction in the number of dividing cells obvious at 24 or 72 hr. Virus heated at $56°$ for 1 hr. did not prevent mitosis, and the inhibition was reduced by human antiserum (capable of neutralizing 10^3 pock units). Normal rabbit or human serum also had a slight protective effect on the cells, but it was significantly less than that of the antiserum ($P < 0·05 > 0·02$).

The proportion of cells yielding virus was small, as in previous experiments, and it was not related to virus input. None of the cells which yielded virus divided, none formed multinucleated giant cells, and most of them had disappeared or were rounded by the time the sample was taken. Assuming that 76 % of cells would have divided if uninfected, the proportion in which mitosis was inhibited can be calculated. When this is compared with the theoretical number containing one or more particles per cell (Table 2), it is seen to correspond closely, whereas the proportion of cells in which infective virus was detected is very low, and (with admittedly small numbers sampled) not related to input.

Infection of synchronously dividing cells. The dynamics of mitotic inhibition can be studied with HeLa cells dividing synchronously after a single chilling according to the method of Wildy & Newton (1958). Dr Newton and I have inoculated HeLa cells during the first stationary phase, at known intervals before cell division was expected to occur. HFEM-HeLa virus was used after concentration by centrifugation so that 1 hr. exposure allowed an input of more than one HeLa plaque unit per cell. A typical experiment is shown in Fig. 5 where mitosis was inhibited by addition of virus 1 hr. before expected cell division. The length of the lag phase, the 24 hr. yield of virus, and proportion of productive

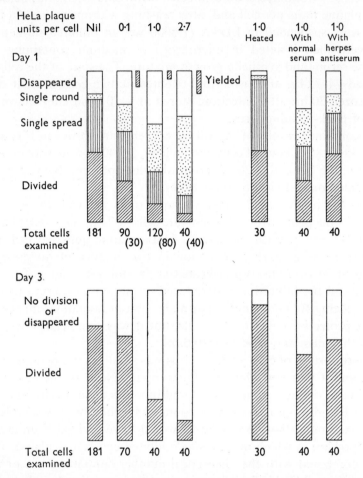

Fig. 4. Inhibition of mitosis of single HeLa cells in drop cultures, obtained from mono-layers inoculated with various amounts of herpes virus. Shaded parts of columns denote proportion of cells in different states on first day (upper) and third day (lower). Number of cells examined is given at base of each column. Smaller columns give proportion of cells yielding infectious, pock-forming, virus sampled 30 hr. after infection. (Numbers of cells examined shown in parentheses.)

(pock-forming) cells, were unaffected by previous synchronization of the cultures. The closest time before cell division at which virus has been added was 1 hr. and even in this short interval mitosis was inhibited. It suggests that the inhibition occurs very rapidly after virus adsorption,

Table 2. *Proportion of isolated single cells dividing and yielding virus after infection of monolayer cultures with different amounts of virus*

Input of virus. HeLa plaque units per cell after adsorption for 2 hr.	Estimated proportion of cells with 1 or more HeLa plaque units $(1-e^{-n})$	Observed proportion of cells failing to divide*	Observed proportion of cells yielding infective virus (numbers examined shown in parentheses)
2·7	0·93	0·84	0·15 (40)
1·0	0·63	0·64	0·05 (80)
0·1	0·09	0·10†	0·10 (20)

* $1 - \dfrac{\text{Proportion of infected cells dividing}}{\text{Proportion of uninfected cells dividing}}$.

† Difference between infected and uninfected not significant $(P > 0.2 < 0.3)$.

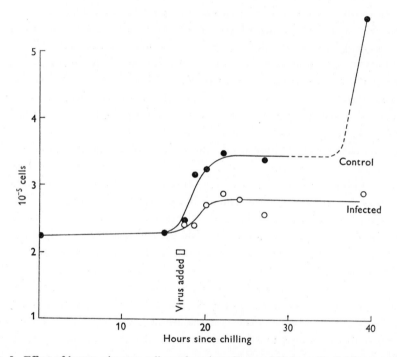

Fig. 5. Effect of herpes virus on cell numbers in cultures of HeLa cells dividing parasynchronously. Because of the formation of multinucleate giant cells the last point for infected cultures denotes numbers of nuclei. Dotted line taken from data in separate experiments.

and it would be interesting to know if it resembles the early killing effect of bacteriophage.

Appearance of excess nucleic acid. Dr Newton has shown that there is an early increase in synthesis of DNA in infected HeLa cells (Newton & Stoker, 1958). With the HFEM-HeLa strain this probably commences

3–6 hr. after infection. The average amount of DNA per cell was increased 40 % by 9 hr. after infection; that is, before there was an average of one pock-forming particle per cell, and at a stage when electron microscopy revealed no virus particles. The increase was confined to the nucleus and was not due to changes in cell numbers or formation of multinucleated cells. By 72 hr. the cells contained nearly double the normal quantity of DNA without any significant change in RNA, compared with uninfected controls. Even if herpes virus contains DNA it is inconceivable that the excess DNA represents assembled virus particles. Assuming 10 % of DNA per particle, it would take 10^6 particles per cell to account for the excess at 72 hr. If this number were distributed evenly, there would just be room for them in HeLa cells with a mean volume of 3·4 cu.μ, but they would appear at 39 per sq.μ in thin sections of all cells. Electron micrographs have never shown this density or anything approaching it. Rough calculation from the number seen gives 10^4 to 10^5 particles in the most heavily populated cells. At 9 hr., when $10^{5·7}$ particles per cell would be required to account for the DNA, no characteristic particles at all can be seen in electron micrographs.

It is still possible that the DNA is specific virus DNA, rather than cell DNA, which, from lack of protein or other cause, is not incorporated into particles. On the other hand, the total DNA is finally almost double the normal, and it seems possible that the excess might be a normal pre-mitotic increase of DNA in cells in which some later stage of mitosis is inhibited by the virus. Newton & Wildy (1958) have shown that, in synchronously dividing HeLa cells, the DNA per cell increases in two separate stages, finally reaching double the minimum about 1 hr. before division. In preliminary experiments with cells infected at this stage, Dr Newton has found further changes in the DNA per cell, which do not suggest that the effect is due simply to inhibition of mitosis in a cell which is normally synthesizing DNA. The excess DNA might, of course, be all cell DNA, whose synthesis is released from control; but it is justifiable to call the excess DNA abnormal, whether or not it is specifically viral.

Appearance of viral antigen. The abnormal DNA was also observed by acridine orange and May Grünwald-Giemsa staining by Ross & Orlans (1958). They showed that the normal, granular DNA staining was replaced in some cells by a diffuse staining concentrated at the nuclear margin nine hours after infection with the HFEM-HeLa strain. This change became more marked and progressively involved more cells. Staining with fluorescent antibody, however, revealed no virus antigen until 16 hr. At this stage redistribution of nuclear DNA had occurred in about half the cells, and in a much smaller proportion nuclear antigen could be detected. Even at 24 hr. when nearly all the cells showed abnormal nuclear DNA staining, there were fewer with virus antigen, and by examining the same cells with fluorescent antibody and then May Grünwald-Giemsa stain, it was found that the same cell could show nuclear change without detectable antigen. It is tempting to suggest that the virus protein is synthesized after the virus nucleic acid, as in the T phages, but the sensitivity of the fluorescent antibody staining technique is not known.

Later changes in cells. A striking change in monolayers of herpes-infected HeLa cells is the appearance of bizarre giant cells sometimes with hundreds of nuclei. In fact in its early stages a herpes plaque probably consists of one giant cell. Giant cells have never been observed to appear from isolated single cells, and Ross & Orlans (1958) suggested that they occurred after breakdown of cytoplasmic membranes between neighbouring cells. This has now been confirmed by Dr Newton and myself in our experiments with synchronously dividing cultures. As early as 9 hr. after an input of 1·0 HeLa plaque units per cell, syncytial sheets of cytoplasm appear with from 2 to 100 nuclei. The number of these syncytial sheets increases, and the total cell count correspondingly drops, while the nuclear count remains approximately the same. The multinucleate syncytial masses or giant cells are not disrupted by EDTA, nor by micromanipulation which breaks up clumps of normal HeLa cells, and they do not become permeable to trypan blue or eosin. Pl. 3, figs. 5 and 6, shows such giant cells in EDTA-treated suspensions prepared for counting.

As in adenovirus infection the giant or single cells remain intact for several days. During this time the pH of the culture medium drops to about 6·2, and Dr Newton has found that glucose utilization is increased during infection without an increase in oxygen uptake. The fall in pH is thus probably due to increased anaerobic glycolysis. Fisher & Fisher (1958) have also reported increased glucose uptake in herpes-infected HeLa cells.

Summary of intracellular events during virus multiplication. Lack of a satisfactory single-cycle experiment with undisturbed monolayer cultures makes it difficult to tell the duration in individual cells of the various changes we have observed. It is also not clear to what extent virus multiplication proceeds asynchronously in different cells. Some isolated single cells released virus between 16 and 26 hr., and others between 26 and 34 hr. after infection, but this could be due to almost simultaneous release between 25 and 27 hr.

Nevertheless it is possible to summarize tentatively the order of first occurrence of some of the events described (Fig. 6). This is largely from data obtained in various experiments with the HFEM-HeLa strain. The virus input, though probably about one infectious particle per cell, has not always been accurately known, however, and may affect the length of the eclipse phase and first appearance of intracellular virus.

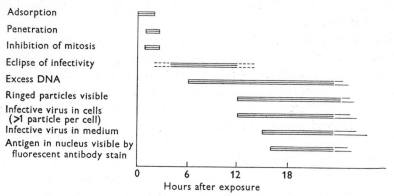

Fig. 6. Summary of findings in HeLa cells infected with herpes virus.

Spread of virus from cell to cell

The spread of virus from cell to cell will be considered next, as seen in the formation of a plaque in a HeLa cell monolayer. When one cell is infected it stops dividing, and later there is a change in the morphology of the contiguous cells, characterized by breakdown of the cell walls and characteristic alterations of the nuclei. This effect might well be due to local spread of infective virus particles through the medium from cell to cell, but there are two objections to this: first, the plaque continues to enlarge in strong antiserum; and second, when infected cells are detached from the monolayer, and placed in isolation, very few of them make or contain infective virus that can be detected by HeLa infectivity or by pock formation. How then can we explain the peculiar spread between contiguous cells? The following hypotheses might be considered:

(1) Removal of the cells from the monolayers is a necessary procedure for estimation of cells yielding virus. This may upset the physiological activity of most of the cells so that virus multiplication does not continue, even when the cells are placed in an environment which is suitable for multiplication of uninfected control cells. This does not explain the fact that, even after suspension, these infected cells can still cause plaques in contiguous cells, even though most release no detectable virus.

(2) The cells may make a large amount of very unstable virus which loses infectivity much more quickly than free virus. Some of this virus may be able to spread to contiguous cells before inactivation and form a plaque, but it will be lost in the experimental conditions of assay of released virus.

(3) Each cell may have adsorbed about ten times more pock-forming (but HeLa incomplete) virus, than HeLa-infectious virus. This incomplete virus may interfere with the production of infectious virus in most of the cells, perhaps depending on the number of incomplete particles adsorbed per cell. If interference takes place, it does not prevent the antimitotic activity or cytopathic effect of the HeLa-infective virus, however, and it does not prevent the spread to contiguous cells to form a plaque. This interference would only be a satisfactory explanation if it stopped the final release of free virus.

(4) The virus may be present in most of the cells in a vegetative state which, released naturally or by cell disintegration into the surrounding fluid, is unable to penetrate new cells and is, therefore, not detected. This vegetative virus may, nevertheless, be able to spread in the conditions of a monolayer culture, by the fusion of contiguous cells. There is little doubt that the giant cells are formed by cell fusion. It is not known if this is due to fusion between two or more infected cells, or between an infected cell and its healthy neighbours. Giant cell formation in anti-serum suggests the latter, which would provide a means for transfer of virus from cell to cell without an extracellular phase.

This last hypothesis is difficult to prove but it has certain attractions. It would explain the efficiency of plaque formation when intact infected cells are placed on uninfected monolayers of HeLa cells, and, as already stated, it would account for cell-to-cell spread in the presence of anti-body. It would explain the lack of secondary plaques even in the absence of antiserum or agar in monolayers with only a few primary plaques, presumably due to absence of released extracellular virus. It would also explain a phenomenon noticed by Ross & Orlans (1958) in their cyto-logical studies. Foci of cytopathic effect involving several adjoining cells could be seen by microscope examination 16 hr. after infection, not long after the first appearance of infectious virus in the cells, and before there would have been time for a second cycle, unless this was considerably shorter than the first. The input of virus was not accurately known in these experiments, but it is unlikely that the particles would fall in a focal distribution. Non-infectious vegetative virus might appear early in the cycle, however, and spread more rapidly, causing these early focal changes.

It is obviously tempting to postulate that the vegetative material concerned is the abnormal DNA or DNA protein, not packed up into effective, cell-penetrating particles. This supposition is not supported by the fact that this DNA is found in the nucleus, though a good deal could be present in the cytoplasm and not be detected by the chemical techniques used.

Latent infection with herpes virus

It has been made clear that our primary object has been to study the growth cycle *per se* before attempting any investigation of latent infection of HeLa cells. It has been observed during the course of our experiments, however, that a small proportion of cells in a monolayer may survive the cytopathic effect after inoculation with relatively high multiplicities of virus. On three occasions these cells have been recovered and grown into large populations by addition of growth medium containing pooled human serum. Not all the medium has been tested for antibody, but representative batches, tested with virus for 2 hr. at 37°, have neutralization indices of 10^3 and tests of individual human sera suggest that it is highly improbable that any of the pools would be devoid of antibody. Dr Carmen Gil has maintained one of these recovered cell lines for 6 months in this medium, and the cells have continued to carry the virus for the whole period. The presence of virus can be shown by replacing the immune by normal serum. If virus is present, a spreading cytopathic effect follows with release of virus into the medium. In monolayers with immune medium, however, plaques appear, and on the assumption that each plaque arises from one infected cell, the proportion of cells carrying virus in the culture is about 10^{-5}. The remaining cells in the culture do not resemble lysogenic bacteria because they can be infected with the original HFEM strain, and though they may be less susceptible, they eventually undergo a cytopathic degeneration in the usual way.

The state of virus in the small number of infected cells is not known. We have seen that freshly infected cells do not continue to divide, but, since virus is known to spread from cell to cell in antiserum, continued infection is quite possible, perhaps involving transfer of vegetative virus as already discussed. Even in freshly infected cultures, plaques enlarge very slowly and, since the generation time of uninfected cells is about 18 hr. (Wildy & Newton, 1958), new cells may be produced as fast as they become infected. Equal rates of virus spread and production of new uninfected cells would lead to an equilibrium with longstanding infection of the culture such as we have observed.

CONCLUSIONS

It is obvious that the study of herpes virus is greatly hindered by its high rate of thermal inactivation at 37°. Loss of infectivity at 30° is slow, however, and HeLa cells produce more infectious virus at 31° than at 37° (Dr Alison Newton, unpublished). This may not be due entirely to greater stability of the virus, but it would be profitable to use lower temperatures for re-examination of some of the problems discussed in this paper.

Important questions which face us are the nucleic acid content of the virus particle, the part played by the abnormal DNA synthesis in the infected cell and the nature of spread of virus between contiguous cells. There also remains the general problem of latent infection: if it turns out to be due to an equilibrium between production of new virus and production of new cells, is this maintained by some feedback mechanism which ensures its stability? For example, infected cells may produce a micro-environment at low pH, where the virus is more rapidly inactivated.

Growth of herpes virus in HeLa cells may prove to be a very wasteful business. In one infected cell the extra nucleic acid might make a million particles; electron micrographs show perhaps ten thousand; a hundred are released as infectious (pock-forming) virus; only ten can infect other HeLa cells; and these are rapidly reduced still further by thermal inactivation. It looks somewhat inefficient, but perhaps we shall find that this is one way to achieve that state of equilibrium with the host which all good viruses so earnestly desire.

I am grateful to my colleagues mentioned in the text for allowing me to quote their unpublished data, and also to Mr William House for expert technical assistance.

REFERENCES

ACKERMANN, W. W. & KURTZ, H. (1952). The relation of herpes virus to host cell mitochondria. *J. exp. Med.* **96**, 151.

BARSKI, G., LAMY, M. & LÉPINE, P. (1955). Culture de cellules trypsinées de rein de lapin et leur application à l'étude des virus du groupe herpétique. *Ann. Inst. Pasteur*, **89**, 415.

BLACK, F. L. & MELNICK, J. L. (1955). Micro-epidemiology of poliomyelitis and herpes-B infections. Spread of the viruses within tissue cultures. *J. Immunol.* **74**, 236.

CARTWRIGHT, S. F., PAY, T. W. F. & HENDERSON, W. M. (1957). Multiplication of the virus of foot-and-mouth disease in culture. *J. gen. Microbiol.* **16**, 730.

COOPER, P. D. (1955). A method for producing plaques in agar suspensions of animal cells. *Virology*, **1**, 397.

CROUSE, H. V., CORIELL, L. L., BLANK, H. & SCOTT, T. F. McN. (1950). Cytochemical studies on the intranuclear inclusion of herpes simplex. *J. Immunol.* **65**, 119.

DULBECCO, R. (1952). Production of plaques in monolayer tissue cultures by single particles of an animal virus. *Proc. Nat. Acad. Sci., Wash.* **38**, 747.

EAGLE, H., HABEL, K., ROWE, W. P. & HUEBNER, R. J. (1956). Viral susceptibility of a human carcinoma cell (strain KB). *Proc. Soc. exp. Biol., N.Y.* **91**, 361.

ENDERS, J. F. (1953). Bovine amniotic fluid as tissue culture medium in cultivation of poliomyelitis and other viruses. *Proc. Soc. exp. Biol., N.Y.* **82**, 100.

FARNHAM, A. E. (1958). The formation of microscopic plaques by herpes simplex virus in HeLa cells. *Virology,* **6**, 317.

DE FONBRUNE, P. (1949). *Technique de micromanipulation.* Paris: Masson & Cie.

FRANCIS, T. & KURTZ, H. B. (1950). Relation of herpes virus to cell nucleus. *Yale J. Biol. Med.* **22**, 579.

FISHER, T. N. & FISHER, E. (1958). Effects of cortisone and herpes simplex virus on HeLa cell metabolism. *Fed. Proc.* **17**, 511.

GOSTLING, J. V. T. (1956). Intracellular site of developing herpes virus. *Nature, Lond.* **178**, 1238.

GOSTLING, J. V. T. & BEDSON, S. P. (1956). Observations on the mode of multiplication of herpes virus. *Brit. J. exp. Path.* **37**, 434.

GRAY, A. & SCOTT, T. F. McN. (1954). Some observations on the intracellular localization of the virus of herpes simplex in the chick embryo liver. *J. exp. Med.* **100**, 473.

GRAY, A., TOKUMARU, T. & SCOTT, T. F. McN (1958). Different cytopathogenic effects observed in HeLa cells infected with herpes simplex virus. *Arch. ges. Virusforsch.* **8**, 59.

KAPLAN, A. S. (1957). A study of the herpes simplex virus–rabbit kidney cell system by the plaque technique. *Virology,* **4**, 435.

LABAW, L. W., MOSLEY, V. M. & WYCKOFF, R. W. G. (1953). Development of bacteriophage in X-ray inactivated bacteria. *J. Bact.* **65**, 330.

LEBRUN, J. (1956). Cellular localization of herpes simplex virus by means of fluorescent antibody. *Virology,* **2**, 496.

LÉPINE, P. & SAUTTER, V. (1946). Étude histochimique des lésions dues aux ultra-virus; les acides nucléiques. *Ann. Inst. Pasteur,* **72**, 174.

MODI, N. L. & TOBIN, J. O'H. (1954). Observations on the growth of herpes simplex virus in the chorioallantois of the developing chick embryo and in tissue culture. *Brit. J. exp. Path.* **35**, 595.

MORGAN, C., ELLISON, S. A., ROSE, H. M. & MOORE, D. H. (1954). Structure and development of viruses as observed in the electron microscope. I. Herpes simplex virus. *J. exp. Med.* **100**, 195.

NEWTON, A. A. & STOKER, M. G. P. (1958). Changes in nucleic acid content of HeLa cells infected with herpes virus. *Virology,* **5**, 549.

NEWTON, A. A. & WILDY, P. (1958). The parasynchronous division of HeLa cells. *Exp. Cell Res.* (in the Press).

O'DEA, J. F. & DINEEN, J. K. (1957). Fluorescent antibody studies with herpes simplex virus in unfixed preparations of trypsinized tissue cultures. *J. gen. Microbiol.* **17**, 19.

PEREIRA, H. G. & KELLY, B. (1957). Dose response curves of toxic and infective actions of adenovirus in HeLa cell cultures. *J. gen. Microbiol.* **17**, 517.

PUCK, T. T., CIECIURA, S. J. & FISHER, H. W. (1957). Clonal growth *in vitro* of human cells with fibroblastic morphology; comparison of growth and genetic characteristics of single epithelioid and fibroblast-like cells from a variety of human organs. *J. exp. Med.* **106**, 145.

PUCK, T. T. & FISHER, H. W. (1956). Genetics of somatic mammalian cells. I. Demonstration of the existence of mutants with different growth requirements in a human cancer cell strain (HeLa). *J. exp. Med.* **104**, 427.

ROSS, R. W. & ORLANS, E. (1958). The redistribution of nucleic acid and the appearance of specific antigen in HeLa cells infected with herpes virus. *J. Path. Bact.* **76**, 393.

SCHAFFER, M. F. & ENDERS, J. F. (1939). Quantitative studies on the infectivity of the virus of herpes simplex for the chorioallantoic membrane of the chick embryo, together with observations on the inactivation of the virus by its specific antiserum. *J. Immunol.* **37**, 383.

SCHERER, W. F. (1953). The utilization of a pure strain of mammalian cells (Earle) for the cultivation of viruses *in vitro*. I. Multiplication of pseudorabies and herpes simplex viruses. *Amer. J. Path.* **29**, 113.

SCHERER, W. F. & SYVERTON, J. T. (1954). The viral range *in vitro* of a malignant human epithelial cell (strain HeLa, Gey). I. Multiplication of herpes simplex, pseudorabies, and vaccinia viruses. *Amer. J. Path.* **30**, 1057.

SCOTT, T. F. McN., BURGOON, C. F., CORIELL, L. L. & BLANK, H. (1953). The growth curve of the virus of herpes simplex in rabbit corneal cells grown in tissue culture with parallel observations on the development of the intranuclear inclusion body. *J. Immunol.* **71**, 385.

SCOTT, T. F. McN., CORIELL, L. L., BLANK, H. & GRAY, A. (1953). The growth curve of the virus of herpes simplex on the chorioallantoic membrane of the embryonated hen's egg. *J. Immunol.* **71**, 134.

SOSA-MARTINEZ, J., GUTIERREZ-VILLEGAS, L. & SOSA, R. M. (1955). Propagation of herpes simplex virus in tissue cultures of rabbit kidney. *J. Bact.* **70**, 391.

STOKER, M. G. P. & ROSS, R. W. (1958). Quantitative studies on the growth of herpes virus in HeLa cells. *J. gen. Microbiol.* **19**, 250.

STOKER, M. G. P., SMITH, K. M. & ROSS, R. W. (1958). Electron microscope studies of HeLa cells infected with herpes virus. *J. gen. Microbiol.* **19**, 244.

STULBERG, C. S. & SCHAPIRA, R. (1953). Virus growth in tissue culture fibroblasts. I. Influenza A and herpes simplex viruses. *J. Immunol.* **70**, 51.

WILDY, P. (1954). The growth of herpes simplex virus. *Aust. J. exp. Biol. med. Sci.* **32**, 605.

WILDY, P. & NEWTON, A. A. (1958). The 'Synchronous' division of HeLa cells. *Biochem. J.* **68**, 14P.

WILDY, P. & STOKER, M. G. P. (1958). Multiplication of solitary HeLa cells. *Nature, Lond.* **181**, 1407.

WILDY, P., STOKER, M. G. P. & ROSS, R. W. (1958). Release of herpes virus from solitary HeLa cells. *J. gen. Microbiol.* (in the Press).

YOSHINO, K. (1956). Infection of one-day-old fertile hen's egg with herpes simplex virus. *J. Immunol.* **76**, 301.

YOSHINO, K. & TANIGUCHI, H. (1956). Quantitative studies on the interactions between herpes simplex virus and ectodermal cell of chorioallantoic membrane of fertile hen's egg by means of the coverslip infection system. *Jap. J. Med. Sci. Biol.* **9**, 303.

YOSHINO, K. & TANIGUCHI, H. (1957). Further studies on the growth of herpes simplex virus in the egg-white-replaced one-day egg. *Jap. J. Med. Sci. Biol.* **10**, 257.

EXPLANATION OF PLATES

PLATE 1

Fig. 1. Pocks on chorio-allantois produced by HFEM strain of herpes virus.

Fig. 2. Plaques in chick cell monolayers produced by HFEM strain of herpes virus (by courtesy of Dr A. P. Waterson).

Fig. 3. Single microscopic plaque in HeLa cell monolayer produced by HFEM strain of herpes virus ($\times 125$).

PLATE 2

Fig. 4. Electromicrograph of section of HeLa cell surface 96 hr. after infection with herpes virus showing extracellular particles ($\times 54,000$) (by courtesy of Dr K. M. Smith).

PLATE 3

Figs. 5 and 6. Giant cells from monolayer cultures of HeLa cells 24 hr. after infection with herpes virus (phase contrast; Fig. 5 $\times 480$, Fig. 6 $\times 180$).

PLATE 1

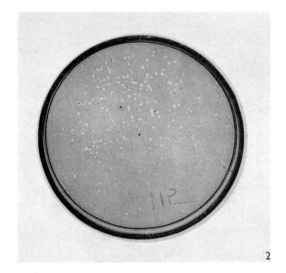

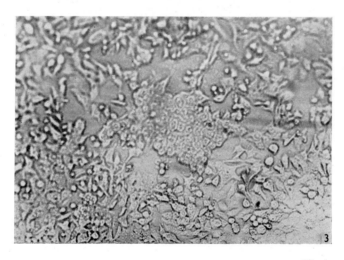

PLATE 2

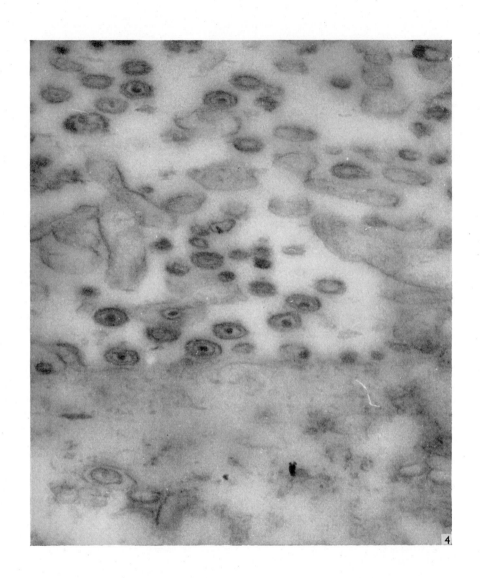

PLATE 3

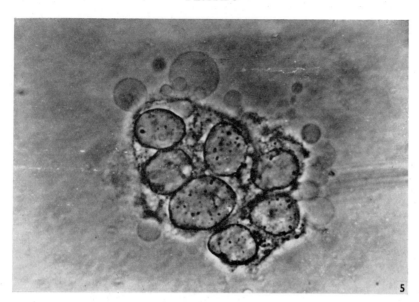

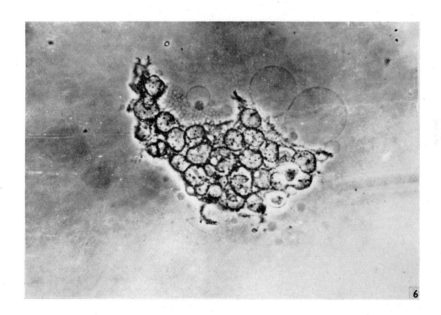

SPECIAL INTERACTIONS BETWEEN VIRUS AND CELL IN THE ROUS SARCOMA*

HARRY RUBIN

Dept. of Virology, University of California, Berkeley, California

In the term 'tumour virus' we acknowledge that several distinctions must exist at the cellular level of infection between this class of virus and the more commonly studied cytocidal viruses. Instead of killing a cell, tumour viruses alter it in a characteristic way. This cellular alteration is, for practical purposes, irreversible and is hereditary in the sense that it is perpetuated in the progeny of the infected cell.

Tumour viruses as a class are more restricted in their host range than are cytocidal viruses. In general they seem to grow well only in the species from which they were first isolated. For example, the Rous sarcoma virus (RSV) has been maintained in continuous passage only in chickens. It is true that under certain conditions, successful infection of other species of fowl has been demonstrated. However, this requires massive inoculation of material in the case of duck infection (Duran-Reynals, 1947) which may result in the selection of variants; or special pretreatment to induce tolerance in the case of turkeys (Harris, 1956).

The viruses associated with mouse mammary carcinoma and mouse leukaemia are not only species specific, but are strain specific as well (Andervont & Dunn, 1953; Woolley & Small, 1957; Gross, 1958).[†]

Tumour viruses are also restricted not only for species and strain but for cell type as well. In the adult animal, RSV can cause tumours only in tissues of mesodermal origin. In the embryo the chorionic cells, which are ectodermal in type, can be infected by the 'wild type' virus (Rubin, 1955), but these cells are at a developmental dead-end and the degree of their differentiation is unknown. In the avian leukosis complex of viruses there are variants whose effects are limited to cells of either the lymphocyte, erythrocyte or myelocyte series (Beard, Sharp & Eckert, 1955).

RSV may under certain conditions produce a haemorrhagic lesion and necrosis of blood vessel walls (Milford & Duran-Reynals, 1943). This phenomenon has never been studied at the cellular level. Since haemorrhage is a prominent feature in many Rous tumours it is difficult to decide

* Supported by grants from the American Cancer Soc and U.S. Public Health Service.

† This specificity may not extend to the cellular level, however, since the mouse mammary tumour agent may multiply in chick embryo cells *in vitro* (Pikovski, 1953), and the polyoma virus multiplies in the cells of several species (Stewart, Eddy & Borghese, 1958).

whether the haemorrhagic lesion is due to the cell necrosis observed or vice versa. It should be noted, however, that the presence of a single layer of entodermal tissue other than endothelium between a virus inoculum and mesoderm reportedly prevents infection even in the embryo (Murphy & Rous, 1912).

Some of these features of tumour virus infection have been recognized since the earliest days of their investigation. To understand these phenomena in molecular terms would give us a great deal of insight into some of the basic problems of carcinogenesis. However, these features are not yet well defined even at the cellular level, and it is to this end that we must first devote our attention before we can ask intelligent questions about virus-cell interaction in molecular terms.

Most of the study in this field has been limited to the pathogenesis and pathology of the disease in the experimental animal, where a large body of useful information has been obtained. Owing to the complex interactions between virus, cell and organism and to the many limitations of a manipulative and quantitative nature which accompany work in animals, relatively little light has been shed on the special relationship between the virus and its primary host, the individual cell.

TECHNIQUES FOR ASSAYING VIRUS AND STUDYING CELL-VIRUS INTERACTIONS

Until recently the most useful RSV assay technique for work of this type involved the production of discrete ectodermal tumours on the chorio-allantoic membrane of the developing chick embryo (Keogh, 1938). This technique was not widely used for a number of years because of the wide variation in host response. However, chicken strains with uniform response have been found and the reliability of the assay clearly demonstrated (Rubin, 1955; Prince, 1957a).

The chorio-allantoic membrane technique has about the same sensitivity for the detection of virus as inoculation into the wing web of susceptible chickens. The number of ectodermal tumours is proportional to the virus concentration, indicating that a single virus particle is adequate to initiate infection (Rubin, 1955; Borsos & Bang, 1957; Prince, 1957a; Manaker & Groupé, 1956).

Virus released from the ectodermal tumours of the chorion ultimately infects the underlying mesoderm, and the two types of altered cells may be seen multiplying side by side in the same tumour. It was concluded from the sum of these observations that the 'wild type' strain of RSV can infect with equal facility cells from connective tissue in adult chickens, and from the chorionic ectoderm and the mesoderm in the chick embryo (Rubin, 1955, 1957).

The chorio-allantoic membrane technique is inadequate for quantitative work in several respects, but chiefly in the fact that the cells can neither be washed, counted nor manipulated in any practical way. A tissue culture assay was needed. The first indications that such an assay was possible came from observations that normal chicken fibroblasts infected by RSV *in vitro* are transformed to a new cell type indistinguishable from Rous sarcoma cells (Halberstaedter, Doljanski & Tennenbaum, 1941; Lo, Gey & Shapras, 1955). It was then found that the transformed cells occurred in discrete groups whose number was proportional to the concentration of the virus inoculum (Manaker & Groupé, 1956). A reproducible technique was evolved for assaying both virus and infected cells on chick fibroblasts *in vitro* (Rubin & Temin, 1958a, 1958b; Temin & Rubin, in the Press) and this has been employed in an investigation of RSV infection at the cellular level.

In distinction to the assays for the more common cytocidal viruses, the RSV assay involves the transformation and multiplication of cells. The morphology of the infected cell is changed in a unique and specific way, and this change is transmitted to all the progeny cells, much as is any normal cell character. The infected cells, which will be referred to as 'Rous cells', differ from normal cells not only in their individual appearance but also in their colonial characteristics, so the Rous cell colonies can be readily distinguished from the background of normal chick fibroblasts. The Rous cell can be cloned and then grown in mass culture for many generations when conditions are favourable. The relationship between cell and virus is therefore shown to be relatively stable, and further infection of normal cells is not required for continued propagation of either the virus or the Rous cell. After prolonged culture, or in an unfavourable environment, giant cell formation and cell death may occur.

QUANTITATIVE FEATURES OF THE TISSUE CULTURE ASSAY

By this technique, the number of cells in a culture which can be infected at any given time is proportional to the concentration of the inoculated virus up to the point where about 10 % of the cells are infected. Further increases in virus concentration fail to increase the number of infected cells. This is true even when the cells have been cloned from a single cell before infection to ensure genetic purity. The remainder of the cells, which initially were refractory to infection, later become infected if left in the presence of virus over a long period of time. It appears, then, that cells undergo a transient period during which they are physiologically competent to be infected (Rubin & Temin, 1958a). The nature of this competence and its relation, if any, to the mitotic cycle is unknown.

The successful infection of a cloned line of fibroblasts with high efficiency should settle once and for all the question whether fibroblasts can be infected or not (Carrel & Ebeling, 1926; Sanford, Likely, Bryan & Earle, 1952; Lo, Gey & Shapras, 1955). Current studies indicate that chick embryo epithelium can also be infected *in vitro* (Olson, personal communication).

Early stages of infection with RSV

Any study of RSV multiplication will show certain peculiar features due to the fate of infected cells and the limits of their competence. A one-step growth curve in the classical sense is not observed because the infected cell continues to multiply and produce virus indefinitely. Furthermore, since only a fraction of the cells can be infected at any given time, there is always a possibility of infecting normal cells with virus newly released from the infected cells. In practice, however, this latter point does not present an important problem in studying the early stages of infection because very little virus is produced for the first day after infection. In fact, there is not a great deal of virus produced at any time by infected cells, and one can follow the rate of multiplication of these cells with minimal danger of reinfection by adding antiviral serum to the growth medium of the cells. In experiments designed to follow the rate of multiplication of Rous cells in the first few days after infection, it is found that the number of infected cells doubles at least every 18–20 hr. (Temin & Rubin, unpublished).

Immediately after entering a cell, the virus loses its infective identity. About 12 hr. later the first new infective virus particles appear both in the cells and in the medium. They increase in amount at a rapid rate in the next 24 hr. or so and then the curve for virus release assumes approximately the same slope as that for Rous cell multiplication (Prince, 1958; Rubin & Temin, 1958a). The average rate of virus production by the Rous cells is about one infective unit per Rous cell every 10 hr. The highest rate of virus production observed by us to date has been about one infectious unit per Rous cell every hour. What this represents in terms of total particles is not known. There has been no accurate estimate made of the ratio of particles to infective units, but recent electron micrographs in our laboratory indicate that it is not excessively high.

Proportion of cells yielding virus

The low average rate of virus production per Rous cell recalls a similar finding with phage production in a population of lysogenic bacteria. In the latter case this is due to the fact that only a very small proportion of cells releases virus. When this occurs, a cell is said to be induced; the induced cell is lysed and a relatively large burst of virus is released. However, there have been indications that an individual animal cell, unlike a bacterium, can release virus over a long period of time (Dulbecco & Vogt, 1954). There is thus a possibility that individual Rous cells can release small amounts of virus continuously and continue to multiply.

Experiments have been carried out to distinguish between the two alternative modes of virus release. In one experiment, established Rous cells* were irradiated to prevent cell division. It was found that this irradiation had no effect on the total virus production by the population; that is, there was no induction. The irradiated cells were plated on the chorio-allantoic membrane or in tissue culture and the number of ectodermal tumours (Rubin, 1955) or foci (Rubin & Temin, 1958a) compared with the number obtained from a plating of fully viable cells. In the case of the fully viable cells, each one has an opportunity to multiply, so that an ectodermal lesion on the chorion could be due to virus produced by one of the cell's descendants; and a Rous focus in the tissue culture assay could theoretically occur in the complete absence of virus release simply by multiplication of the Rous cells. The irradiated cells cannot divide, however, and only those in the original inoculum which release virus can initiate a focus. It was found that the irradiated cells caused as many foci as the fully viable cells, indicating that all Rous sarcoma cells release virus. Since there are very few, if any, dead cells found in Rous cell clones, it follows that the Rous cells survive the production of infective virus. This conclusion is supported by more direct experiments in which individual Rous cells were maintained in microdrops, where they could be continuously observed, and the fluid repeatedly sampled. To date, virus has been isolated from seven such cells which divided at least once after the virus had been released (Temin & Rubin, unpublished).

---

* Established Rous cells are those in which the capacity for virus production has reached its full radioresistance (see section on radiation).

Transmission of the ability to produce virus

The Rous sarcoma virus seems to have a very persistent relation to the infected cell. The sarcoma has been maintained by cell and virus passage without loss of the agent for almost fifty years since its initial discovery. In our own laboratory more than forty serial transfers of Rous sarcoma cells were carried out in chickens, and the ability of the cells to produce virus was tested at different stages. Results indicated that the cells all retained the ability to produce virus (Rubin, 1955). It is evident that some very efficient mechanism must be operating for the transmission of this property from one cell generation to the next. Because of the low rate of virus production, it seems unlikely that reinfection plays an important role in maintaining the continuity of infection. Of course, it could be argued that any Rous cell which might lose the ability to produce virus might also become normal in appearance, and would no longer be counted as a Rous cell in the virus release experiments. We might thus get a false impression of the efficiency of perpetuating the ability to produce virus. Such segregation of normal cells from Rous cells cannot occur with a very high frequency, however, or it would be detected in the cloning of Rous sarcoma cells, and, to date, it has not been detected in our laboratory. The absence of significant segregation of normal cells is also supported by experiments which show the immediate and continuing rapid exponential growth of Rous cells after infection under conditions which minimize reinfection.

An investigation has been made of the role which reinfection might play in preserving the information for virus production. Rous sarcoma cells were cloned in the presence of antiviral serum to reduce reinfection and their growth continued in this serum for many generations. At the end of this treatment the cells were still producing virus at the same rate as cells grown in the absence of serum, suggesting that reinfection plays a minor role in maintaining the continuity of infection among the progeny of the cells infected initially.

Since reinfection appears a poor candidate for providing continuity of infection, some intracellular mechanism must be invoked. The two most obvious possibilities are (*a*) the random apportionment of 'vegetative' virus units among the progeny of Rous sarcoma cells and (*b*) the segregation of provirus-like units under control of an exact mechanism, such as that which governs cell division. Evidence will be considered which tends to favour, but does not prove, the latter hypothesis.

RADIATION EXPERIMENTS WITH BACTERIOPHAGE

As a result of recent genetic and radiological experiments evidence has accumulated that indicates a close interaction between the genomes of temperate phages and their host bacteria. The genetic evidence includes transduction, the localization of prophages at a specific region of the bacterial chromosome and the segregation of prophage as a single marker in bacterial crosses (Wollman, Jacob & Hayes, 1956; Hartmann, 1957; Bertani, 1958).

The radiological evidence which complements the genetic evidence consists of studies on the radiosensitivity of the infectivity of free virus and of the capacity of bacteria to support phage growth.

Both virulent and temperate phages vary in their sensitivity to inactivation by X-rays according to the amount of DNA they contain (Epstein, 1953). Temperate phages, however, are found to be more resistant to u.v. light than virulent phages of comparable DNA content (Garen & Zinder, 1955; Stent, 1958). It has been suggested that the resistance of temperate phages to u.v. is due to the fact that the photochemical damage which results from u.v. can be repaired by interaction of the damaged phage genome with a homologous region of the bacterial genome (Garen & Zinder, 1955). The agreement of X-ray sensitivity with DNA content is presumed to be due to the high energy electrons which result from X-rays and cause damage to the viral DNA, such as rupture of phosphodiester bonds, which cannot be repaired by interaction with the host cell.

When the bacterial cells are irradiated and their capacity to support phage growth is studied, another interesting difference between temperate and virulent phages is encountered. The capacity of bacteria to support the growth of temperate phages is much more radiosensitive than is their capacity to support the growth of virulent phages. Stent (1958) has suggested that the interaction between a relatively intact bacterial genome and temperate phage is a prerequisite for the multiplication of the latter. Virulent phage multiplication is presumed to be practically independent of the intact host genome.

Radiation of free RSV and NDV

Radiological experiments similar to those described above have been carried out with RSV (Rubin & Temin, 1958a, 1958b); NDV was used as a representative virulent animal virus to compare with RSV. It was deemed appropriate because, like RSV, it grows in chick fibroblasts, can be readily assayed by the plaque technique, and both are probably RNA viruses (Franklin, Rubin & Davis, 1957; Bather, 1957).

When irradiated with X-rays, RSV proves to be only slightly more resistant than NDV. This suggests that both viruses, assuming both contain RNA, have similar amounts of nucleic acid per infective particle (Epstein, 1953). When irradiation is carried out with u.v., however, RSV is found to be ten times more resistant than NDV.

We can ask if the apparent resistance of RSV to u.v. is due to the fact that only a small part of the virus is involved in transforming cells, and that this part survives the loss of the ability of the virus as a whole to multiply. Such a situation would be analogous to the transduction of bacteria by a small piece of the bacterial genome carried by phage. That this is *not* the case is already suggested by the fact that the sensitivity of RSV to X-rays is similar to that of NDV. A transduction-like mechanism has been completely ruled out by the demonstration that all the cells transformed by u.v.-treated RSV release infectious virus. These results indicate that the entire genome of the virus is required to effect the characteristic change seen in Rous cells.

The paradoxical u.v. resistance of RSV is similar in degree to that of temperate phage. It is tempting to speculate that the resistance of RSV is due to the repair of u.v. damage by interaction with a homologous region in the host cell genome, as has been suggested for phage.

Capacity of cells to initiate RSV and NDV growth

The ability of animal cells to divide and form colonies can be measured quantitatively by the cloning technique of Puck, Ciecura & Fisher (1957). The ability of chick embryo cells to form colonies is found to be relatively sensitive to X-rays, the dose for 37 % survival being 300 to 600 r. At 100 times this dose, a large proportion of the cells still retain their capacity to support the multiplication of NDV. However, the capacity of cells to initiate RSV growth is apparently lost at the same dose of irradiation as their ability to multiply. Further experiments suggest that the correlation between the curves for inactivation of colony-forming ability and RSV capacities is not merely fortuitous, but that a cell must have the ability to divide in order to initiate the growth of RSV.

The requirement that cells be *able* to divide in order to initiate virus production does not mean that they must actually divide. On the contrary, cells which are infected with RSV and kept in the presence of 5-fluorouracil develop the radioresistant capacity (see below), albeit more slowly than cells infected in the absence of the compound. Treated cells do not divide, although they can divide when the 5-fluorouracil is removed. They are incapable of synthesizing vaccinia virus, a DNA virus, in the presence of this compound. NDV growth is unaffected by the compound, however, suggesting that DNA synthesis is preferentially inhibited in this system (Fairman, personal communication). Therefore it appears that only certain processes essential for cell division are also essential for the initiation of RSV growth.

The capacity of established Rous sarcoma cells to continue virus production

If the irradiation of cells is carried out at various times *after* infection, it is found that the capacity to support RSV growth becomes increasingly resistant with time. By 2 days after infection the dose required to prevent further virus production by Rous cells is about two orders of magnitude larger than the dose required to destroy the RSV capacity of cells irradiated before infection.

Cells in which the RSV capacity has attained its full resistance will be referred to as established Rous cells. Such cells continue to release virus at a normal rate for at least 5 days after their colony-forming ability has been destroyed by irradiation.

Recapitulating, we can divide the multiplication of RSV into two distinct stages. If the cell is irradiated before infection or up to 6 or 8 hr. after infection, the capacity of the cell to initiate virus production is as radiosensitive as the ability of the cell to divide. After this time the radioresistance of the capacity increases rapidly and in 24 to 36 hr. it has become several orders of magnitude more resistant. Can we find some rationale for this behaviour? One interpretation of these findings might be as follows. In order that virus multiplication be initiated the virus genome must be integrated with that of the cell, and this can only occur when some genetically competent portion of the cell, whether it be RNA or DNA, is being duplicated. Once the proper integration has occurred, the virus genome can function in cell division and metabolism like other individual components of the cell's genome. Thus we get continued virus production after killing an established Rous cell, just as we get continued synthesis of most normal constituents in cells which have lost the ability to divide following irradiation.

What radiosensitive structure in the cell and what radiosensitive process might be required for both cell division and the initiation of RSV production? There is no direct evidence along this line about the requirements for RSV multiplication, but some light has been thrown on the critical radiosensitive structures in animal cells which are required for cell division. Irradiation of grasshopper neuroblast cells with a u.v. microbeam has shown that the nucleolus is the most radiosensitive structure in the cell (Gaulden & Perry, 1958). What is more, the time of greatest sensitivity coincides with the period of nucleolar RNA synthesis. This, of course, raises the possibility that the nucleolus and RNA synthesis may play an important role in the establishment of RSV infection. Since we require that the information for virus production be preserved at cell division, it would be important to find evidence of genetic and physical continuity of the nucleolus if it is involved in this preservation. There is some cytological support for this in the observation that the nucleolus contains Feulgen-negative threads, and these remain intact throughout the mitotic cycle even when the amorphous part of the nucleolus disappears. It has been proposed that these nucleolar threads may be carriers of genetic information (Estable & Sotelo, 1954; Bernhard, Hagenau & Oberling, 1952).

It is obvious from recent experiments with plant and animal viruses that RNA can transmit genetic information (Gierer & Schramm, 1956; Colter, Bird & Brown, 1957). Genetic evidence of a similar role for RNA within cells in the absence of virus infection is not so well established, although the nucleolar irradiation experiments imply a critical role for nucleolar RNA, which may be genetic. Studies with *Escherichia coli* have suggested that the primary effect of u.v. in causing mutations is on the precursors of RNA (Doudney & Haas, 1958). For the present it is on such speculative grounds that our working hypotheses about the site of RSV action in the cell admittedly must rest.

ANTIGENS OF THE CELL AND OF THE VIRUS

A number of contradictory reports have appeared concerning the presence of normal chicken antigens in RSV. The positive reports have been based on the neutralization of the virus by antiserum to normal chicken tissues (Gye & Purdy, 1933; Amies & Carr, 1939). The negative reports have been based on a failure to demonstrate such neutralization (Keogh, 1938; Barrett, 1940; Kabat & Furth, 1941) and the failure of purified RSV to fix complement with anti-chick serum (Dmochowski, 1948). The disagreement in the neutralization results can be attributed to the use of different techniques for carrying out the neutralization. It was recently shown that the neutralization of the virus by anti-chick serum is only apparent, and is actually due to the inhibitory effect of the anti-chick serum on tumour growth rather than to direct inactivation of the virus (Rubin, 1956). This is clearly demonstrated by two observations.

(*a*) The neutralizing effect of anti-chick serum is completely reversed when the serum virus mixture is diluted, whereas neutralization by antiviral serum is reversed to only a minor extent.

(*b*) Addition of the anti-chick serum *after* infection inhibits tumour growth, whereas antiviral serum has no effect unless added to the virus before infection.

These observations have recently been confirmed by Borsos (1958), who also found that when the virus is assayed by the haemorrhagic lesion technique, where formation of a gross tumour is not required, anti-chick serum has no effect whatsoever on the virus titre.

Recent observations (Harris & Simons, 1958) on the multiplication of RSV in cells of a different species have raised some interesting questions about the role of immunological reactions in modifying the growth of tumours. Turkeys, which are usually refractory to RSV infection, may be made susceptible by pretreating them with normal chicken materials. This may be interpreted as a phenomenon similar to either immunological tolerance or immunological enhancement (Brent, 1958; Kaliss, 1956). But tolerance to what—the virus or the infected cell? It seems most unlikely that antibodies directed against the virus could be elicited in time to account for the usual refractory state in the turkey, and there is no evidence for the presence of neutralizing antibodies in the serum of normal turkeys. Also against any role for antiviral antibody in explaining these observations is the fact that such antibody can be placed in high concentration directly on the chorio-allantoic membrane or on tissue culture cells as early as 1 hr. after infection without effect on the transformation or growth of infected cells. Certainly a turkey cannot produce antiviral antibodies before the infecting virus has penetrated the host cells and such antibodies can therefore have no significance in the normal resistance of turkeys. Even the presence of antiviral antibody in the recipient animal at the time of infection has been found to have little influence on the outcome (Prince, 1957*b*). It follows, then, that the induction of immunological tolerance to the *virus* particles can have little influence on the outcome of infection.

The observations can be better understood if we suppose that RSV infection of turkey cells causes them to make some cellular antigen normally found in chickens but absent in turkeys. An immunological response to this new *cellular* antigen would be expected to prevent growth of the tumour just as it would prevent the growth of grafted tissue from a chicken. A turkey made tolerant to chicken antigens would not react to the appearance of this new antigen, and the tumour would grow unmolested. This phenomenon would be very similar to lysogenic conversion, where the multiplication of temperate phage is accompanied by the appearance of new cellular antigens (Uetake, Luria & Burrous, 1958). A similar interpretation can be made of Gye and Purdy's observations with Fujinami virus infection in chickens and ducks (1933.)

CONCLUSIONS

The detailed study of interactions between cells and tumour viruses is only beginning, and it would be a rash individual indeed who proposed rigorous models for these interactions based on the information presently at hand. It may be useful, however, to offer some speculations based on fundamental knowledge in other relevant biological systems, especially if they can be tested by experiment or will accentuate the need for particular techniques to enable such tests to be made. Thus on these grounds, and from the experiments described above, it seems reasonable to propose as a working hypothesis that the *maintenance* of the malignant properties of a Rous sarcoma cell line is the result of a close integration of virus and cell genomes. The nature of this integration should prove a fruitful area for future investigation. Whether the cellular alteration itself is due to a specific genetic change in the cell which is directly associated with integration of the virus genome, or is a by-product of restricted virus multiplication, is a completely open question. In trying to answer this question it would be extremely useful to have reliable genetic markers for both cell and virus, and there appears to be no insuperable barrier to their being found. More efficient methods for cloning and synchronizing chicken cells are also needed. When these become available we may be able to answer inquiries about the mechanism of virus carcinogenesis with more than an embarrassed smile.

REFERENCES

AMIES, C. R. & CARR, J. G. (1939). Immunological experiments with a highly concentrated suspension of Rous No. 1 tumour producing agent. *J. Path. Bact.* **49**, 497.

ANDERVONT, H. B. & DUNN, T. B. (1953). Influence of heredity and the mammary tumor agent on the occurrence of mammary tumors in hybrid mice. *J. nat. Cancer Inst.* **14**, 317.

BARRETT, M. K. (1940). The antigenic nature of purified chicken tumour agent. *Cancer Res.* **1**, 543.

BATHER, R. (1957). The nucleic acid content of partially purified Rous No. 1 Sarcoma virus. *Brit. J. Cancer*, **11**, 611.

BEARD, J. W., SHARP, D. G. & ECKERT, E. A. (1955). Tumor viruses. *Advanc. Virus Res.* **3**, 149.

BERNHARD, W. F., HAGENAU, F. & OBERLING, C. (1952). L'ultra-structure du nucléole de quelques cellules animales, revélées par le microscope électronique. *Experientia*, **8**, 58.

BERTANI, G. (1958). Lysogeny. *Advanc. Virus Res.* **5**, 151.

BORSOS, T. (1958). Absence of neutralization of Rous sarcoma virus by anti-normal chicken embryo serum, and complement. *J. nat. Cancer Inst.* **20**, 1215.

BORSOS, T. & BANG, F. B. (1957). Quantitation of hemorrhagic lesions in the chick embryo produced by the Rous sarcoma virus. *Virology*, **4**, 385.

BRENT, L. (1958). Tissue transplantation immunity. *Progr. Allergy*, **5**, 271.

CARREL, A. & EBELING, A. H. (1926). The transformation of monocytes into fibroblasts through the action of Rous virus. *J. exp. Med.* **43**, 461.

COLTER, J. S., BIRD, H. H. & BROWN, R. A. (1957). Infectivity of ribonucleic acid from Ehrlich ascites cells infected with Mengo encephalitis. *Nature, Lond.* **179**, 859.

DMOCHOWSKI, L. (1948). Investigations on the properties of agents causing fowl tumors. I. Attempts at isolation of the fowl tumor agents by differential centrifugation. *J. nat. Cancer Inst.* **9**, 57.

DOUDNEY, C. O. & HAAS, F. L. (1958). Modification of ultraviolet induced mutation frequency and survival in bacteria by post-irradiation treatment. *Proc. nat. Acad. Sci., Wash.* **44**, 390.

DULBECCO, R. & VOGT, M. (1954). One step growth curve of Western equine encephalomyelitis on chicken embryo cells grown *in vitro*, and analysis of virus yields from single cells. *J. exp. Med.* **99**, 183.

DURAN-REYNALS, F. (1947). A study of three new duck variants of the Rous chicken sarcoma. *Cancer Res.* **7**, 99.

EPSTEIN, H. T. (1953). Identification of radiosensitive volume with nucleic acid volume. *Nature, Lond.* **171**, 394.

ESTABLE, C. & SOTELO, J. R. (1954). *Fine Structure of Cells. VIIIth Congress of Cell Biology.* Leiden (1955). New York: Interscience.

FRANKLIN, R. M., RUBIN, H. & DAVIS, C. (1957). The production, purification and properties of Newcastle disease virus labelled with radiophosphorus. *Virology*, **3**, 94.

GAREN, A. & ZINDER, N. D. (1955). Radiological evidence for partial genetic homology between bacteriophage and host bacteria. *Virology*, **1**, 347.

GAULDEN, M. E. & PERRY, R. P. (1958). Influence of the nucleolus on mitosis as revealed by ultraviolet microbeam irradiation. *Proc. Nat. Acad. Sci., Wash.* **44**, 553.

GIERER, A. & SCHRAMM, G. (1956). Die Infectiosität der Nucleinsäure aus Tabakmosaikvirus. *Z. Naturf.* **11***b*, 138.

GROSS, L. (1958). Viral etiology of 'spontaneous' mouse leukaemia. A Review. *Cancer Res.* **18**, 371.

GYE, W. E. & PURDY, W. J. (1933). The infective agent in tumour filtrates. A further investigation by means of antisera to normal tissues. *Brit. J. exp. Path.* **14**, 250.

HALBERSTAEDTER, J., DOLJANSKI, L. & TENNENBAUM, E. (1941). Experiments in the cancerization of cells *in vitro* by means of the Rous sarcoma agent. *Brit. J. exp. Path.* **22**, 179.

HARRIS, R. J. C. (1956). Acquired tolerance of turkeys to Rous sarcoma agent. *Proc. roy. Soc. B*, **146**, 59.

HARRIS, R. J. C. & SIMONS, P. J. (1958). Nature of the antigens responsible for the acquired tolerance of turkeys to Rous sarcoma agent. *Nature, Lond.* **181**, 1485.

HARTMAN, P. E. (1957). Transduction: A comparative review. In *The Chemical Basis of Heredity*. Edited by W. D. McElroy and B. Glass, p. 408. Baltimore: Johns Hopkins Univ. Press.

KABAT, E. A. & FURTH, J. (1941). Neutralization of the agent causing leukosis and sarcoma of fowls by rabbit antisera. *J. exp. Med.* **74**, 257.

KALISS, N. (1956). Course of production of an isoantiserum effecting tumor homograft survival in mice. *Proc. Nat. Acad. Sci., Wash.* **42**, 269.

KEOGH, E. V. (1938). Ectodermal lesions produced by the virus of Rous sarcoma. *Brit. J. exp. Path.* **19**, 1.

LO, W. Y., GEY, G. O. & SHAPRAS, P. (1955). The cytopathogenic effect of the Rous sarcoma virus on chicken fibroblasts in tissue cultures. *Johns Hopk. Hosp. Bull.* **97**, 248.

MANAKER, R. A. & GROUPÉ, V. (1956). Discrete foci of altered chicken embryo cells associated with Rous sarcoma virus in tissue culture. *Virology*, **2**, 838.

MILFORD, J. & DURAN-REYNALS, F. (1953). Growth of a chicken sarcoma virus in the chick embryo in the absence of neoplasia. *Cancer Res.* **3**, 578.

MURPHY, J. B. & ROUS, P. (1912). Behaviour of chicken sarcoma implanted in the developing embryo. *J. exp. Med.* **15**, 119.

PIKOVSKI, M. A. (1953). The survival of mammary tumor agent in cultures of deterologous cells. *J. nat. Cancer Inst.* **13**, 1275.

PRINCE, A. M. (1957a). Quantitative studies on Rous sarcoma virus. 1. The titration of Rous sarcoma virus on the chorioallantoic membrane of the chick embryo. *J. nat. Cancer Inst.* **20**, 147.

PRINCE, A. M. (1957b). Quantitative studies on Rous sarcoma virus. II. The mechanism of the resistance of chick embryos to chorioallantoic inoculation of Rous sarcoma virus. *J. nat. Cancer Inst.* **20**, 843.

PRINCE, A. M. (1958). Quantitative studies on Rous sarcoma virus. III. Virus multiplication and cellular response following infection of the chorioallantoic membrane of the chick embryo. *Virology*, **5**, 435.

PUCK, T. T., CIECURA, S. J. & FISHER, H. W. (1957). Clonal growth of human cells with fibroblastic morphology. *J. exp. Med.* **106**, 145.

RUBIN, H. (1955). Quantitative relationships between causative virus and cell in the Rous No. 1 chicken sarcoma. *Virology*, **1**, 445.

RUBIN, H. (1956). An analysis of the apparent neutralization of Rous sarcoma virus with antiserum to normal chick tissues. *Virology*, **2**, 545.

RUBIN, H. (1957). The production of virus by Rous sarcoma cells. *Ann. N.Y. Acad. Sci.* **68**, 459.

RUBIN, H. & TEMIN, H. (1958a). Studies of infection with the Rous sarcoma virus *in vitro*. To be published in *Fed. Proc.* Dec. 1958.

RUBIN, H. & TEMIN, H. (1958b). Radiation studies on lysogeny and tumor viruses. *Texas Rep. Biol. Med.* (in the Press).

SANFORD, K. K., LIKELY, G. D., BRYAN, W. R. & EARLE, W. R. (1952). The infection of cells in tissue culture with Rous sarcoma virus. *J. Nat. Cancer Inst.* **12**, 1317.

STENT, G. S. (1958). Mating in the reproduction of bacterial viruses. *Advanc. Virus Res.* **5**, 95.

STEWART, S. E., EDDY, B. E. & BORGHESE, N. (1958). Neoplasms in mice inoculated into a tumor agent carried in tissue culture. *J. nat. Cancer Inst.* **20**, 1223.

TEMIN, H. & RUBIN, H. Characteristics of an assay for Rous sarcoma virus and Rous sarcoma cells in tissue culture. *Virology* (in the Press).

UETAKE, H., LURIA, S. E. & BURROUS, J. W. (1958). Conversion of somatic antigens in salmonella by phage infection leading to lysis or lysogeny. *Virology*, **5**, 68.

WOLLMAN, E. L., JACOB, F. & HAYES, W. (1956). Conjugation and genetic recombination in *E. coli. Cold Spr. Harb. Symp. quant. Biol.* **21**, 141.

WOOLLEY, G. W. & SMALL, M. C. (1957). Strain specificities of leukemia agent. *Ann. N.Y. Acad. Sci.* **68**, 533.

STUDIES ON VACCINIA VIRUS IN HeLa CELLS

H. B. MAITLAND AND ROY POSTLETHWAITE

Department of Bacteriology, University of Manchester

In studying the behaviour of vaccinia virus in tissue culture the experimental system has been kept as simple as possible. Young cultures of HeLa cells in a chemically defined medium (Eagle, 1955) were used. With a well dispersed suspension of elementary bodies, a homogeneous population of cells, a medium which avoided unknown factors such as those found in serum, embryo extract, etc., and an experimental design intended to give results of maximum quantitative significance, it was hoped to obtain more precise information about the processes of viral infection of cells than has usually been attempted in work relating to this virus. Particular attention was directed toward the possible occurrence of an eclipse phase as part of the growth cycle. By simplifying the culture system the conditions for virus growth may not have been optimal, but the processes of infection and multiplication may be expected to be similar in any system where growth occurs.

MATERIALS AND METHODS

Virus

The Lister Institute strain of vaccinia, used for preparing smallpox vaccine, has been maintained by passage in the skin of rabbits. Elementary body suspensions were prepared by the method of Hoagland, Smadel & Rivers (1940) from infected rabbit skin, using a Spinco centrifuge for the high-speed centrifugings. They were suspended in McIlvaine's buffer 0·004M, pH 7·3, and stored at $-20°$; their titre before storage ranged from $70–500 \times 10^6$ pock-forming units/ml. Stained films revealed considerable, but not complete, dispersion of elementary bodies and very little extraneous material. The clumps could be broken up by dilution in McIlvaine's buffer and vigorous pipetting, yielding a preparation which consisted largely of single elementary bodies. For inoculation, a similar suspension was made in Earle's solution. Examination by the electron microscope indicated the degree of dispersion achieved: in thirty-two representative fields, two from each of sixteen grid-squares, 213 elementary bodies were counted, of which 182 (85 %) were single; there were eight pairs, one clump of three and one of about twelve.

HeLa cells

These were maintained by weekly subculture in a medium consisting of 10 % each of human and horse serum, and 0·2 % lactalbumin hydro-lysate in Hanks's solution with penicillin, streptomycin and mycostatin.

Cultures for experiments were prepared from well-grown 7-day cultures by trypsinizing the monolayers, making a suspension of cells in the medium and transferring 4 ml. containing, in separate experiments, $1·0–1·5 \times 10^6$ cells, to 50 mm. pyrex Petri dishes. These were incubated at 37° in 5 % CO_2 in air for 24 hr. By this time a monolayer of cells, usually not completely confluent, had formed. The medium was then replaced with Eagle's medium and incubation was continued overnight. The change of medium was made to diminish the possibility of carrying over any serum constituents into the experiment.

Recovery of virus from cells by ultrasonic treatment

A 'Mullard' 50 Watt ultrasonic drill with a 1:1 ratio chromium-plated stub has been found satisfactory for releasing virus from HeLa cells. The stub was placed in contact with the surface of the liquid in the Petri dish; the machine was switched on and allowed to act for 60 sec. while the Petri dish was moved constantly so that all parts of it came under the vibrating stub. This movement may not be necessary for the release of virus, but if the dish was kept stationary the vibrations affected the glass after a few exposures. The optimal conditions for obtaining the required results have to be determined for each type of experiment. Such factors as shape of stub, shape and size of the vessel, whether the stub is im-mersed or merely in surface contact, volume of liquid, nature and tem-perature of suspending medium, and time of operation, affect the result.

It was found that with 4 ml. of liquid in a 50 mm. Petri dish, treatment for 60 sec. at room temperature disintegrated the cells of monolayer cultures or cells in suspension, but it did not reduce the infective titre of an elementary body suspension in Earle's solution, nor cause a rise in temperature sufficient to harm the virus. Rises from 26° to 30–33° and from 28° to 37° have been noted with 3 ml. of water in a Petri dish (Magrath, unpublished).

The advantages of the method are that it is quick, can be applied to a culture without any preliminary manipulation and completely breaks up virtually all the cells. Macpherson (1958) found that ultrasonic treat-ment (using another type of apparatus) was more effective in releasing virus from HeLa cells than grinding or freezing and thawing, and about as effective as shaking with glass beads.

If treatment is prolonged unduly the stub becomes heated, the temperature in the suspension rises and the overall effect is to reduce the infective titre of the virus.

Titration of virus

The chorio-allantoic membrane of 13-day chick embryos was inoculated with 0·05 ml. of material diluted in Hanks's solution. The mean number of pocks per membrane was determined after incubation at 37° for 2 days from unweighted counts on seven or eight eggs.

In experiments involving a series of titrations, results were frequently expressed as percentages of a control. Each titration was carried out on the material from two dishes pooled immediately after disintegration of their contents in order to reduce any individual differences in cultures, which were as far as possible identical.

Antiserum

Rabbits were inoculated with elementary body suspensions, at first intradermally and 3 weeks later by intravenous injections given on three consecutive days in each of 4 or 5 weeks. The serum was inactivated at 56° and stored at −20°. Before further bleeding, another three daily injections were given.

EXPERIMENTAL

Data are presented on the adsorption of virus, its neutralization by antiserum, changes in infectivity preceding growth, and release of virus from cells treated with trypsin.

Adsorption of virus by HeLa cells

The Eagle's medium was removed from monolayer cultures and the cultures were washed once in Earle's solution. Two ml. of virus in Earle's solution were then added and removed again after the required time at room temperature. The cells were finally washed three times with 2 ml. of Earle's solution and disintegrated in 4 ml. of Eagle's medium. The virus was titrated immediately.

During a 30 min. period of adsorption full recovery of virus in the system could be demonstrated. The total amount of virus at the end of adsorption, that is, the supernatant along with the virus in the washes and on the cells, was usually more than the amount originally in the inoculum (Table 1).

Such enhancement of infectivity has often been found in titrations of vaccinia virus exposed to tissue or tissue extracts. It is probably caused by disaggregation of virus clumps. The occurrence of enhancement

Table 1. *Adsorption of virus in Earle's solution to a monolayer of HeLa cells for* 30 *min. at room temperature. Percentage distribution of virus in cells, supernatant and washings*

		Percentage of virus in inoculum					
			In washings				
Experi-	Infective units	In supernatant				Remaining	
ment	in inoculum	after adsorption	1st	2nd	3rd	on cells	Total
1	119,000	151	9	0·8	—	15	175·8
2	7,130,000	78	6	0·5	0·3	20	104·8
3	6,960,000	118	5	1·0	0·5	18	142·5
4	3,684,000	40	3	0·5	0·02	56	99·5
5	3,260,000	77	4	0·3	0·6	64	145·9

reveals the inaccuracy of estimating the amount of virus adsorbed by subtracting what is left in the supernatant from what was originally in the inoculum. Further, although no loss of virus in the whole system was detectable during the period of adsorption, there may have been some loss which was compensated by enhancement.

Three washes adequately removed loosely attached virus from the cells, as shown by the decreasing amount of virus in successive washes (Table 1). Further washing, by pipetting 2 ml. of Earle's solution on and off twenty times, removed no more than 4% of the total virus in the system. The virus remaining on the cells after three washes was therefore regarded as adsorbed virus.

Table 2. *Recovery of virus after adsorption by HeLa cells in monolayer cultures*

	Experiment 1. Inoculum 69,000 infective units per dish		Experiment 2. Inoculum 1,380,000 infective units per dish	
Duration of adsorption (min.)	No. of infective units adsorbed	Virus detected expressed as % of inoculum	No. of infective units adsorbed	Virus detected expressed as % of inoculum
0·5	—	—	14,400	1·0
5	2,000	3·0	54,400	4·0
15	3,400	5·0	118,000	8·0
25	3,700	5·4	—	—
30	—	—	104,000	7·6
40	6,500	9·4	—	—
60	9,700	12·6	320,000	23·2
120	19,300	28·0	608,000	44·0

The amount of virus adsorbed by the cells depended chiefly on the strength of inoculum and duration of contact. Some virus was adsorbed in ½ min. The amount detectable in disintegrated cells increased steadily with time, giving a straight line relationship over a 2 hr. period. Typical results are shown in Table 2. To obtain a base-line figure which represents virus adsorbed to cells before the occurrence of any further processes which might take place, a short period of adsorption is desirable and has been used in many of the experiments.

An interesting consequence of adsorption of virus to HeLa cells is the marked degree of protection this gives against the deleterious effect of the overlying medium. Thus, the titre of virus incubated at 37° in Eagle's medium fell to about 10 % of its original titre in an hour and thereafter declined more slowly during several hours. When cells with adsorbed virus were incubated in Eagle's medium at the same temperature there was a fall in titre of about 25 % in 6–8 hr. The cause of the protection is unknown.

Neutralization of adsorbed virus by antiserum

It is frequently assumed that virus which has been adsorbed by cells and is still neutralizable by antiserum is 'on' the cell surface, whereas virus that is not neutralizable is 'inside' the cell. This may perhaps be too simple a view and it is conceivable that the position of the virus in relation to an irregular surface may affect its accessibility to antibody. Ease of neutralization might thus vary with the stage of cell-virus combination and penetration of virus into the cell as well as with the physiological state of the cell, especially its ability to support the growth of virus. Much of the adsorbed virus in our experiments was neutralizable by antiserum and may be presumed to have been on the cell surface; virus which was not neutralizable may be regarded as that fraction from which infection arose. Thus the amount of adsorbed, non-neutralizable virus appeared to be the best base line available for studying changes in infectivity, though it was an empirical one. The difficulty was to know when maximum neutralization of adsorbed virus had been attained.

Two sera prepared in rabbits were used. When mixed with virus in McIlvaine's buffer, pH 7·3, plus 10 % skimmed milk (in which the titre of virus was stable for 4 hr.) for 30 min. at 30°, and inoculated without further dilution, each reduced the virus titre to 50 % of the controls at serum dilutions of 10^{-5} and 10^{-7} respectively. Serum diluted 1/10 and 1/100 neutralized 98–99 % of virus.

For the neutralization of adsorbed virus, the culture was washed, 2 ml. of 1/100 serum in Earle's solution were applied, and left at room temperature for the required time. The serum was removed, the cells washed twice with 2 ml. of Earle's solution and 4 ml. of Eagle's medium was added. This was followed immediately by disintegration of the cells and titration of the virus. Controls were treated in parallel with saline in place of serum.

These strong antisera had a rapid effect. About 70 % of the adsorbed virus was neutralized during the first minute, but with longer periods of contact the rate of neutralization became markedly slower. We have used periods up to 30 min. to neutralize adsorbed virus in order to obtain a base line on which to construct a growth curve; at 30 min. the unneutralized fraction was about 15 %. It has already been noted that virus adsorbed to cells is less rapidly inactivated by the medium than free virus and it is possible that such virus might also be less readily neutralized by antiserum.

The amount of unneutralizable virus accumulated roughly in proportion to the increase in total adsorbed virus over an adsorption period of about 2 hr.; the proportion of adsorbed virus that was not neutralizable did not change significantly during this time. Thus only a small proportion of the virus adsorbed to HeLa cells could be regarded as virus which infected them. There may have been differences in the infectivity of virus elementary bodies or differences in the susceptibility to infection of individual cells in the culture. Either virus or cells, or perhaps both, appeared to be heterogeneous. It would be of interest to compare other lines of cells and other adapted strains of virus in this respect.

It has already been mentioned that virus began to be adsorbed to cells immediately after contact and that some of this rapidly became unneutralizable. It would seem that the unneutralizable virus is committed to infecting cells because an increase in virus concentration was demonstrable in cells exposed to virus for 1 min., washed and incubated for 24 hr. in a 1/100 dilution of antiserum in Eagle's medium.

GROWTH CURVES

In studying the changes in infectivity which may occur in cultures during the early phases of virus growth it is important to decide what base line to adopt so that subsequent titrations can be related to it. It is clear from the preceding section that the total amount of adsorbed virus, even after a short period of adsorption, is not a suitable base line since about 85 % of this virus was neutralizable by antiserum in 30 min. and was presumably not then concerned in infection. The ideal base line would be the amount of adsorbed virus at a time, very soon after its adsorption, before any further processes that could be part of a growth cycle rendered it non-infective. This is difficult to achieve. It has been shown that some virus infects cells in 1 min. but it takes 15–30 min. for serum to be fully effective, and during this time an eclipse phase, if such exists, may already have begun. Therefore in order to obtain a base line a compromise has to be adopted the object of which is to adsorb virus for as short a time as is practicable and to apply serum for as short a time as will at least neutralize almost all the neutralizable virus.

Growth curves obtained in different ways have been compared.

The basic technique was uniform throughout. Cultures prepared as described were washed once with Earle's solution. For adsorption 2 ml. of virus in Earle's solution were applied at room temperature for the required time. This was removed and the carpet of cells was washed three times, each time with 2 ml. of Earle's solution. Four ml. of Eagle's medium was added. Cultures were disintegrated and titrated immediately to provide a base line, and again at intervals after incubation at 37° in 5 % CO_2 in air. When antiserum was used for neutralization, 2 ml. of 1/100 dilution were added to cultures after adsorption and washing and left in contact at room temperature for the required time. The serum was removed and the cells washed twice with Earle's solution before adding Eagle's medium as above.

Results were expressed as percentages of the titre of the control culture, disintegrated at zero hour, before incubation. Growth of virus always occurred in cultures incubated for 24 hr.

(a) Growth curve when the base line at zero hours was the total amount of adsorbed virus

After adsorption for 30 min. there was a gradual loss during incubation of up to 25 % of the titre at zero hours. The lowest point was at 7–10 hr. while at 12 hr. the titre was rising.

This result in itself has little significance in relation to the mechanism of virus growth, because the cells carry a large proportion of neutralizable virus which would tend to mask any loss of infectivity that might have occurred in the much smaller amount of non-neutralizable virus which initiated infection. The observed reduction in titre might be attributed to either or both fractions of virus. The neutralizable virus was protected to a marked degree from inactivation by the medium, but it might not have been completely stable. The result was instructive, however, when this curve was compared with other curves.

(b) Growth curve when cells with adsorbed virus were treated with antiserum before incubation and the base line at zero hours was unneutralized virus

In some experiments 30 min. were allowed for adsorption and 30 min. for neutralization. Neutralization should then be virtually maximal and the base line should consist almost entirely of virus concerned in infection. The disadvantage of this procedure was that during the hour which elapsed between inoculation and titration some virus could already have become non-infective by passing rapidly into an eclipse phase.

In view of this possibility some experiments were carried out in which the base-line titration was made as soon as practicable after first contact of virus with cells. Periods of 1 min. were allowed for both adsorption and neutralization and, with washing, about 5 min. elapsed before the cells were disintegrated. The antiserum acting for this short time would not have achieved maximal neutralization of adsorbed virus, but it did reduce the titre by about 70 %. The base line was not therefore a measure of unneutralizable virus alone. Nevertheless, during incubation there was a gradual fall in titre of about 70 %; and this drop in titre would tend to be underestimated by the procedure used for the experiment. The lowest titre was found between 8 and 10 hr. Increase in titre due to growth was evident in 13–14 hr.

Similar results were obtained with periods of adsorption and neutralization of 30 min. This suggests that no marked loss of virus had taken place in the hour before making the base-line titration. But the evidence on this point is inferential, as the base lines in the two experiments were not strictly comparable.

The result indicates that loss of infectivity was brought about by cell–virus interaction. All the virus did not disappear. Whether the virus which did disappear had become 'eclipsed' was not apparent from these experiments. It is possible that the loss of infectivity of virus could have been caused by such a mechanism of multiplication, but virus in cells may become non-infective apart from processes leading to replication. The residuum of virus that did not lose its infectivity could have been (a) virus that had not penetrated the cells even though it had become unneutralizable, or (b) virus within the cell that would eventually multiply, or even (c) virus within the cell which was not destined to yield infective progeny.

(c) Growth curve when cells with adsorbed virus were incubated and then treated with antiserum before titration

In order to find out whether virus adsorbed to cells continued to become unneutralizable during incubation, cultures were washed after adsorption of virus for 30 min. and then incubated at 37°. Subsequently they were treated with antiserum for 15 min. before titration. The results of two experiments are shown in Table 3. In the first experiment the control growth curve I (which starts with total adsorbed virus and shows the

Table 3. *Growth curves comparing cultures treated with antiserum after incubation and before disintegration* (II *and* IV) *with those untreated* (I) *and with those treated before incubation* (III)

| | Experiment 1 | | | | Experiment 2* | | | |
| | I | | II | | III | | IV | |
Time (hours)	No. of I.U. (in thousands)	%	No. of I.U. (in thousands)	%	No. of I.U. (in thousands)	%	No. of I.U. (in thousands)	%
0	1,864	100	80	100	33	100	31	100
1	1,742	93	80	100	21	63	30	99
2	1,232	66	76	95	18	54	19	64
3	1,600	86	120	150	15	44	42	136
4	1,304	70	168	210	17	50	32	106
5	—	—	—	—	19	58	32	106
5½	1,288	69	180	225	—	—	—	—
6	—	—	—	—	11	34	24	78
7	1,988	106	190	237	9	28	19	61
8	—	—	—	—	13	39	37	121
8½	1,360	75	164	205	—	—	—	—
9	—	—	—	—	14	41	48	158
10	—	—	—	—	14	41	90	295
10½	1,200	64	696	870	—	—	—	—
11	—	—	—	—	20	60	274	895
12	1,976	106	1,248	1,560	13	39	422	1,390
14	2,568	138	4,120	5,140	—	—	—	—
24	—	—	—	—	2,032	6,100	23,120	76,000
25	51,360	2,750	55,360	70,000	—	—	—	—

* Recovery from control culture untreated with serum $= 1176 \times 10^3$. I.U. = infective units.

amount still present at each point during incubation) reveals a loss of about 35%—thus agreeing with the similar growth curves noted in section (*a*). In comparison, the growth curve II of this experiment shows the amount of unneutralizable virus at the start, and during incubation, at points corresponding with curve I. At the start about 5% of the adsorbed virus was unneutralized. During incubation the amount of unneutralized virus did not decrease; if anything it rose slightly until growth began. This absence of fall is significant. It has already been shown that a fall in titre occurred when cells with adsorbed virus were incubated without the use of antiserum, as in section (*a*) above, and that a more marked fall of about 70% was seen on incubation of cells carrying unneutralizable virus (section (*b*) above). If all the cultures forming growth curve II had been treated with serum at the start, there would have been a fall in titre during incubation, as in section (*b*). The reason for its absence appears to be that virus continued to become unneutralizable during incubation, thus compensating for the loss of infectivity that was taking place concurrently. This virus may have penetrated the cells or it may have been on the surface but inaccessible to antiserum.

The second experiment in Table 3 confirmed this conclusion. Here the cultures from which the control growth curve (III) and the experimental one (IV) were obtained were set up simultaneously and had the same base line of unneutralizable virus. In curve III the unneutralizable virus was incubated and the titre fell by 65–70 % as expected. In curve IV, which was similar to curve II in the first experiment, the cells were incubated with all their adsorbed virus before treatment with antiserum and there was again no significant fall in titre.

In both experiments it was noticeable that increase of titre due to growth began earlier in the curves of unneutralized virus (curves II and IV) than in the others. This presumably reflects the continued conversion of neutralizable to unneutralizable virus and a corresponding increase in the amount of infecting virus.

The mechanism by which vaccinia virus combines with cells and initiates their infection is not understood. There is clearly a marked difference between the infectibility of the chorio-allantoic membrane *in situ* and HeLa cells in culture. Only a small proportion of the virus that infected the membranes infected HeLa cells. This may stem from an essential difference in type of cell, but possibly also from an alteration in the susceptibility of cells, depending on whether they are infected *in vivo* or *in vitro*. The data derived from the experiments reported here relate to HeLa cell cultures observed between the time of inoculation and the beginning of virus growth, and some features of adsorption and infection in this system have been clarified. The adsorption of elementary bodies to the cell did not always lead to virus multiplication. A large proportion of adsorbed virus remained neutralizable by antiserum and therefore non-infective. Some of the adsorbed virus, however, infected the cells almost immediately after contact. In contrast to virus which caused rapid initiation of infection, some adsorbed virus took longer, the process continuing for several hours. Further investigation is needed to decide how far this difference in rate of initiating infection is attributable to variability of the elementary bodies and how far to variability of the cells.

(d) Growth curve when cells with adsorbed virus were incubated in a medium containing antiserum

The most effective way to eliminate neutralizable virus is to incubate cells with adsorbed virus in a medium containing antiserum, replacing it with a serum-free medium before disintegration and titration.

After adsorption for 1 min. and washing, cultures were incubated in Eagle's medium containing 1/100 antiserum. Before disintegration the medium was removed, the cells were washed and Eagle's medium added. Controls to determine the amount of adsorbed virus were titrated before adding antiserum. In this system there was a marked decline in titre during the first few hours, but the virus did not entirely disappear and multiplied later.

In an attempt to determine how much of the decline was due to neutralization of virus by antiserum and how much, if any, was due to action of cells on the virus, the rate of neutralization of virus in suspension was compared with that of virus adsorbed on cells. But this was not an entirely valid comparison because virus on cells may not have been so readily accessible to antibody, owing to its physical environment, and neutralization may have been slower. Further, the neutralizing effect of antiserum on adsorbed virus might be considered to have ended when the initial rapid fall in titre became much slower. But again this is relative and cannot be assumed because some virus may be only slowly neutralized. Our conclusion therefore about this must remain tentative until further investigations have been made. A growth curve of this type is shown in Table 4.

Table 4. *Growth curve when cultures were incubated in Eagle's medium with* 1/100 *antiserum*

Period of incubation	Virus recovered (% of control)
Control (no serum)	100
1 min.	32·5
15 min.	18·3
30 min.	15·1
45 min.	9·2
1 hr.	10·0
2 hr.	9·4
3 hr.	5·5
4 hr.	5·8
5 hr.	4·3
6 hr.	2·8
7 hr.	4·8
8 hr.	3·9
9 hr.	1·8
10 hr.	6·4
11 hr.	5·2
12 hr.	6·8
13 hr.	3·4
24 hr.	171·4

Neutralization of virus in suspension was carried out at room temperature with antiserum diluted 1/200. Virus of titre 4×10^6 infective units/ml. was suspended in McIlvaine's buffer + 10 % skimmed milk, in which it was stable for some hours. For titration, samples were put in ice-cold solution and further diluted as necessary. The amount of virus on cells was $10–20 \times 10^3$ infective units/ml. and the final dilution of anti-serum was 1/100. The conditions of virus in suspension were therefore not strictly comparable with those of virus on cells.

With virus in suspension virtually the full neutralizing effect of anti-serum was obtained in about 15 min. On cells, about 75 % of virus was neutralized in 1 min. and thereafter the fall in titre slowed markedly. If one accepts the neutralization of virus in suspension as a guide and 15 min. as the time when maximum neutralization has occurred on cells, it appears that a considerable further loss of infectivity (about 80 %) was due to interaction with cells. If one allows a little longer for neutralization to be complete and 30 min. as the base line, the further loss of infectivity is still high, about 70–75 %. These figures are similar to the findings in (b), p. 191 above, when neutralization for 1 min. or 30 min. was carried out at the start of the incubation period and cultures were incubated in Eagle's medium.

On the other hand, the final amount of virus left in cells incubated in antiserum was but a small fraction, in the region of 2–4 %, of the total adsorbed virus and this amount did not differ greatly from the amount which was unneutralized in suspension. It might be argued that all the reduction of virus on cells was due to slow neutralization by the anti-serum. But this seems unlikely since, as noted in section (b), the fall in titre during incubation in antiserum, as seen in Table 4, was similar to that occurring when antiserum was left in contact for a short time and then removed before incubation. How efficiently or completely the anti-serum was removed has not been tested. But presumably pipetting off the antiserum, washing three times and adding fresh medium would reduce greatly the neutralizing effect so that further fall in infectivity of virus during incubation could be attributed to an interaction with cells rather than a continued action of serum. On balance therefore, with the evidence at present available, it seems probable that the fall in titre of virus adsorbed on cells and incubated in a medium containing antiserum was due partly to neutralization by antibody and partly to an interaction with cells.

Whether this action of the cells is to produce what is called an eclipse phase does not appear from these results. The loss of infectivity brought about by cells may, however, be related to the processes of viral multi-plication.

Titration of infected cells

In theory, if the loss of virus which occurs during incubation of infected cells is due to an eclipse phase, it should be possible to show that the number of infected cells does not decline in parallel with the fall in titre of virus. This proposition assumes that cells in a culture could at any time be adequately dispersed and that after transfer to the chorio-allantoic membrane each cell would remain sufficiently intact to ensure the multiplication of virus which would ultimately infect the membrane and produce one pock. Thus cells containing eclipsed virus would ultimately show that they were infected even though little or no virus could be obtained by disintegrating them, whereas, if the virus had been completely inactivated the cells would be non-infective.

The cultures of vaccinia in HeLa cell monolayers were particularly suitable for such experiments because almost all the virus was still in the cells even after incubation for 24 hr.; that is at a time when some multiplication had occurred. In cultures incubated with the total amount of adsorbed virus, about 1–1·5 % of the virus in the whole system was in the medium after incubation for 5 hr., and 0·1–0·7 % after 24 hr. To obtain cell suspensions from these cultures the medium was removed, the cell carpet treated with trypsin (0·25 % B.D.H. trypsin in phosphate buffered saline) for 15 min. at 37° and the medium replaced. Well dispersed cell suspensions were readily obtained by gentle pipetting. The cells were deposited in the centrifuge and the supernatant removed and titrated. The deposit of cells was re-suspended in Eagle's medium and titrated either intact or after disintegration.

In attempting experiments of this kind some unexpected sources of error were found. A surprising finding was that cells treated with trypsin released as much as 50 % of their virus into the supernatant, and this occurred after incubation for 7 or 24 hr. as well as at zero hours. Ethylenediaminetetra-acetic acid (EDTA), used in place of trypsin, also appeared to release virus from cells. This effect of trypsin was observed even when the cultures, after adsorption of virus, were incubated for 6 hr. in Eagle's medium containing 1/100 antiserum. Whatever the reason for this release of virus, titration of trypsinized cells will clearly not accurately measure the number of infected cells. Indeed, disintegrated and intact cells yielded the same amount of virus if the cells were dispersed first with trypsin or EDTA.

The experiments on these lines have not therefore assisted the main purpose of these studies. Nevertheless, the action of trypsin on cells containing virus seems well worth further investigation.

SUMMARY

An elementary-body suspension of a rabbit-skin-passaged strain of vaccinia was grown in monolayer cultures of HeLa cells in a chemically defined medium. Virus was recovered from cells by ultrasonic disintegration.

The amount of virus adsorbed by cells depended on its concentration and the duration of contact. Some virus was adsorbed in $\frac{1}{2}$–1 min., and the amount increased linearly with time during a period of 2 hr.

About 70 % of adsorbed virus was neutralized by antiserum in 1 min. and 85–90 % in 30 min. Neutralization was never complete. It is assumed that neutralizable virus had not yet entered the cell and that unneutralizable virus, although not necessarily all of it, was engaged in processes leading to penetration and replication. The actual situation of unneutralizable virus was not evident; it could have been inside the cells, or on the surface combined in such a way that it would soon penetrate and replicate, or possibly merely protected in some way by the surface without being able to advance further in the growth cycle.

Adsorbed virus was protected from the rapid inactivating action of the Eagle's medium in which the infected cells were incubated. There was little loss of the neutralizable fraction of adsorbed virus when cells were incubated in Eagle's medium for several hours.

During incubation of cells carrying adsorbed virus some of the neutralizable virus became unneutralizable; thus the processes leading to penetration of cells by adsorbed virus continued in a culture for several hours.

It would appear that, whatever the explanation may be, only a small fraction of the elementary bodies adsorbed to cells was able to multiply in them. Some elementary bodies penetrated cells very rapidly after adsorption, whereas others showed a considerable interval between adsorption and penetration. This raises questions about variability in the infectivity of virus, lack of uniformity of cells, the essential mechanism by which the virus enters the cell and the possible relation of adaptation to these factors.

When cells with adsorbed virus were incubated in Eagle's medium a fall in titre of 20–30 % occurred in 7–10 hr. An increase in titre due to growth was detectable in about 12 hr. When cells carrying only the unneutralizable fraction of adsorbed virus were similarly incubated a fall in titre of about 70 % during 8–10 hr. was found, and an increase due to growth, in 13–14 hr. This loss of virus appeared to be due to an action of cells on the virus. The action was a gradual one and there was neither a sudden nor rapid drop in titre.

An early or rapid loss of virus has not been noted in any of the experiments in spite of the fact that some virus very rapidly infected cells in the early stages of adsorption. But even if this virus did become rapidly 'eclipsed' its amount would probably be too small to be detected.

In experiments with cells carrying unneutralizable virus, virus never disappeared completely. About 20–30 % remained and the opinion may be held that this is the virus which eventually multiplied. There is no evidence from these experiments for or against this view.

When cells with adsorbed virus were incubated in medium containing antiserum there was a marked decline in titre during several hours; this seems to have been caused by neutralization at first, and later by an action of cells on the virus. Growth of virus occurred.

In cultures of infected cells incubated in Eagle's medium virtually all the virus was in the cells, at least up to 24 hr. Attempts to titrate infected cells by making trypsinized suspensions from the monolayer cultures failed because the trypsin caused up to 50 % of the virus to be released from cells into the medium. Ethylenediaminetetra-acetic acid also caused a similar release of virus. The reason for this is not at present understood.

There is no certainty from these experiments that the loss of infectivity of adsorbed virus which has been attributed, on the balance of evidence, to interaction with cells, indicates an eclipse phase, although this is one possible interpretation of the findings. The loss of infectivity brought about by cell-virus interaction may in some way be part of a multiplication process, but these experiments do not afford any evidence for or against that interpretation.

REFERENCES

EAGLE, H. (1955). The specific amino acid requirements of a human carcinoma cell (strain HeLa) in tissue culture. *J. exp. Med.* **102**, 37.

HOAGLAND, C. L., SMADEL, J. E. & RIVERS, T. M. (1940). Constituents of elementary bodies of vaccinia. I. Certain basic analyses and observations on lipid components of the virus. *J. exp. Med.* **71**, 737.

MACPHERSON, I. A. (1958). The liberation of cell-bound vaccinia virus by ultrasonic vibration. *J. Hyg., Camb.* **56**, 29.

THE CHEMICAL APPROACH TO THE STUDY OF ANIMAL VIRUS GROWTH

P. D. COOPER

Virus Culture Laboratory, Medical Research Council Laboratories, Carshalton, Surrey

Abbreviations used in this article are: pfu = plaque forming unit, TCD_{50} = tissue culture dose infective for 50 % of the cultures, RNA = ribonucleic acid, DNA = deoxyribonucleic acid, CPE = cytopathogenic effect.

DEFINITION OF SCOPE

There are, broadly speaking, four levels of complexity at which one can study an animal virus infection: (*a*) the events inside a cell, (*b*) the events inside an organ, (*c*) the events inside an animal, (*d*) the events inside a population of animals. Each has its own importance and information is needed on all for reasons both academic and applied. However, understanding all ultimately depends upon understanding the first. The study of the first in isolation has only recently been technically feasible, and it is an important task of modern virology to emulate the bacteriology of the late nineteenth century in the study of the micro-organism in its simplest environment. Therefore the 'virus growth' here given a chemical approach will mean the way in which virus progeny are produced from an infected animal cell.

GENERAL VIEW OF THE PROBLEM

The intricacies of animal virus growth are still hidden from humankind, particularly during the important 'eclipse' phase, and a direct way to reveal them is to make the correct chemical analyses. Unfortunately this has proved to be quite difficult, partly because unsuitable systems have prevented strict interpretation (Bauer, 1953); more recently, cell culture has in some degree allowed the use of the fruitful methods familiar to bacteriophage work (in particular the habit of thinking of an animal virus infection in terms of the fate of an individual cell, whatever the size of the population studied).

It is clear, however, from the limited data to hand that such a discipline has not ended our troubles. The animal cell, unlike the bacterial cell, is so large compared with its virus yield that small changes may be masked, and big changes are suspect as they may be unrelated to the primary growth process. The difficulty in choosing the 'correct' chemical analyses then becomes apparent and is still very much with us.

Furthermore, what might be called the overall mechanics of infection are still obscure, and a prior knowledge of them is most important in the design of the most informative chemical experiments. For example, mutual exclusion between virus particles may or may not occur; it is not useful to employ high multiplicities of labelled virus to look for the site of nucleic acid replication if 99 % of the label is diverted by genetic exclusion. Chemists might indeed feel that any chemical investigation is premature until the system is better understood biologically.

Happily for us this feeling has not been general, and this reviewer does in fact find himself with material for his review. This contribution will first consider current experience of experimental pitfalls, then review recent work using a chemical approach to simplified cell-virus systems and lastly attempt a synthesis and discuss indications for further work.

SOME FURTHER RESTRICTIONS

It is necessary to restrict somewhat further the scope of this contribution. Cytochemical aspects, including fluorescence and fluorescent-antibody microscopy, are a legitimate if qualitative chemical approach but will be the concern of other contributors to this symposium. Growth-curve studies using serological techniques will also not be included.

Chemical work relating to virus structure *per se*, while very relevant to virus growth, is properly the subject of others and will not be included unless directly contributing to knowledge of the growth cycle. Some effects of inhibitors and substrates on virus growth, perhaps the inverse of the present topic, have been reviewed by Tamm (1958). Studies on the action of chemotherapeutic agents undoubtedly did, or will, give information on the normal growth pathways which they disturb, but experience with the antibiotics suggests that interpretation is a lengthy business. The main lesson from the use of inhibitors so far is that the cell-virus complex has a very similar metabolism to that of the uninfected cell.

The main restrictions will arise, however, because it is not felt useful at this stage to discuss work which cannot give a direct idea of the fate of a single infected cell. It is in any case probable that most current work, even when ideally planned, cannot be interpreted in precise chemical terms, but in some cases it can at least be said that certain things do or do not happen to a cell-virus complex at a particular stage of its development. These can be reproduced in other laboratories, despite small differences in technique leading to perhaps growth cycles of differing length, and one can hope that such facts will in time build a composite detailed picture. It is therefore disappointing to find that, despite the clear lessons of the last ten years in all aspects of virus work, extensive chemical work is still being done with the unsuitable systems or concepts which were the only ones available ten or twenty years ago. Some reasons for their unsuitability are discussed in the next section.

CRITERIA FOR SUITABILITY OF EXPERIMENTS

It is essential that some at least of the following criteria should be strictly applied to any virus-cell system intended for chemical study. Similar criteria have been discussed by Dulbecco (1955), but with emphasis more on suitability for infectivity than for biochemical studies.

One-step growth

Probably the most important single criterion is that one-step growth conditions must apply. The importance of this is that very many chemical changes must occur in an infected cell as its passes from the normal healthy state to the final stages of lysis and complete disintegration. Thus it is of little interest to record a change unless one can say to what aspect of virus growth it relates. The simplest form of one-step growth system is the single cell, but chemical methods are mostly too insensitive for such very small samples. Furthermore, chemical handling usually destroys the cell-virus complex, so that to cover all stages of infection one needs a number of single cells large enough to overcome their individual asynchrony, which may itself be large. It is therefore easier to use a large cell population in the hope that this represents a fair average, but it is clearly essential that *all* cells should be at a nearly identical stage of virus development. One-step virus growth *per se* can be obtained in any cell population if subsequent or previous growth cycles are isolated, for example, by cell dilution, short time-sequences or the use of an anti-serum, but chemical studies further demand that one-step growth be applied to the whole culture, as the infected cells cannot be segregated for chemical handling. The metabolism of even a small proportion of healthy cells may mask changes due to virus, and the presence of cells in advanced stages will obscure early changes in later starters. Several authors have taken the trouble to record absence of change in systems where most cells were not infected.

Thus all cells present must be infected at the beginning of the experiment and samples should be taken for chemical assay at intervals during the complete cycle of virus growth (this may not apply to the use of labelled virus). As we now conceive it, the virus cycle consists of (*a*) virus adsorption, (*b*) penetration, (*c*) growth (of apparently non-infective units), (*d*) maturation (becoming infective), (*e*) release.

Examples of systems in which these conditions cannot be fulfilled are intracerebral inoculations, infections of minced-tissue suspensions and of chorio-allantoic membranes in intact or de-embryonated eggs or as *in vitro* pieces. Allantoic cells in the intact egg (but not as pieces *in vitro* because of the presence of differently reacting cell types), on the other hand, are suitable for some experiments with labelled virus, although they suffer from the difficulty of disrupting the cells cleanly. Minced tissue is not suitable, owing to the presence of many dead cells.

In vitro *versus* in vivo

To study a disease itself one must at some stage consider the intact animal, but to study the simplest cell–virus relationships the animal must be eliminated. Use of an intact animal will vitiate all the criteria here proposed, but another reason for avoiding animals is the complication of their hormonal and specific and non-specific defence responses; these need looking at separately.

Virus assay

It is essential to measure infective virus, and not rely solely on other methods of assay such as haemagglutinin titration. The most accurate and sensitive methods applicable should be used and methods such as pock or plaque assays are much preferable to limiting dilution assays. Occasionally one has to choose between an accurate method and a sensitive one, and in this case the best, if perhaps more tiresome, course is to avoid the choice by using both. This is important, as one should define the stage of virus growth precisely; clearly an accurate assay helps this, but one needs to know the largest amount of infective virus involved (for example, to calculate the multiplicity of infection, the end of the latent period or the non-infective particles), so that the titration must also be sensitive. Virus non-infective for one system but infective for another (as detected by systems of different sensitivity) constitutes a form of incomplete virus, which is discussed below as a hazard in interpretation. For these reasons also it is clear that virus must be released into a fluid medium and not extracted in unknown yield from intact tissue.

Early changes the most important

As mentioned above, since the cell eventually dies and disappears almost entirely, there must ultimately be many large changes. Probably the bulk of these can be regarded as remote effects of virus action rather than effects intimately connected with virus growth and their elucidation may arouse scant interest. It follows that most chemical attention should be given to early phases of the growth cycle, particularly the latent and early release phases.

Purity and reproducibility of system

It is self-evident that ideally one should have pure (clone-picked) virus and cell systems, that virus growth curves and assays should be highly reproducible, and that one should be able to take representative samples easily. Unhappily, for many systems this is still easier (or more often) said than done; use of cell suspensions rather than monolayers simplifies the sampling problem, but may increase the proportion of non-viable cells unless adapted to growth in suspension.

HAZARDS OF INTERPRETATION DUE TO MIXED OR MULTIPLE INFECTION

The foregoing section describes means of resolving known technical hazards of interpretation. Further difficulties still exist which are only partly understood at present, and which all stem from the likelihood of a cell receiving more than one particle, dead or alive. They may or may not apply to all systems, but when appreciated should be resolvable. Unlike those of the foregoing section, experiments with these pitfalls are likely to be very informative because the growth processes are directly modified rather than merely obscured, but such modifications will be mistaken for the original processes unless they can first be noticed and eliminated.

Exclusion and interference by inactivated virus particles

It appears that, like phage, adsorption of a very small number of inactivated Newcastle disease virus particles (Baluda, 1957) can rapidly prevent the growth of identical particles adsorbing subsequently (exclusion). On the other hand, dilute passage stocks of vesicular stomatitis virus (VSV) (Cooper, 1958 b) and influenza virus (Frazer, 1953) are free of this difficulty in that homotypic exclusion or interference does not develop in the time usually employed for adsorption. It is clear that if most of added, isotopically labelled virus is 'excluded' in this way little information can be obtained regarding transmission of label to progeny, although much information on exclusion mechanisms may result. Similarly, interference without exclusion, as shown by reduced rate of virus release, may occur in a cell multiply infected with live virus, although this does not apply to VSV (Cooper, 1958 a); the effect of interference and exclusion on the chemical pathways involved is unknown, as are the pathways themselves.

'Incomplete' virus

Apart from the influenza group, several ether-sensitive viruses such as VSV (Cooper & Bellett, 1958), Rift Valley fever virus (Mims, 1956), and western equine encephalomyelitis virus (Chambers, 1957) may give rise to transmissible interfering components, which, in influenza at least, can be labelled 'incomplete' virus as they are easily recognized serologically as similar to the infective particle. It should be noted that 'incomplete' is not a very satisfactory term, since it has developed a number of different meanings in different hands. The interference of the VSV transmissible interfering component (present in stocks serially passaged undiluted) is manifest largely as exclusion.

Thus the avoidance of multiple infection with live or killed particles is not sufficient to ensure freedom from complications due to exclusion or interference. Like that of influenza virus, the transmissible interfering component of VSV is formed on serial undiluted passage; for viruses other than influenza, however, the dilutions and times of harvest of seed pools are rarely given in published articles on virus growth.

Two special difficulties which are similar are (a) the excess of noninfective over infective particles present in, for example, poliovirus (Schwerdt & Fogh, 1957), and (b) differing sensitivities of two assay systems, for example, HeLa cells and chorio-allantoic membranes for herpesvirus (Newton & Stoker, 1958). In both cases fully or partly (that is, for one cell type only) inactivated virus may be present, or all particles may be potentially infective but with a low or variable probability of achieving infection. In the latter case it may be that the probability of interference is higher than that of infection, in which case the excess of particles will function as 'incomplete'.

Interferon

The discovery of a viral product which is unlike a virus particle and which interferes with virus growth (Isaacs & Lindenmann, 1957) means that complications may exist even with a single multiplicity of 'complete' virus fully infective for the system used. Here, as with 'incomplete' VSV, one does not have as simple a serological guide as with incomplete influenza virus; thus the need for purified virus as an inoculum becomes apparent and this need has been almost entirely overlooked so far. Some other virus preparations also contain 'toxic' components (Pereira & Kelly, 1957; Ackermann, Payne & Kurtz, 1958).

Shortened latency

In some viruses (Cooper, 1958*a*), increasing the multiplicity of infection decreased the time before appearance of the first progeny particle; that is, shortened the latent period. Two possible explanations among others are that virus grows as a pool equally accessible to all adsorbing virus, and/or that there is a probability of delay in starting an infection which becomes less the more particles are added. Whatever the explanation, there is no guarantee that the chemical changes, particularly the early ones, will be the same for single and multiple infection.

Lysis-from-without

Infected animal cells do not 'burst' in quite the same way as bacteria and such a mechanism for releasing virus from enclosure within a thick rigid cell wall is not necessary. Poliovirus does not appear prematurely to damage monkey kidney cells up to a multiplicity of 1000 particles per cell (Fogh, 1955). Nevertheless, possible damage should be sought when contemplating experiments with very high multiplicities.

Multiplicity reactivation

Multiplicity reactivation is not noticeable in u.v.- or heat-inactivated VSV preparations (Cooper, 1958*a*, *b*), although marker recombination has been found in inactivated influenza virus preparations (Gotlieb & Hirst, 1956). The complication may arise in, for example, experiments with isotopically labelled virus, where some cells receive a single live virus particle and others receive several inactive particles; the chemical mechanisms of producing progeny may be different in the different cells, again particularly in the early stages.

HAZARDS OF INTERPRETATION DUE TO
PROBABILITY EFFECTS

Due to the Poisson distribution of adsorbed virus, and the likelihood that even virus particles simultaneously adsorbed at the same multiplicity may not start growing at the same time, it is likely that the chemical changes in a population of multiply-infected cells will be neither synchronous nor identical. The presence of shortened latency makes such asynchrony inevitable for VSV (Cooper, 1957*a*, 1958*a*), and this difficulty seems unavoidable where one insists on multiple infection yet cannot handle a single cell.

The only recourse seems to be to say that this may not matter very much providing the discrepancies are small or cancel one another, so that one can observe an average (although an average of what is open to question). The greatest difficulty is to decide whether to ascribe a small effect to a small change in all the cells or to a big change in some, perhaps in those few which happen to be very advanced in lysis, that is at a stage less relevant to the main mechanisms of growth.

THE IDEAL EXPERIMENT

To illustrate all these difficulties it may be helpful to construct an ideal experiment as a basis for following the chemical changes accompanying virus growth in animal cells. Leaving aside the beautiful but unrealizable concept of performing successive quantitative chemical assays on the same single cell throughout a growth cycle, we are left with the usual cell population.

The experiment should run as follows: the cells are first derived by a minimum number of subcultures from a single cell, and maintained frozen as a master culture. Thus cells for all experiments have the same history, as they are derived from this master. A thick agitated suspension of such cells in buffered saline is completely infected with virus under conditions where adsorption is complete before growth begins. The virus seed has been derived from a single plaque, has been maintained by a minimal number of dilute-passage subcultures from a master stock, and is free of incomplete, inactivated and interfering particles; 1 infectious unit = 1 electron-microscopic particle. The virus is completely stable at 37°, and the seeds used have been extensively purified chemically and physically before use. Since the cells are also growing systems, their growth processes have been synchronized or halted, but 100 % of the cells present are still viable, or at least able to liberate the maximum yield of virus. Surface damage, by, for example, trypsin or versene, has been overcome before the experiment is started. After adsorption, free unadsorbed virus is eliminated, and virus growth started in all cells at once, still in suspension in a completely defined synthetic medium and under conditions where virus readsorption does not occur. After a short time for penetration, adsorbed virus which has not penetrated is also eliminated. Samples are then taken for total-cell, infected-cell, and free-virus assays. At intervals during the entire growth cycle samples are removed for chemical and infectious unit assays in both cell and supernatant fractions; infectious units are measured at once by plaque assay in the most sensitive system available. Virus growth is rapid and yield per cell is high (for example, 1000 pfu/cell).

The multiplicity and state of infecting virus, etc., can of course be varied, inhibitors can be used to detect different stages, and the possibilities for chemical and other assays are large; clearly the more different are the assays made on the same system under different conditions the more detailed can be the conclusions.

The results are then interpreted in terms of the events occurring during virus adsorption, penetration, organization into a replicating form, vegetative growth, maturation and release or other stages detected, and correlated with existing information on virus structure (for example, RNA or DNA content, number and nature of lipid or protein subunits) and with information from cytochemical studies, for which monolayer cultures may be more suitable.

Although this form of presentation is necessarily somewhat naïve, it should suffice to show that no published experiments are ideal, and that the obstacles to such an ideal are formidable. It is also little consolation to the animal virologist to know that the bacterial virologist has had almost such a system available with much less effort for many years; consequently much of the preceding sections will surprise phage workers by stating the obvious yet again. Nevertheless, technical difficulties are still so considerable for the animal virologist that the obvious needs restating.

WHERE TO LOOK

One further source of difficulty needs mention. It derives from the fact that the animal cell is a relatively large and complicated structure, containing at least four 'compartments' (namely, nucleus, mitochondria, microsomes, soluble fraction), some of them with double membranes and nearly all themselves highly complex structurally when observed under the electron microscope. When considering that each structure must contain extremely complex chemical pathways, one might be excused some despair of being able to unravel anything useful. Our methods of dissecting cells for examination are still very crude, and methods for separating the contained chemical fractions not much better.

Clearly one needs some sort of a lead, for example from the early fate of labelled virus RNA, or early cytological changes. It is not certain whether cell-virus systems showing large early changes are better than those showing small ones, since the small ones may be the more simple to follow. The writer is inclined to feel that a good approach to this problem will not be apparent until we have better techniques and more information on the general behaviour of the system (for example, whether the nucleic acid of the particular virus is synthesized in the nucleus and the protein in the cytoplasm).

CURRENT INFORMATION ON PARTICULAR VIRUSES

In such an early stage, it is inevitable that chemical information on intracellular growth mechanisms will come to hand in a piecemeal fashion. So as to derive as much order as possible, work which can definitely be interpreted in terms of happenings at the cellular level will be summarized below under the heading of the individual virus.

Poliovirus

Several very marked changes have been observed during poliovirus growth. Maassab, Loh & Ackermann (1957) studied one-step growth of poliovirus type 1 (Mahoney) in HeLa cell cultures using sufficient virus to infect all cells initially, and followed the phosphate changes in DNA and in cytoplasmic and nuclear RNA. Starting within an hour of infection the total cytoplasmic RNA phosphate increased 2–3-fold over control values. This was substantiated by a simultaneous increase in the rate of cytoplasmic RNA ^{32}P incorporation, which continued up to 7 hr., and then declined, whilst the first infective virus particle appeared in the 'average' cell at about 3 hr. Thus virus maturation was preceded by a large synthesis of cytoplasmic RNA, at least some of the phosphorus coming from inorganic phosphate. The interest of this finding is enhanced by the fact that poliovirus contains RNA rather than DNA (Schwerdt & Schaffer, 1956). There was also a simultaneous but smaller incorporation into DNA and nuclear RNA.

More recently, Ackermann (1958) has found that the base ratios of the newly formed cytoplasmic RNA are very similar to those of uninfected cytoplasm and quite distinct from those of the virus, so that this does not seem to be a cytoplasmic accumulation of virus RNA. There was a large early increase in protein.

The further interpretation of these findings runs into the difficulties encountered by Cooper (1957a, b). For example, in the poliovirus studies, cytoplasmic 'RNA' phosphate was separated by the Schneider method, and no attempt was recorded of a separation from phosphoprotein and hot-acid-labile phosphates which occur in significant amount in animal cells. Also, separation of nuclei may extract loosely bound components so that more than one cell-fractionation procedure is desirable; the cytoplasm itself contains many particulate and soluble components. Smaller but still significant changes also occurred in the nucleus, and it is possible for an animal virus—for example, that of vesicular stomatitis (Cooper, 1957b)—to grow well with much smaller chemical changes than those of poliovirus. Thus one cannot decide from these results whether or not poliovirus RNA is replicated in the nucleus or the cytoplasm. Nevertheless, the presence of such large and early changes makes poliovirus in cell culture seem an interesting system for further study.

Miroff, Cornatzer & Fischer (1957) have also investigated the uptake of ^{32}P into various phosphate fractions of the HeLa cell in monolayer culture during infection with type 1 (Mahoney) poliovirus. The inoculum was insufficient to infect more than 30 % of the cells initially, but the ^{32}P uptake of the uninfected cells was sufficiently low (perhaps because a non-growth-producing maintenance medium was used) to detect changes from control cell values during the early part of the first cycle (up to 4 hr. after infection). In support of the findings of Maassab *et al.* (1957), there was an increase in specific activity of total nucleic acid (Schneider separation) and phospholipid fractions. Virus yields appeared atypically low, however (less than 10 TCD_{50} per cell after a full cycle): methods of preparing seed pools were not given.

On the other hand, Goldfine, Koppelman & Evans (1958) found that, during one-step growth of poliovirus type 3 in HeLa cells completely infected with a high multiplicity, the rate of incorporation of cytidine ^{14}C into RNA was slightly less than in the controls during the first half of the cycle (up to 5 hr. after infection), returning to normal later (up to 11 hr.). This may indicate that the rate of *de novo* synthesis of bases was increased. The incorporation into DNA was greatly decreased during this time.

Some information is also available, in general terms, of the effect of poliovirus infection on the metabolism of small molecules. Levy & Baron (1957) compared glycolysis and uptake of ^{14}C glycine by monkey kidney cell monolayers untreated and infected with type 3 poliovirus at a multiplicity of 70. Lactic acid production was noticeably faster by the first hour after infection in this one-step growth system, and the high rate continued until the 7th hour, when it fell to control values. The effect was also found with partially purified virus. The virus stimulation occurred with anaerobic as well as aerobic glycolysis, so that it was not due simply to blockage of oxygen pathways; infected cells also showed the Pasteur effect. Therefore presumably the changes represent an overall increase of glucose utilization, rather than a switch from one pathway to another. On the other hand, glycine uptake was much slowed by infection, being manifest by the first hour, and continuing all through the cycle.

Becker, Grossowicz & Bernkopf (1958) found very similar changes in the uptake of glucose during one-step growth of type 2 (MEF$_1$) poliovirus on human amnion or monkey kidney cell monolayers. Sufficient virus was added to infect all cells initially (multiplicity = 5), and in comparison with identically treated uninfected cells the infected cells used very much more glucose during the period immediately preceding the bulk of virus release (0–10 hr. after infection). The rate of glucose uptake later fell to control values. The rate of phosphate uptake was also higher in the first 10 hr., but the phosphorus that accumulated was soon afterwards released into the medium. Cyanide, azide and fluoroacetate increased the glucose utilization of infected cells even more than that of controls, without affecting virus yields. It seems, therefore, that anaerobic glycolytic pathways can be used for virus synthesis, but the oxidative ones also play a part.

This conclusion is also derived from the observation that poliovirus grew in the apparent absence of oxygen, but the provision of oxygen as air greatly increased the virus growth rate (Gifford & Syverton, 1957). It was noted that the cells (HeLa and monkey kidney) behaved like facultative anaerobes in the absence of virus.

Ackermann, Rabson & Kurtz (1954) found that *p*-fluorophenylalanine inhibited viral synthesis during one-step poliovirus growth in HeLa cell monolayer cultures. The inhibition was reversed by phenylalanine, provided this was added within 6 hr. of adding the inhibitor. Although virus growth was stopped, CPE was not. Eagle & Habel (1956) found that salts, dialysed serum, glucose and glutamine were the only nutriments necessary for maximum virus yields, but glucose could be largely replaced by a group of other nutriments added together. Some interesting observations of considerable significance to pathogenicity studies, but of as yet unknown significance to growth studies, are the growth requirements of some strains for the bicarbonate ion (Vogt, Dulbecco & Wenner, 1957) and cystine (Dubes, 1956).

Kovacs (1956 *a*, *b*) has presented much data on the effect of poliovirus *in vitro* on various nucleases and phosphatases, mostly using monkey kidney cells in roller-tube culture. Although most of the changes are decreases, many appear before CPE and may therefore have a bearing on processes of virus growth rather than cell lysis, but since one-step growth was not used, the stage of the growth cycle at which changes commence is unknown.

In summary, therefore, poliovirus-infected cells show a generalized, enhanced metabolism in the eclipse period in which one might expect virus synthesis to be most active. These changes were largely cytoplasmic. The cytological changes which are also apparent at this time are largely nuclear (Dunnebacke, 1956).

Adenovirus

Fisher & Ginsberg (1957) investigated the reasons for the more acid appearance of HeLa cell cultures infected with type 4 adenovirus. They found that this was due to stimulation of glycolysis resulting in a higher production of non-volatile acids (lactic, pyruvic, acetic and α-keto-glutaric). In the case of lactate, at least, the proportion of glucose converted to non-volatile acid was unchanged by infection, so that, as with poliovirus, the overall utilization of glucose was increased 3–5 fold during the complete period of virus growth without any overt rearrangement of pathways. One-step growth conditions were not used, however, so that one cannot say at which stage the increase occurred; the authors point out that it cannot be said whether or not increased glucose utilization is an inherent part of adenovirus growth.

Levy and co-workers (1957) described several metabolic changes during one-step growth of adenovirus type 2 in HeLa cells. All cells were infected initially, and the changes were not due to the component giving early CPE, but to the virus itself; adenovirus, however, may be a difficult biochemical subject because of a high degree of asynchrony during infection. Levy *et al.* found within 2–4 hr. a great increase in the incorporation rate of ^{32}P phosphate into all phosphate fractions without any effect on their total concentrations, and of glycine-2-^{14}C into the acid-soluble fraction. They also found an increase in lactic acid production, but were able to show that this occurred much later (8–24 hr. after infection).

Newcastle disease virus (NDV)

Franklin, Rubin & Davis (1957) prepared purified NDV containing ^{32}P. They found that while some acid-soluble phosphorus could be lost without loss of infectivity, the phospholipid could not, even if removed enzymically. Rubin & Franklin (1957) used this labelled virus to show that most virus particles neutralized by adsorbing a very few antibody molecules could adsorb to chick lung epithelial cells *in vitro* without entering them. They felt therefore that 'viropexis' (engulfment by the cell) could only account for a small proportion of successful viral penetrations, and that the usual mechanism was more rapid and specific, perhaps enzymic.

Vesicular stomatitis virus (VSV)

Cooper (1957b) compared the paths of phosphate transfer in normal chick embryo cell monolayer cultures with those completely infected with VSV under conditions of one-step growth. In view of the small changes found, some pains were taken to ensure that these conditions did in fact apply, and that substantially all cells were able to liberate good yields of virus (Cooper,1955, 1957 *a*); however, purified virus seeds could not be used. The rates of transfer (gain, loss or exchange) of ^{32}P between acid-soluble inorganic and organic phosphates, lipid, RNA and DNA phosphates, were all unaffected until uptake ceased in most fractions soon after the end of the latent period; the only other change was a 30–50 % decrease in sucrose-soluble RNA towards the end of the exponential release, which may be the first stage of lysis in a minority of early-starting cells. Cell particulates appeared undamaged by this time, although at 20 hr., when CPE was extensive, most of the cellular ^{32}P from all fractions was released into the medium. Thus the early changes due to virus synthesis must be quite small; those found indicated an overall inhibition of metabolism. Meanwhile Turco (1959), concurrently using the same system in the same laboratory, found the same in general but also a small but significant change in the RNA base ratios of the nucleus, the mitochondria-plus-microsomes and of the sucrose-soluble fraction. The relative proportion of uridylic acid increased; in '^{32}P gain' experiments (^{32}P moving into the cells) the relative specific activity of uridylic acid dropped progressively, but in '^{32}P loss' experiments it rose slightly. The other nucleotides were unaffected. This suggested the coincidental sythesis of virus nucleic acid and a copious new high-uridine RNA, with equivalent loss of old RNA; the new RNA, although of unknown relation to virus material, was equivalent to very much more than the infective virus yield.

Evidence was also presented (Cooper, 1957 *c*) that the cells possessed a phosphate-impermeable membrane which allowed reciprocal transport of phosphate by presumably specific mechanisms. The rate of phosphate exchange across this membrane was used to show that VSV could enter, grow within, and leave the host cell without grossly damaging the cell surface.

Fowl plague virus

Wecker & Schäfer (1957*b*) completely infected chick embryo cells in monolayer culture with a low multiplicity (1–2) of purified fowl plague virus labelled with ^{32}P (Wecker & Schäfer, 1956). Chorio-allantoic membrane pieces were treated similarly. The virus was allowed to grow for periods up to 3 hr., when the cells were harvested, washed and homogenized. Between one-third and one-half of the ^{32}P was then extractable with water, the rest being firmly bound to the cell debris. Of the extract, nearly one-half was not sedimented by centrifugation sufficient to sediment intact virus; some of this 'soluble' material was precipitated by antisera to *gebundenes antigen* (which can be obtained from purified intact virus by ether treatment, Schäfer, 1957). The remaining ^{32}P was in phospholipid, acid-soluble phosphate and free RNA (that is, lysed by ribonuclease).

Thus on infection some fowl plague virus seemed to break down to *gebundenes antigen*, plus smaller-molecule phosphates and soluble RNA which may or may not be derived from *gebundenes antigen*. However, most of the ^{32}P remained attached to the cell debris; also the haemagglutinin: pfu ratios (Wecker & Schäfer, 1956) of the purified virus seed suggest the presence of a large excess of non-infectious haemagglutinin, so that these very interesting results must be interpreted with caution at present.

The virus particle, 70 mμ diameter, is composed of lipid and two particulate protein-containing components, the haemagglutinin (HA), 30 mμ diameter, and the *gebundenes antigen*, 10–15 mμ diameter, which latter also contains the bulk of the RNA (Schäfer, 1957). Franklin (1958 d) compared the effect of proflavine on the intracellular appearance of infective virus, the soluble antigen (which closely resembles *gebundenes antigen*) and the HA of fowl plague virus, in chick embryo cell monolayers. He found that HA and virus synthesis were inhibited at much lower proflavine doses than was soluble antigen, and the former showed much more nearly 'single-hit' exponential dose-response relationships than the latter. Soluble antigen appeared first in the nucleus, whereas HA appeared first in the cytoplasm (Breitenfeld & Schäfer, 1957; Franklin, 1958 b), and several papers were quoted which suggested that proflavine will inhibit cytoplasmic more than nuclear syntheses.

Influenza virus

Hoyle & Frisch-Niggemeyer (1955) examined the fate of purified ^{32}P-labelled influenza virus after infection of the allantoic sac *in ovo*. After 1½ hr. when about half the radioactivity was adsorbed to the cells, part of the ^{32}P recovered from the disintegrated membranes was found, as in the case of fowl plague virus, to be in material of smaller particle size than the intact virus. The remainder was attached to the cell debris, but was eluted with molar sodium chloride. The fate of the RNA ^{32}P was not clear-cut and probably represented a mixture of fates; little further can be deduced since the chemical and physical separation methods employed would not rigorously define the various fractions obtained.

Again, a difficulty of these experiments is the possible presence of non-infectious haemagglutinin and the need to use large multiplicities of infection in order to detect the small quantities of label, although homotypic exclusion may not be important in influenza virus infections

(Frazer, 1953). A further snag which seems inherent with the myxovirus group, and possibly with all ether-sensitive viruses, is the presence of large amounts of phospholipid ^{32}P which may be rapidly broken down in the cell and may enter the metabolic pool, thus obscuring the fate of the labelled virus nucleic acid.

Hoyle & Finter (1957) have similarly examined the fate of influenza virus labelled with ^{35}S-methionine. Their results also indicated a minor but rapid change of physical or chemical state. At least 20 % of the protein ^{35}S changed to small molecular weight material within $1\frac{1}{2}$ hr., and the rest became associated with some poorly soluble component. All haemagglutinin and 98 % of the infectivity was lost.

One can therefore say that some of the invading virus particles were broken down to smaller pieces, but the fate of the remainder is unknown. Which group leads to infective progeny is also unknown.

Liu (1956) also found that, of the purified ^{32}P-labelled influenza virus which adsorbed to the cells of the allantoic sac, some alcohol-soluble ^{32}P appeared to be transferred to the cold acid-soluble fraction within 6 hr., but the hot acid-soluble fraction did not change. However, nearly all of the virus ^{32}P added to the eggs appeared unchanged but did not adsorb, although most of the haemagglutinin and infectivity was lost; perhaps this was due to non-specific virus inhibitors which may also have affected the adsorbed virus.

Henle, Girardi & Henle (1955) used the incorporation of ^{32}P to show that the small amounts of haemagglutinin found in HeLa cell cultures after influenza virus infection was not residual inoculum but did in fact arise from *de novo* production of a form of incomplete virus. The cells were destroyed, despite the fact that little infective virus was produced.

Ackermann & Maassab (1955) were able to indicate two stages of influenza virus development, the earlier of the two inhibited by methoxinine and the later by *p*-fluorophenylalanine. Between 4 and 6 hr. after infection virus synthesis appeared to pass through a stage after which it was insensitive to both inhibitors.

An observation (Le Clerc, 1957; Burnet, Lind & Perry, 1957) which may have important implications is that influenza virus infections pass through a stage early in the latent period in which they are relatively sensitive to ribonuclease; influenza virus contains RNA, which seems likely to be responsible for the infectivity (Ada & Perry, 1956).

Herpes virus

Newton & Stoker (1958) followed chemically the change in nucleic acid content during one-step growth of herpes virus in HeLa cell monolayer cultures, when all cells were infected initially. In comparison with controls they found a marked increase of DNA per cell which started well within the eclipse phase. Even after 72 hr., when the DNA per cell was doubled, all DNA was confined to the nucleus. The total DNA produced was very much larger than might be accounted for by infective virus progeny, and it would be interesting to compare its base ratios with those of host cell and virus. RNA was not affected. Electron microscopical and fluorescent-antibody studies in the literature were quoted which also suggest that this virus is synthesized in the nucleus.

SOME GENERALIZATIONS

Viewed in the light of the disciplinary restrictions which are discussed in the preliminary sections, the foregoing summaries show that we have, as yet, little detailed chemical information on the intracellular growth of any one animal virus. Nevertheless, certain findings, when coupled with measurements of infectivity, may permit some generalizations.

A most important property which now gives good promise of being general among RNA viruses is that infective material can be extracted in the form of free RNA rather than necessarily bound as virus ribonucleoprotein. The viruses for which this information is now available are those of Mengo encephalitis (Colter, Bird & Brown, 1957), poliomyelitis type 2 and West Nile encephalitis (Colter, Bird, Moyer & Brown, 1957), eastern equine encephalomyelitis (Wecker & Schäfer, 1957a), poliomyelitis type 1 (Alexander et al. 1957), Semliki forest (Cheng, 1958), foot-and-mouth disease (Brown, Sellers & Stewart, 1958), and encephalomyocarditis (EMC) (Huppert & Sanders, 1958).

In general the RNA preparations were more infective in vivo than in vitro, and some question of cellular 'competence' may be involved. Several criteria have been held to show that the infectivity is in fact due to free RNA, but Huppert & Sanders (1958) have shown that the only reliable criterion of this is its sensitivity to ribonuclease, the other criteria at best showing only that the infectivity behaves somewhat differently from intact virus at comparable infectivity concentrations.

An interesting outcome of the work with EMC virus is that the extraction procedure used did not yield infective RNA from purified EMC virus per se but only from a component of infected cells or crude lysates sedimenting more slowly than virus and which was resistant to ribonuclease. Infective RNA of the other viruses was all extracted from cell homogenates or crude or partially purified lysates. One's thoughts turn in this connection to the 'soluble antigen', a virus-specific microsome-like small particle component (7–15 mμ) of unknown function nearly universally present in cells infected with the smaller animal viruses, and, in the case of fowl plague virus at least, containing RNA. However, its relationship to the small-particle source of infectious RNA remains speculative for the moment.

The lack of penetration of antibody-neutralized NDV (Rubin & Franklin, 1957) suggests that the impetus to penetration comes from the virus rather than the cell, and this is supported by the findings of Allison (personal communication). He found that pretreatment of isotope-labelled fowl plague virus with p-chloromercuribenzoate (PCMB) or diisopropyl fluorophosphonate (DFP) did not alter the kinetics of virus adsorption but prevented penetration (the PCMB effect was re-versed by cysteine). The same applied to vaccinia virus except that DFP did not prevent penetration. Possibly the adsorption sites on the virus surface which lead to successful penetration are sterically blocked by inhibitor and are few compared with those allowing non-infective adsorption, but it is more likely that penetration is mediated by virus enzymes, as DFP is a potent anti-esterase and PCMB inhibits sulphydryl-activated enzymes.

Franklin (1958 a) has pointed out the relationships existing between the ether sensitivity of a number of viruses and the way in which they are released from infected cells. Certain ether-sensitive viruses— for example, western equine encephalomyelitis (Rubin, Hotchin & Baluda, 1955) and VSV (Franklin, 1958 c)—remain associated with the cell for only a few minutes after maturation, and if VSV (Cooper, 1957 c) is typical, are released by a 'secretory' mechanism rather than a 'burst'. Franklin makes the interesting suggestion that all ether-sensitive viruses are completed at the cell periphery with a lipid coat which is essential for infectivity. Removal of this lipid by lipid solvents or enzymes destroys the infectivity of NDV (Franklin, Rubin & Davis, 1957). Viruses such as poliovirus in which lipid is absent, or others in which it is inaccessible (not as a coat?) and so are ether-resistant, are suggested to be not depen-dent on the cell surface for maturation and in fact accumulate inside the cell until released by a burst-like process (Howes & Melnick, 1957). The sensitivity to desoxycholate of a number of viruses (Theiler, 1957) also seems to parallel closely their ether sensitivity; since by definition 'entero-viruses' need to be bile-resistant, this particular classification of viruses according to their habitat may have some foundation in chemical struc-ture. Dulbecco & Vogt (1955) noticed a marked difference between the sensitivities to nitrogen mustard of poliovirus on the one hand, and a group consisting of VSV, NDV and western equine encephalomyelitis virus on the other, and this difference may also be related to their lipid content.

Another generalization of relevance to growth mechanisms and based on chemical data has been summarized by Frisch-Niggemeyer (1956). It is that while size, and therefore particle weight, vary widely among the smaller viruses (both plant and animal but all RNA-containing), the content of RNA is approximately constant, suggesting that the fundamental replicating unit is similar. In spite of this, however, the sensitivity to u.v. light is much lower (smaller target?) for poliovirus (Dulbecco & Vogt, 1955, 37% survival dose = 360 ergs mm.$^{-2}$) which is 27 mμ diameter, than for VSV (Cooper & Bellett, unpublished data, 37% survival dose = 50 ergs mm.$^{-2}$) which is 70–80 mμ diameter. There also appears to be a grouping of the weights of these viruses around values which are small integral multiples of a smaller subunit (Polson, 1953); this might suggest a common simple assembly pattern from similarly constituted subunits. However, interpretation of this must await further data on size from other methods (for example, electron microscopy) and on chemical composition; some of the viruses may contain lipid, others do not. There is also evidence that individual viruses can exist as particles falling in more than one of these size-groupings.

We might summarize our present knowledge of the 'typical growth cycle' by the following examples from specific viruses. Like phages, animal viruses appear first to adsorb to cells by electrostatic mechanisms (for example, poliovirus; Bachtold, Bubel & Gebhardt, 1957), become rapidly fixed and then penetrate the cell membrane by the action of viral enzymes rather than by phagocytosis by the cell (for example, fowl plague, NDV and vaccinia viruses). Infectivity is now no longer detectable inside most cells later releasing infective virus, so that an eclipse phase in this sense seems well established for all the smaller viruses examined.

Unfortunately we cannot yet say from the chemical data that the eclipse is due to a physical breakdown of the particle. That some degree of breakdown and subsequent assembly of new particles does occur, however, seems likely from the separate synthesis of fowl plague soluble antigen (in the nucleus) and haemagglutinin (in the cytoplasm). Free RNA can certainly play a part in the infective process, but it is not known whether a normal infection with intact virus must necessarily pass through a stage in which the nucleic acid is in free state.

The eclipse phase of poliovirus and adenovirus is accompanied by increased chemical activity in both nucleus and cytoplasm, particularly marked in the latter, which appears at present to be an all-round increase of the normal phosphate and carbohydrate metabolism rather than a selective change. Herpesvirus causes an increase in nuclear DNA during the eclipse phase. On the other hand, VSV probably produces as much virus nucleic acid in the form of infective particles as does poliovirus, but brings about no gross disturbance of phosphate metabolism in the eclipse phase. Cells appear damaged at similar times after infection with poliovirus or VSV, and big changes are to be expected and may be found in both systems at these times.

Finally poliovirus (and a number of other ether-insensitive viruses) are completed and accumulate within the cell until released by partial cell dissolution, whereas VSV (and a number of other ether-sensitive viruses) appear to be completed at the cell periphery and released at once, and therefore continuously, by a secretory-like process. It remains to be seen whether large and small changes are typical of the two types of maturation.

CONCLUSIONS

Virus synthesis can only be conceived as proceeding in stages, and it is likely that the initiation of the transition from one stage to another is to some extent a matter of chance. If this is so, the operation of chance in the earlier stages, particularly while the virus is organizing into a replicating state and before any replication has begun, will mean that some cell-virus complexes will be more delayed than others in starting to replicate, and the overall chance of delay will increase with the number of preliminary stages. Cairns (1957) has found evidence of some delay in completing the first cycle of influenza virus infections (although he maintains an open mind about which stage in the growth process it occupies), and shortened latency (Cooper, 1958a) could be accounted for partly in this way, although multiple contributions to a vegetative pool seem more likely as an explanation (unpublished considerations). However, if a vegetative pool is formed during replication, the operation of chance will increasingly allow units to be drawn at random from it into another partly-assembled-particle pool, and samples may be drawn at random from such a pool into a matured pool and thence released. Thus, after the early stages, the probability of delay in passing from one stage to another should express itself in the relative sizes of the different pools rather than in a further distribution in time at which virus release takes place. In other words, the time at which individual particles start to replicate may vary widely, but once started the rates of development of individual cell-virus complexes should be similar.

This picture is, of course, speculative, but the point in describing it is that in the infected cell at the height of virus synthesis there may be quite large co-existing pools of virus components or precursors of all stages of development, increasing at earlier times but constant in amount later, and for a time at least bearing a constant relation to each other. The pools may be much larger than the amount of virus produced if the probability of correct (infective) assembly is low, and this probability may be reflected in the difference in infective yield per unit cell mass between animal viruses on one hand and plant and bacterial viruses on the other. There is indeed some evidence that the scale of the infective processes is similar for all three virus groups; this, if true, would be a useful unifying concept.

Thus, one important step is to find the number of stages and pools involved, particularly the early ones; their nature can be investigated subsequently. If their presence can be established by some means, perhaps serological, use of isotopically labelled components may reveal the sequence in which they are started or assembled, and their age.

There is thus much to be done in deciphering the mechanisms of virus growth; as with phage, probably much is to be gained by concentration on a few well-chosen model systems. Animal viruses are more diverse than bacterial ones, and so more model systems may be desirable. The difficulty remains of making the choice so that the ideal criteria apply as much as possible, and the present phase seems likely to be an exploratory one in which the relationships among the viruses become better known, and more information becomes available on which to base our choice.

I wish to thank all those who were kind enough to show me their manuscripts and data in advance of publication.

REFERENCES

ACKERMANN, W. W. (1958). Biosynthetic activities of HeLa cells infected with poliovirus. *7th Int. Congr. Microbiol., Stockholm*, p. 229.

ACKERMANN, W. W. & MAASSAB, H. F. (1955). Growth characteristics of influenza virus. Biochemical differentiation of stages of development. II. *J. exp. Med.* **102**, 393.

ACKERMANN, W. W., PAYNE, F. E. & KURTZ, H. (1958). Concerning the cytopathogenic effect of poliovirus; evidence for an extraviral toxin. *J. Immunol.* **81**, 1.

ACKERMANN, W. W., RABSON, A. & KURTZ, H. (1954). Growth characteristics of poliomyelitis virus in HeLa cell cultures: lack of parallelism in cellular injury and virus increase. *J. exp. Med.* **100**, 437.

ADA, G. L. & PERRY, B. T. (1956). Influenza virus nucleic acid: relationship between biological characteristics of the virus particle and properties of nucleic acid. *J. gen. Microbiol.* **14**, 623.

ALEXANDER, H. E., KOCH, G., MOUNTAIN, I. M., SPRUNT, K., DAMME, O. V. (1957). Infectivity of ribonucleic acid of poliovirus on HeLa cell monolayers. *Virology,* **5**, 172.

BACHTOLD, J. G., BUBEL, H. C. & GEBHARDT, L. P. (1957). The primary interaction of poliomyelitis virus with host cells of tissue culture origin. *Virology*, **4**, 582.

BALUDA, M. A. (1957). Homologous interference by ultraviolet-inactivated Newcastle disease virus. *Virology*, **4**, 72.

BAUER, D. J. (1953). Metabolic aspects of virus multiplication. *Symp. Soc. gen. Microbiol.* **2**, 46.

BECKER, Y., GROSSOWICZ, N. & BERNKOPF, H. (1958). Metabolism of human amnion cell cultures infected with poliomyelitis virus. I. Glucose metabolism during virus synthesis. *Proc. Soc. exp. Biol., N.Y.* **97**, 77.

BREITENFELD, P. M. & SCHÄFER, W. (1957). The formation of fowl plague virus antigen in infected cells, as studied with fluorescent antibodies. *Virology*, **4**, 328.

BROWN, F., SELLERS, R. F. & STEWART, D. L. (1958). Infectivity of ribonucleic acid from mice and tissue culture infected with the virus of foot-and-mouth disease. *Nature, Lond.* **182**, 535.

BURNET, F. M., LIND, P. E. & PERRY, B. (1957). The action of ribonuclease on the multiplication of influenza viruses in the de-embryonated egg. *Aust. J. exp. Biol. med. Sci.* **35**, 517.

CAIRNS, H. J. F. (1957). The asynchrony of infection by influenza virus. *Virology*, **3**, 1.

CHAMBERS, V. C. (1957). The prolonged persistence of western equine encephalomyelitis virus in cultures of strain L cells. *Virology*, **3**, 62.

CHENG, P. (1958). Infectivity of ribonucleic acid from mouse brains infected with Semliki forest virus. *Nature, Lond.* **181**, 1800.

COLTER, J. S., BIRD, H. H. & BROWN, R. A. (1957). Infectivity of ribonucleic acid from Ehrlich ascites tumour cells infected with Mengo encephalitis. *Nature, Lond.* **179**, 859.

COLTER, J. S., BIRD, H. H., MOYER, A. W. & BROWN, R. A. (1957). Infectivity of ribonucleic acid isolated from virus-infected tissues. *Virology*, **4**, 522.

COOPER, P. D. (1955). A method for producing plaques in agar suspensions of animal cells. *Virology*, **1**, 397.

COOPER, P. D. (1957*a*). Some characteristics of vesicular stomatitis virus growth curves in tissue culture. *J. gen. Microbiol.* **17**, 327.

COOPER, P. D. (1957*b*). Paths of phosphate transfer in normal chick embryo cells and in cells infected with vesicular stomatitis virus. *J. gen. Microbiol.* **17**, 335.

COOPER, P. D. (1957*c*). An osmotic barrier for inorganic phosphate in chick embryo cells and its stability during the latent and release periods of infection by vesicular stomatitis virus. *J. gen. Microbiol.* **17**, 353.

Cooper, P. D. (1958*a*). Shortened latency as a result of multiple infection by vesicular stomatitis virus in chick cell culture. *J. gen. Microbiol.* **19**, 340.

COOPER, P. D. (1958*b*). Homotypic non-exclusion by vesicular stomatitis virus in chick cell culture. *J. gen. Microbiol.* **19**, 350.

COOPER, P. D. & BELLETT, A. J. D. (1958). A transmissible interfering component analogous with an incomplete form of vesicular stomatitis virus. *7th Int. Congr. Microbiol., Stockholm*, p. 232.

DUBES, G. R. (1956). Cystine requirement for normal poliovirus action on monkey kidney tissue cultures. *Proc. Soc. exp. Biol., N.Y.* **93**, 129.

DULBECCO, R. (1955). Interaction of viruses and animal cells. A study of facts and interpretations. *Physiol. Rev.* **35**, 301.

DULBECCO, R. & VOGT, M. (1955). Biological properties of poliomyelitis viruses as studied by the plaque technique. *Ann. N.Y. Acad. Sci.* **61**, 790.

DUNNEBACKE, T. H. (1956). Correlation of the stage of cytopathic change with the release of poliomyelitis virus. *Virology*, **2**, 399.

EAGLE, H. & HABEL, K. (1956). The nutritional requirements for the propagation of poliomyelitis virus by the HeLa cell. *J. exp. Med.* **104**, 271.

FISHER, T. N. & GINSBERG, H. S. (1957). Accumulation of organic acids by HeLa cells infected with type 4 adenovirus. *Proc. Soc. exp. Biol.*, *N.Y.* **95**, 47.

FOGH, J. (1955). Relation between multiplicity of exposure, adsorption and cytopathogenic effect of poliomyelitis virus in monkey kidney tissue culture. *Virology*, **1**, 324.

FRANKLIN, R. M. (1958*a*). An hypothesis to explain the relation between the synthesis and release of animal viruses from infected cells and the lipid content of the viruses. *Experientia*, **14**, 346.

FRANKLIN, R. M. (1958*b*). The growth of fowl plague virus in tissue cultures of macrophages and giant cells. *Virology*, **6**, 81.

FRANKLIN, R. M. (1958*c*). Studies on the growth of vesicular stomatitis virus in tissue culture. *Virology*, **5**, 408.

FRANKLIN, R. M. (1958*d*). The synthesis of fowl plague virus products in a proflavine-inhibited tissue culture system. *Virology*, **6**, 525.

FRANKLIN, R. M., RUBIN, H. & DAVIS, C. A. (1957). Production, purification and properties of Newcastle disease virus labelled with radio-phosphorus. *Virology*, **3**, 96.

FRAZER, K. B. (1953). Genetic interaction and interference between the MEL and NWS strains of influenza A virus. *Brit. J. exp. Path.* **34**, 319.

FRISCH-NIGGEMEYER, W. (1956). Absolute amount of ribonucleic acid in viruses. *Nature, Lond.* **178**, 307.

GIFFORD, G. E. & SYVERTON, J. T. (1957). Replication of poliovirus in primate cell cultures maintained under anaerobic conditions. *Virology*, **4**, 216.

GOLDFINE, H., KOPPELMAN, R. & EVANS, E. A. (1958). Nucleoside incorporation into HeLa cells infected with poliomyelitis virus. *J. biol. Chem.* **232**, 577.

GOTLIEB, T. & HIRST, G. K. (1956). The experimental production of combination forms of virus. VI. Reactivation of influenza virus after inactivation by ultraviolet light. *Virology*, **2**, 235.

HENLE, G., GIRARDI, A. & HENLE, W. (1955). A non-transmissible cytopathogenic effect of influenza virus in tissue culture accompanied by formation of non-infectious haemagglutinin. *J. exp. Med.* **101**, 25.

HOWES, D. W. & MELNICK, J. L. (1957). Growth cycle of poliovirus in monkey kidney cells. I. Maturation and release of virus in monolayer cultures. *Virology*, **4**, 97.

HOYLE, L. & FINTER, N. B. (1957). The use of influenza virus labelled with radio-sulphur in studies of the early stages of the interaction of virus with the host cell. *J. Hyg., Camb.* **55**, 290.

HOYLE, L. & FRISCH-NIGGEMEYER, W. (1955). The disintegration of influenza virus particles on entry into the host cell. Studies with virus labelled with radio-phosphorus. *J. Hyg., Camb.* **53**, 474.

HUPPERT, J. & SANDERS, F. K. (1958). An infective 'ribonucleic acid' component from tumour cells infected with encephalomyocarditis virus. *Nature, Lond.* **182**, 515.

ISAACS, A. & LINDENMANN, J. (1957). Virus interference. I. The interferon. *Proc. roy. Soc.* B, **147**, 258.

KOVACS, E. (1956*a*). Comparative biochemical studies on normal and poliomyelitis infected tissue cultures. IV. Enzyme changes in host cells. *Proc. Soc. exp. Biol.*, *N.Y.* **92**, 183.

KOVACS, E. (1956*b*). Comparative biochemical studies on normal and on poliomyelitis virus infected tissue cultures. V. Profound alteration of acid and alkaline phosphatase activity in infected rhesus kidney cells. *J. exp. Med.* **104**, 589.

LE CLERC, J. (1957). L'action de la ribonucléase sur la multiplication du virus de la grippe. *Ann. Inst. Pasteur*, **93**, 772.

LEVY, H. B. & BARON, S. (1957). The effect of animal viruses on host cell metabolism. II. Effect of poliomyelitis virus on glycolysis and uptake of glycine by monkey kidney tissue culture. *J. infect. Dis.* **100**, 109.

LEVY, H. B., ROWE, W. P., SNELLBAKER, L. F. & HARTLEY, J. W. (1957). Biochemical changes in HeLa cells associated with infection by type 2 adenovirus. *Proc. Soc. exp. Biol., N.Y.* **96**, 732.

LIU, O. C. (1956). Isotopic labelling of virus. II. The labelling of influenza virus with radio-active phosphorus. *Trans. N.Y. Acad. Sci.* **18**, 249.

MAASSAB, H. F., LOH, P. C. & ACKERMANN, W. W. (1957). Growth characteristics of poliovirus in HeLa cells: nucleic acid metabolism. *J. exp. Med.* **106**, 641.

MIMS, C. A. (1956). Rift Valley fever in mice. IV. Incomplete virus; its production and properties. *Brit. J. exp. Path.* **37**, 129.

MIROFF, G., CORNATZER, W. E. & FISCHER, R. G. (1957). Effect of poliomyelitis virus type I (Mahoney strain) on the phosphorus metabolism of the HeLa cell. *J. biol. Chem.* **228**, 255.

NEWTON, A. & STOKER, M. G. P. (1958). Changes in nucleic acid content of HeLa cells infected with herpes virus. *Virology*, **5**, 549.

PEREIRA, H. G. & KELLY, B. (1957). Dose-response curves of toxic and infective actions of adenovirus in HeLa cell cultures. *J. gen. Microbiol.* **17**, 517.

POLSON, A. (1953). Weight relationships among animal viruses. *Nature, Lond.* **172**, 1154.

RUBIN, H. & FRANKLIN, R. M. (1957). On the mechanism of Newcastle disease virus neutralisation by immune serum. *Virology*, **3**, 84.

RUBIN, H., HOTCHIN, J. & BALUDA, M. (1955). The maturation of western equine encephalomyelitis virus and its release from chick embryo cells in suspension. *J. exp. Med.* **101**, 205.

SCHÄFER, W. (1957). Units isolated after splitting fowl plague virus. In *Ciba Foundation Symposium on the Nature of Viruses*. Edited by G. E. W. Wolstenholme and E. C. P. Miller, p. 91. London: Churchill.

SCHWERDT, C. E. & FOGH, J. (1957). The ratio of physical particles per infectious unit observed for poliomyelitis viruses. *Virology*, **4**, 41.

SCHWERDT, C. E. & SCHAFFER, F. L. (1956). Purification of poliomyelitis viruses propagated in tissue culture. *Virology*, **2**, 665.

TAMM, I. (1958). Selective inhibition of virus multiplication. *Symp. Soc. gen. Microbiol.* **8**, 178.

THEILER, M. (1957). Action of sodium desoxycholate on arthropod-borne viruses. *Proc. Soc. exp. Biol., N.Y.* **96**, 380.

TURCO, G. L. (1959). Growth of vesicular stomatitis in tissue culture. Changes in cellular RNA during the infectious cycle (manuscript in preparation).

VOGT, M., DULBECCO, R. & WENNER, H. A. (1957). Mutants of poliomyelitis viruses with reduced efficiency of plating in acid medium and reduced neuropathogenicity. *Virology*, **4**, 141.

WECKER, E. & SCHÄFER, W. (1956). Einbau von radioaktivem Phosphor in das Virus der klassischen Geflügelpest. *Z. Naturf.* **11**b, 181.

WECKER, E. & SCHÄFER, W. (1957a). Eine infektiöse Komponente von Ribonukleinsäure-Charakter aus dem Virus der amerikanischen Pferde-Enzephalomyelitis (Typ Ost). *Z. Naturf.* **12**b, 415.

WECKER, E. & SCHÄFER, W. (1957b). Studien mit ^{32}P-markiertem Virus der klassischen Geflügelpest. 1. Untersuchungen über das Verhalten des Virus beim Eindringen in die Wirtszelle. *Z. Naturf.* **12**b, 483.

FLUORESCENCE MICROSCOPY: OBSERVATION OF VIRUS GROWTH WITH AMINOACRIDINES

E. S. ANDERSON, J. A. ARMSTRONG, AND JANET S. F. NIVEN

Central Enteric Reference Laboratory and Bureau, Public Health Laboratory Service, Colindale Avenue, London, N.W. 9, and National Institute for Medical Research, London, N.W. 7

The possible value of the fluorescence microscope in microbiological research was appreciated soon after the introduction of the fluorescent dyes, or fluorochromes. With an adequate activating light source, dark field illumination and objectives of high numerical aperture, outstanding optical resolution is possible. Unlike orthodox light microscopy the image observed with the fluorescence microscope is formed by the emission of light from the specimen itself, and detection of the object depends primarily upon the intensity of the light emitted. Thus the presence of dispersed objects, the dimensions of which are close to or even beyond the limits of precise delineation by transmitted light, may be detected as a pattern of linear or point sources of light against a black background; but the size of the fluorescent image formed by an ultramicroscopic object does not, from its nature, permit absolute measurement of the object itself (Levaditi & Panthier, 1945).

Primulin, thioflavine-S, berberine sulphate and trypaflavine have been recommended as fluorochromes for microbiological purposes, with optimal activation in the blue-violet region of the visible spectrum. Hagemann (1937), Haitinger (1938) and Levaditi and his associates (1940, 1945, 1948) found such methods of value in the study of virus elementary bodies of the pox group, typhus rickettsiae and the host-cell inclusion bodies of rabies and herpes-infected tissues. More recently, work in this field has been directed towards an understanding of the factors underlying the selective affinities of certain fluorochromes. This trend was stimulated to a large extent by the discovery of the unusual polychromatic fluorochroming properties of the compound 2,8-*bis*-dimethylaminoacridine, known as acridine orange. This basic substance is only one of the many fluorescent amino-derivatives of acridine. Strugger (1940) and Bukatsch & Haitinger (1940) demonstrated its potentialities as a vital stain for bacteria, yeasts, certain plant cells and vertebrate spermatozoa. Multicoloured effects have since been noted by many workers using acridine orange as a vital fluorochrome, but the differential fluorescence of cells and their components has been variously interpreted. The so-called 'Strugger effect', differential fluorescence of living and dead components (green and red fluorescence respectively), has been the subject of conflicting reports and much controversial discussion (see Gärtner, 1943; Levaditi, 1944; Strugger, 1949; Krebs & Gierlach, 1951; Bogen, 1953). From the evidence now available it seems reasonable to conclude that as a valid means of determining the viability of cells this technique has a limited range of application under controlled conditions, making it of little value for general use.

In spite of the widely differing experimental conditions employed by workers in the fields of plant, animal and bacterial cytology it soon became apparent that acridine orange and some related acridine derivatives showed, amongst other affinities, a definite partiality for particular cell components, notably those with a high nucleic acid content (Gössner, 1949; De Bruyn, Robertson & Farr, 1950; De Bruyn, Farr, Banks & Morthland, 1953; Zeiger, Harders & Müller, 1951; Schuler, 1952, 1954; Krieg, 1953a, 1953b). Krieg (1954) noted that bodies believed by him to be the nuclei of yeast cells fluoresced yellow-green after treatment with acridine orange, whilst cytoplasmic granules suspected of containing RNA exhibited red fluorescence. Research in other directions also pointed towards the existence of a specific interaction of nucleic acids with those acridines already known for their antibacterial and antimalarial properties (McIlwain, 1941; Irvin, Irvin & Parker, 1949; Irvin & Irvin, 1954). Other reports disclosed that aminoacridines inhibited mitosis and cell growth in living tissue cultures (Lasnitzki & Wilkinson, 1948), obstructed the maturation of bacteriophage (DeMars, Luria, Fisher & Levinthal, 1953), and were mutagenic in yeasts (Ephrussi & Hottinguer, 1950), Drosophila (Clark, 1953) and bacteriophage (DeMars, 1953). Investigations followed dealing directly with the physico-chemical interaction of aminoacridines and the nucleic acids (Peacocke & Skerrett, 1956; Lawley, 1956).

A systematic study of the fluorescent properties acquired by animal tissues after treatment with acridine compounds was undertaken by Armstrong (1956, 1957). Initial tests were carried out on thin paraffin sections of a wide range of normal animal tissues after fixation by routine methods. Of several acridine derivatives tested two were far superior to the rest as fluorochromes; they were acridine orange and its 5-phenyl derivative, acridine orange R. Both dissolve readily in acetate buffers to give clear, orange-coloured solutions with absorption peaks at 2670 Å and 4920 Å (Fig. 1). Different tissues and cell components showed characteristic affinities for the fluorochrome, and presented a pattern of polychromatic fluorescence when activated on the fluorescence micro-scope by the blue-violet emission (i.e. about 4500 Å) from a high-pressure mercury vapour lamp. Quartz optical components are necessary. The method of tissue fixation was not critical, although fluorescence was usually most brilliant in specimens fixed in Carnoy's fluid. Fixatives containing picric acid or osmium tetroxide, however, seriously impaired

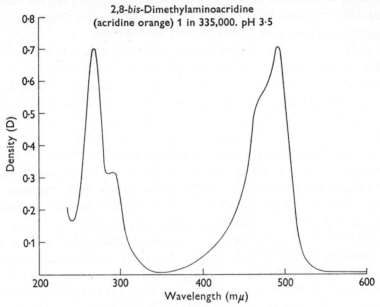

Fig. 1. Absorption curve of acridine orange.

the uptake of the stain. Excellent results were obtained in unfixed tissues preserved at −70° and sectioned at −20°. Concentration of fluoro-chrome and the duration of staining had little bearing on the results; and the most important factor controlling the fluorescence of the tissues was the pH of the solution. Using acridine orange within the range of pH 1·5–3·5 (or pH 3·5–5·0 for acridine orange R) the differential fluorescence of the various tissue elements was most sharply delineated. The fluor-escence of nucleic-acid-containing structures was particularly in evi-dence. Nuclear chromatin emitted a bright greenish-yellow fluorescence, contrasting sharply with a flame-red colour shown by nucleoli and the basophilic cytoplasmic components of neurons, pancreatic acinar cells, peptic cells of the gastric mucosa, and other cells with a substantial content of ribonucleic acid (RNA). At higher pH values the specificity was not maintained, the specimens became visibly coloured and the fluorescent image progressively more diffuse and completely red in colour. Such observations were correlated with nuclease digestion tests, model tests on purified preparations of nucleic acids, and the parallel study of test objects by the Feulgen, ultraviolet absorption and methyl green–pyronin techniques. This showed that under adequately controlled conditions of tissue preparation and treatment it is possible with the fluorescence microscope to detect and distinguish between intracellular localizations of DNA and RNA. A similar conclusion was reached by von Bertalanffy and his associates (Bertalanffy & Bickis, 1956; Bertalanffy, Masin & Masin, 1956), who found the method of value in routine exfoliative cytology.

Advantages of the acridine orange technique are (i) its simplicity, (ii) its relatively high level of sensitivity compared with existing cytochemical methods, (iii) the simultaneous demonstration of both DNA and RNA, and (iv) the fact that fluorochromed specimens are readily stained by other methods after first being studied with the fluorescence microscope. Within the specified pH range only structures containing acid muco-polysaccharides (for example, mast cell granules, cartilage, elastic tissue) acquire fluorescent properties at all similar to those of the nucleic-acid-containing elements, and identification of these presents no serious difficulty. It should be emphasized, however, that the cytochemical specificity of fluorochroming methods applied to the *living* animal cell has yet to be established, and caution must therefore be exercised in their interpretation. Preliminary studies by Stockinger (1958) suggest that complex factors in addition to the distribution of nucleic acids are concerned in the vital fluorochroming of tissue cultures.

The mechanism of the differential fluorescence of cellular nucleic acids has yet to be satisfactorily explained. Certain features of the dye uptake process, and the stability of the induced fluorescence, seem to indicate that the factors concerned in the affinity of acridine orange for the two types of nucleic acid are distinct. The interaction with DNA-containing elements occurs almost instantaneously, with the formation of a fairly stable complex showing greenish yellow fluorescence, whilst the induction of red fluorescence in RNA-containing structures is by comparison a slow process requiring several minutes to become fully established in a 3μ section. Furthermore, the red fluorescence is gradually diminished by prolonged activation with intense blue light and abolished almost instantaneously by immersion of the specimen in alcohol. In a spectrophotometric study of the interaction of nucleic acids with several amino-acridines Morthland, De Bruyn & Smith (1954) found a significant shift of the absorption peak of the dyes when DNA or RNA was added. Their findings suggested the formation of a complex bond consisting partly of an electrostatic attraction between positively charged ions of the dye and negatively charged components of the nucleic acid molecule, and partly (especially with regard to DNA) of firmer linkages depending upon complementary molecular configuration. The same authors noted that depolymerization of DNA with deoxyribonuclease (DNase) substantially impaired the formation of an acid-dye complex; and Schümmelfeder, Ebschner & Krogh (1957) found that after acid hydrolysis, DNA-containing structures would combine with acridine orange to form a red-fluorescing complex similar to that formed normally by cellular RNA. Steiner and his co-workers (Steiner & Beers, 1958; Beers, Hendley & Steiner, 1958) have recently proposed two types of inter-action between acridine orange and the nucleic acids, resulting in the formation of two complexes which they have designated I and II. These may be responsible for the polychromatic fluorescence. In complex I they believe that the linkage involves the bases and inter-nucleotide phosphates of polyribonucleotides; in complex II it is thought to involve the terminal phosphates of both polyribonucleotides and DNA. The latter appears to form only complex II.

The acquired fluorescence of intracellular nucleic acids, and the optical advantages of the fluorescence microscope, offer intriguing possi-bilities of supplementing information afforded by methods already available for cytological studies of virus growth. Indeed, it has been shown that significant and specific changes are demonstrable by this means in vertebrate and insect tissues, and also in tissue cultures after infection with viruses of widely differing character (Armstrong & Niven, 1957; Tenenbaum, 1957). Results of interest have also been reported concerning the multiplication of bacteriophage in lysogenic bacterial cells induced with ultraviolet (u.v.) irradiation (Anderson, 1957). The following account is an extension of these observations.

CHANGES OBSERVED IN BACTERIA DURING GROWTH OF BACTERIOPHAGE

Although a great deal of research has been directed to the quantitative aspects of phage synthesis, especially changes in the amount and charac-ter of proteins and nucleic acids in the host cell during the latent period of infection, comparatively little has been done on the direct cytological study of phage development. This is not surprising, for the bacterial cell itself is a structure unhappily close to the limit of resolution of the light microscope, while its structural subunits, such as nuclei or their equivalents, actually lie on or beyond that limit. The interpretation of changes that can be visualized in such regions tends therefore to draw perhaps more greedily than usual on the imagination of the observer. Even in the cytology of uninfected bacteria differences of opinion concerning the interpretation of 'normal' cell cycles are not unknown. It is understandable, therefore, that the worker with the light microscope feels himself to be in particularly dangerous country when he attempts to translate bacterial pathology into acceptable dynamic terms. Nevertheless, visual observation of the course of phage growth in individual cells, if it were possible, might offer the advantage of relating known biochemical changes to observable, more or less regular, progressions of cytological events; and abnormalities in the biochemical sequence might be paralleled by irregularities in the morphological picture.

Luria & Human (1950) extended the earlier observations of Luria & Palmer (1946), using the technique developed by Robinow (1942, 1944, 1945) to follow the sequence of events occurring in cells of *Escherichia coli* B infected with phages T1, T2, T4 and T6. They showed that each phage precipitated characteristic cytopathological changes. For example, in infection with phage T2 the chromatinic material of the bacteria migrated to the cell wall. Cellular swelling took place, and after 7–9 min. finely granular chromatin appeared. By 15–20 min. after infection, coarsening of these granules occurred and cells evidently began to lyse, although as the lysis resulted in disappearance of the cells its course and products could not be seen. When cells were infected with phage inactivated by u.v. irradiation, the changes progressed only as far as margination of the original bacterial chromatin. After this, the chromatin disappeared altogether from infected cells. Murray, Gillen & Heagy (1950), using acid hydrolysis followed by Giemsa or Feulgen staining, and also fixation with Bouin's fluid followed by thionin staining, made similar observations to those of Luria and Human in infection with T2 and its *r* (rapid lysing) mutant. Murray & Whitfield (1953) explored the effects of infection with T5 and with phages related to it. Phage T5 caused disappearance of nuclear structures within 15 min. New chromatin was synthesized within 22–25 min., showing itself as granules increasing in number and eventually forming a core almost filling the infected cell. Infected organisms increased progressively in length and thickness and lysed after 45–48 min. The lysis was usually polar in origin, the opposite end of the affected cell frequently remaining visible after lysis. Small granules were apparent around the lysed cell. Murray and Whitfield also examined the results of infection with recombinants of phage T5 and other phages. Their observations confirmed that the cytological effects were characteristic of particular phages and they suggested that the pattern of such effects might be useful in phage taxonomy. In phage hybrids it was observed that the cytopathological picture segregated independently of other genetic markers. In subsequent work, these authors (Whitfield & Murray, 1954) traced the morphological changes accompanying lysogenization of *Shigella dysenteriae* with phages P1 and P2 (Bertani, 1951, 1953a, 1953b). With phage P1, the bacterial nuclei fused into axial filaments which subsequently expanded to form a chromatin reticulum. When lysogenization occurred, this reticulum recondensed to form normal nuclear elements. When the cell was destined to lyse, the chromatin reticulum appeared to be rather finer in texture, and the cell swelled, developed a 'spongy' appearance and disintegrated suddenly. The decision as to whether the cell is to undergo lysogenization or lysis is dependent on temperature with phage P1 (Bertani, 1953b; Bertani & Nice, 1954); by lowering the temperature of incubation within 20 min. of infection the proportion of cells undergoing lysogenization is increased. Later work by Whitfield and Murray (1956) showed that condensation of bacterial chromatin into a central core could be precipitated by alterations in the ionic composition of the environment. As the alterations in chromatin distribution in infection of *S. dysenteriae* with phages P1 and P2 resembled those caused in infected cells by variations in electrolyte concentration, they suspected (Whitfield & Murray, 1957) that phage infection affected the cell wall so as to disturb ionic equilibrium. Adsorption of 'ghosts' of phage T2 to bacterial cells produced central chromatin aggregation, which suggested that the effect was due to the adsorption only and was not connected with phage multiplication proper.

The optical and electron microscopes have been used to follow the course of infection of *Escherichia coli* B with phage T2 by Mudd and his co-workers (see Beutner, Hartman, Mudd & Hillier, 1953; Mudd, Hillier, Beutner & Hartman, 1953; Hartman, Mudd, Hillier & Beutner, 1953). In addition to confirming the cytological changes described by earlier workers, this group stated that bacterial mitochondria were unaffected by growth of T2 and showed that reductase activity continued unchanged in phage-infected cells.

Kellenberger (1953), using acid hydrolysis followed by Giemsa staining, and also electron microscopy, examined the normal cytology of a number of strains of *Escherichia coli*, some of which were lysogenic. He also described the changes demonstrable by light and electron microscopy in u.v.-irradiated lysogenic and non-lysogenic cells. The nuclear elements in such cells fragmented and then united in the centre of the organisms. The chromatin fragments then increased in number and were dispersed throughout the cell. No obvious difference could be seen between cells destined to lyse and those destined to recover. It was impossible by staining methods to study cells immediately before lysis, but phase-contrast studies showed that when lysis of lysogenic organisms was imminent the cells blew up into spheres and exploded. When recovery from the induction was to occur, the diffusely scattered chromatin recondensed and became reorganized into nuclear elements. In cells which lysed the mitochondria persisted until just before lysis. Lysogenic and non-lysogenic organisms seemed to show identical chromatin changes.

Experimental

The bacterial strains and phages employed were as follows:

Salmonella typhi Vi-type D6—strain 1691. This strain has been shown to carry a temperate phage designated d_6 which determines its type specificity (Felix & Anderson, 1951; Anderson & Felix, 1953).

S. typhi Vi-type A. This is the type strain described by Craigie & Yen (1938).

S. typhi strain A(d_6). This is type A lysogenized with phage d_6, a procedure which converts it into type D6.

Escherichia coli B. Phage T2.

Media. Bacto dehydrated nutrient broth (Difco Laboratories) in a strength of 2% was used as the basis of all nutrient media. For solid media, 1·3% powdered New Zealand agar (Davis) was added.

Methods. Irradiation was always carried out in phosphate buffer at pH 7·0. The source of u.v. radiation was a 30-watt G.E.C. germicidal lamp. Cells were irradiated for 5 sec. in buffer at a distance of 45 cm.

As it had previously been established that incubation in liquid media gave similar results to those on the surface of solid media, bacterial and phage development were followed entirely on the latter. About 0·25 ml. of the suspensions containing about 5×10^8 cells/ml. was spread over an area roughly 1×5 cm. on nutrient agar plates preheated to 37°. These plates were incubated at 37° and sample slips of agar approximately 1 cm. square were cut at selected time intervals. Smears were made from these on specially cleaned slides, allowed to dry, and were transferred to Carnoy's fixative. In some cases smears were stained without fixation. Staining was carried out in 1:2000 acridine orange. In contrast to animal tissues, in which optimal fluorescent differentiation of RNA and DNA is obtained by staining at a pH between 1·5 and 3·0, the optimum pH for bacterial systems was found to be 5·0. At this pH the

RNA fluoresced red and the DNA green or greenish yellow. After staining, smears were mounted in acetate buffer at pH 5·0. Fluorescence microscopy was carried out using as a primary filter either a 2 % solution of ammoniacal copper sulphate or an Ilford 304 glass-gelatine sandwich. The secondary filter was an Ilford 110 minus-blue gelatine film.

Giemsa staining after acid hydrolysis was carried out by the method described by Murray, Gillen & Heagy (1950); the Feulgen technique was also used.

Results

Normal bacterial morphology. The strains of *Salmonella typhi* used are morphologically indistinguishable from each other. The nuclei show the green or greenish yellow fluorescence characteristic of DNA, while the cytoplasm exhibits the red fluorescence of RNA. Most cells are binucleate, but organisms with four or more nuclei are not uncommon and mononucleate cells are occasionally found. The nuclei appear predominantly as transverse subterminal rods. When dividing they thicken and separate into two units which often remain united at one end so as to produce the V or U formation commonly encountered in the Gramnegative bacteria. One arm of the V sometimes lies along the cell wall, and nuclei which have apparently newly separated may remain connected by a fine filament of DNA. The morphology of *Escherichia coli* B is similar to that of *S. typhi*. No difference has been detected between the morphology of lysogenic and non-lysogenic cells.

Induction of lysogenic cells by irradiation with u.v. light. The changes taking place in type D6 after u.v. irradiation have already been summarized (Anderson, 1957). Within a few minutes of irradiation the nuclei were somewhat dimmer and more diffuse. They then moved to the cell centre where they fused to form a single mass of DNA, rather bandlike at first, but later more compact and circular in outline. This change was complete by between 15 and 30 min. after irradiation (Pl. 1, fig. 1). It was succeeded by the appearance of an axial filament of DNA extending from the central mass towards each bacterial pole. This filament was frequently wavy in outline and thickened progressively (Pl. 1, fig. 2). As the thickening occurred, the central mass of DNA was submerged in the newly formed material. Sixty minutes after induction most cells were practically full of DNA. Round dark bodies could be seen in the bacterial cell at this stage, often subterminal in position, and appearing by darkground illumination as bright circles almost as wide as the cell. From 60 min. onwards bursting cells were frequently apparent (Pl. 1, fig. 3) and free DNA appeared in increasing quantities. This released DNA fluoresced a brilliant greenish yellow and contained darker round bodies, about 0.3μ in diameter, which sometimes seemed to show a rather dim DNA fluorescence. By dark-ground illumination these bodies showed as bright granules of circular outline and uniform size. Occasionally, they were found in clusters embedded in the DNA emerging from individual bursting cells, and under favourable conditions they were visible as multiple dark points in the DNA of unruptured cells. It was then possible to observe that they were distinct from the intracellular bodies described earlier. The latter were larger and fewer (1–3 per cell) than those released at cell lysis. It is possible that the larger bodies are the mitochondrial equivalents that have been described by a number of workers, but the nature of the smaller particles is still obscure. A third type of body, about 0.5μ in diameter and showing DNA fluorescence but no dark-ground image, also appeared when cell lysis became frequent. Its identity is also unknown. The period of maximum phage release, which was about $1–1\frac{1}{2}$ hr. after irradiation, coincided with that of maximum cell bursts. At this time there was massive liberation of DNA, which was found in large patches containing many of the smaller of the bodies referred to above. These bodies increased in number in parallel with the frequency of cell bursts but, although they were clearly associated with the process of phage formation, their large size would seem to preclude the possibility of their being phage particles. Induced cells increased in length and to a lesser extent in thickness; they were often four or more times their original length by the time they burst. Cells rarely divided after induction, but exceptionally a septum formed in the central DNA mass shortly after irradiation, leaving half the DNA on each side.

As the amount of DNA increased, the red (RNA) fluorescence diminished, until little or none was visible in cells ready to burst. However, a fragment was often found in a polar position in cells ready to lyse, and such points showed up brightly on dark-ground illumination. In some cells the DNA of the central mass seemed to fragment and disperse throughout the cell, later to attenuate still further and disappear, leaving cells exhibiting only RNA fluorescence, which neither burst nor showed signs of recovery. In other cells, however, DNA dispersal followed by recondensation reproduced apparently normal nuclei, and healthy cells commenced to separate from such units. This recovery from irradiation was found from about $2\frac{1}{2}$ hr. after irradiation onwards, but was rare at the dosage of u.v. used, which resulted in loss of over 99 % of viable cells.

Irradiation of a 'non-lysogenic' culture. A culture cannot be said to be non-lysogenic unless it has been tested for lysogenicity on all possible indicator strains under all possible conditions, and unless the presence of defective lysogeny has also been excluded. In the face of such an impossible task, non-lysogeny can only be defined in terms of a particular phage. The behaviour of non-lysogenic and lysogenic cultures can thus be compared only when a given strain has been lysogenized with a defined phage. It is then possible to contrast the properties of the newly lysogenized culture, on the one hand with its non-lysogenic precursor, and on the other with other cultures known to carry the temperate phage employed. Such possibilities exist in certain strains of *Salmonella typhi*. The classical strain of Vi-type A (Craigie & Yen, 1938) has not so far been shown to be lysogenic. In any event, it does not carry phage d_6. Vi-type D6, on the other hand, as we have already indicated, carries phage d_6, and the events visible in the fluorescence microscope following u.v. induction of this culture have been described above. Type A can be lysogenized with phage d_6 to yield a strain which may be designated A (d_6) and the lysogenized culture behaves in relation to the Vi-typing phages as type D6 (Felix & Anderson, 1951; Anderson & Felix, 1953). If the changes undergone by this newly lysogenized culture after u.v. irradiation differ from those found in type A, but resemble those found in type D6, such special features may be attributed to the presence of the prophage.

The early changes found after u.v. irradiation of type A were similar to those found in type D6. The nuclei became rather hazy in outline and fluoresced less intensely. They then migrated to the centre of the cell where they fused. From this point onwards, the train of events in the non-lysogenic strain differed from that found in type D6. The DNA in the central spot seemed to disperse as a fine reticulum or as fine granules throughout the cell. The density of this reticulum remained roughly constant for some time as the cell increased in length. By about $1\frac{1}{2}$–2 hr. after irradiation, however, the bacteria began to show whether irradiation was to be followed by death or recovery. In the majority of cells, the DNA reticulum disappeared, and these cells, now exhibiting only RNA fluorescence, started to fragment. In cells destined to recover, the DNA recondensed and, although bizarre chromatin configurations were evident for a considerable time, normal-looking nuclei began to appear and ultimately cells of healthy appearance started to separate. By the time this process was evident, the mean cell length was often many times that of the unirradiated culture. The healthy-looking cells appeared as units separating from the poles of such elongated filaments. Recovering cells were seen occasionally from $2\frac{1}{2}$–3 hr. after irradiation. It may be mentioned here that the dose of u.v. radiation used in these experiments resulted in a loss of over 90 % of viable centres. From about 15 min. after irradiation, small dark patches appeared within the cells, and the number of these patches steadily increased as time passed. In many instances they extended across the entire width of the affected cells. Under ordinary dark-ground illumination, the patches sometimes seemed to represent bodies within the bacterial cell, but they more often appeared to be indentations or gaps in the cell wall. Cell disintegration was common, and of at least two sorts. In the first, cells without visible DNA fragmented and thereafter lost density in the fluorescence and dark-ground fields. In the second, cells still containing reasonably large amounts of DNA as a single axial filament ruptured at one end and lost their DNA. It was even possible in some cases to see the space formerly occupied by this DNA as a black track in the cell. Such DNA emergence was not accompanied by the release of granules of the sort found in induced type D6, nor did the DNA accumulate in large masses as it did in the irradiated lysogenic culture. Many small fragments of bacteria were present from about 2 hr. onwards. Such fragments appeared to have intact walls but exhibited only RNA fluorescence.

As we have already pointed out, although we have never been able to isolate a phage from type A, we do not know whether it is lysogenic but, if it is, and if the phage it carries is inducible by u.v. light, then the pattern of its multiplication and release is very different from that of phage d_6 in type D6. On the other hand, when a strain of type A lysogenized with phage d_6 was irradiated with u.v. light, the sequence of events observed was exactly similar to that found in type D6. It is clear, then, that this alteration in response of the cells to u.v. irradiation is connected with the presence of the d_6 prophage.

Escherichia coli B *infected with phage T2*. For these experiments a concentration of *E. coli* B of about $5 \cdot 0 \times 10^8$ cells/ml. was infected with phage T2 in adsorption medium (Hershey & Chase, 1952) in a phage-to-organism ratio of 3 to 1. Adsorption was allowed to proceed for 10 min. at 37° with agitation, and the mixture was then inoculated on to well-dried Difco agar plates prewarmed to 37°. The plates were incubated at 37° and the preparations were sampled immediately after transfer to solid medium, and thereafter at 5 min. intervals for 60 min. A sample was also taken immediately after mixing the phage and cells: in common with all others, this was allowed to dry on nutrient agar before being smeared on slides as previously described. The interval between mixing the phage and cells and transfer of this first sample to slides for staining was about 2–3 min.

The normal cytology of *Escherichia coli* B is quite similar to that of

Salmonella typhi, but the cells are rather smaller and mononucleate cells are commoner than in the latter organism. The nuclei are more compact than in *S. typhi* and frequently assume a wedge shape. During growth, single nuclei elongate and develop rather clubbed poles and a central constriction. The cell divides and the nuclei for some time occupy a position on each side of and close to the newly formed contiguous cell walls. Even in the earliest infected samples, fixed on slides less than 5 min. after infection and without appreciable preliminary incubation on nutrient medium, it was exceptional to find nuclei of normal appearance. A considerable proportion of the cells showed nebulous DNA concentrations which were perhaps the dispersing nuclei described by authors using other staining methods. The striking feature of this early sample, however, was the fact that, even at so short an interval after infection, a large number of cells showed sharply concentrated DNA of totally different distribution from that of the normal nuclei. This DNA mass, which at that time was usually single, was either polar or lateral in position. Its fluorescence was rather greener than the normal nuclear DNA, and in the cells in which it appeared the nuclei were no longer visible. In some instances the mass extended from a bacterial pole along the cell margin. At this stage, marginal concentrations were usually unilateral.

The samples taken immediately after the 10 min. adsorption period showed much the same appearance as that described above. Five minutes later, however, the DNA had extended as a diffuse green or greenish yellow haze from its original situation. Some cells showed an axial DNA filament, but this was rare, and did not appear to represent a constant phase in phage development in this system. A larger proportion of cells than before showed marginal concentrations of DNA. As time passed, the infected cells increased somewhat in diameter and length and their DNA content also increased, so that by 15 min. most cells were practically full of greenish yellow fluorescing material, which had now assumed a coarsely patchy appearance with residual red (RNA) fluorescence between the patches. In spite of this patchiness, the DNA gave the impression of continuity and this was particularly evident in unfixed preparations. At about this time occasional lysing cells were seen. The DNA was released in a small splash from each burst and a cluster of minute particles fluorescing as DNA and apparently of uniform size were visible around the burst cell. A small residuum of the cell was often present in these bursts. The DNA particles were sufficiently distinct to be easily countable, and numbered up to 100 or more per lysed cell. As time advanced, the cellular content of DNA increased and the mottled appearance described above was thus less evident. Cells packed with DNA often seemed distended but did not increase greatly in length. Bursts became progressively more frequent, but under the experimental conditions employed the peak burst frequency in the wild type of T2 did not occur until long after the 20 min. latent period characteristic of the phage.

The minute particles released from cells and showing fluorescence characteristic of DNA started to appear in the general background about 15 min. after infection, and their number steadily increased thereafter. By one hour after infection they had reached a high concentration. An interesting feature of the study of phage development by fluorescence microscopy is that the DNA from lysed cells is at least as visible after release as it was before. This has already been noted in induced lysogenic *Salmonella typhi* and is equally true of T2 infections of *Escherichia coli* B. Thus, from 25 min. after infection, free DNA accumulated in extensive masses showing brilliant greenish yellow fluorescence. The discrete DNA particles were especially abundant at the periphery of such masses, and it is reasonable to conclude that their concentration was even higher in the centre of the free DNA, although they would naturally be obscured by the brilliant fluorescence of the latter. Some disrupted cells appeared to release only DNA without detectable particles. Acridine-orange-stained smears of a 4-year-old T2 lysate, and also of a purified T2 preparation, fluoresced a brilliant greenish yellow, and on suitable dilution the fluorescent material resolved itself into discrete particles indistinguishable from those released from bursting phage-infected cells. These particles in the T2 lysate were resistant to DNase digestion in the unfixed state but sensitive to it after treatment with Carnoy's fixative. Our thanks are due to Mrs E. A. Asheshov for a supply of purified phage T2.

Discussion

Comparison of the findings in the study of phage growth by fluorescence microscopy with those in the methods used hitherto shows that in many instances the two approaches give similar results. The fluorescence method, however, possesses certain advantages which may allow it to add to the picture already built up by the use of the acid hydrolysis-Giemsa, Feulgen, phase-contrast and other techniques. In observation by bright-field microscopy, it is frequently difficult, even with monochromatic filters, to obtain satisfactorily crisp images of bodies near the limit of visibility. In fluorescence microscopy on the other hand, each body emits its own light against a black background, with consequent gain in resolution. Giemsa and Feulgen staining of parallel samples after acid hydrolysis was carried out in all the systems described. The appearances of intracellular DNA broadly resembled those found in the fluorescence microscope. However, the definition in the transmitted light preparations was considerably inferior to that observed in the fluorescence microscope, and the products of lysed cells were either much less distinct or not detectable.

As far as the development of phage T2 in *Escherichia coli* B is concerned, there are general similarities between the findings outlined above and those of workers using other techniques. For example, the rapid displacement of bacterial chromatin after phage infection, and the later development of coarsely granular chromatin have been described by a number of investigators. The fluorochrome acridine orange, however, is a sensitive agent for the cytochemical detection of nucleic acids. Treatment of fixed or living bacteria with ribonuclease (RNase) before staining removes the material showing red fluorescence, while deoxyribonuclease removes the material that fluoresces green (the latter enzyme is active on fixed preparations and free DNA only). In virtue of the specificity of this method, the distribution of nucleic acids in bacteria can be determined with precision. In addition to this, unfixed preparations can be stained, so that the effects of fixation can be clearly distinguished. It may be noted here that unfixed preparations of uninfected bacteria gave much the same sort of picture as did preparations fixed in Carnoy's fluid, except that the nuclear elements appeared to be rather broader than those of fixed cells. Moreover, in unfixed smears the developing phage DNA of infected cells showed greater continuity than in fixed material, and both intracellular and extracellular DNA fluoresced more brilliantly when stained without preliminary fixation. As the general pattern of DNA changes in *E. coli* B infected with T2 is similar in the unfixed preparation stained with acridine orange to that found in the acid-hydrolysed Giemsa-stained smear, it is probable that the latter method has given a reasonably close picture of the cytopathology of this particular system. However, this fluorescence study suggests that DNA newly formed during phage multiplication may be present, not in granules as previously described, but as a continuous reticulum with centres in which production is sufficiently active to produce a mottled or quasi-granular appearance. A striking feature of acridine-stained preparations is the ease with which DNA is detectable after release from the disrupted organisms and hence the results of cell lysis are visible. With the possible exception of the electron micrographs of Kellenberger & Séchaud (1957) and Kellenberger & Kellenberger (1957) in which filaments that may be DNA are visible, no other techniques enable the distribution of DNA to be accurately observed after its liberation. The free DNA resulting from lysis is presumably the residuum of the DNA pool formed during phage growth (Visconti & Delbrück, 1953) and is an interesting visual confirmation of the fact that an excess of DNA is released, as well as mature phage particles, when an infected organism disintegrates.

Although Murray, Gillen & Heagy (1950) observed the presence of faintly basophilic dots in the released cytoplasmic contents of T2-infected *Escherichia coli* B, they did not claim these dots to be T2 particles. In any event, the fact that the head of T2 is only 85 mμ in its largest diameter, and therefore beyond the limit of resolution of the light microscope, enforces caution in the interpretation of the nature of any small particles released during lysis of phage-infected cells when examined by bright-field staining methods. It is of course important to maintain equal caution when interpreting the picture presented by such systems in the fluorescence microscope, but we suggest that the minute particles which are easily visible in this method may in fact be T2 particles. We offer the following observations in support of this. First, the particles fluoresce as DNA, and no other discrete particles of high DNA content are released when T2 lyses *E. coli* B. Second, purified preparations of T2, which show only DNA fluorescence, resolve themselves after suitable dilution into similar particles. Third, treatment of purified preparations of phage T2 with high-titre phage antiserum before staining with acridine orange results in the formation of large aggregates of these particles, while their general background density, which is high in control preparations, is greatly reduced.

It seems probable that the fluorescent intensity of the DNA in the head of the phage is sufficiently strong for each particle to register as a point source of light, the detection of which is made possible by the dark field against which the observations are made. The DNA content of phage T2 is about $2 \times 10^{-10} \mu$g. per particle (Hershey, Kamen, Kennedy & Gest, 1951; Hershey, 1953) and if individual particles are indeed rendered visible by this technique, its sensitivity as a means of detecting DNA is of a very high order. So far, we have been unable to identify these particles with confidence in the ordinary dark field after removal of the primary blue filter of the fluorescent system; nor can they be seen in acid-hydrolysed preparations stained with Giemsa. If it can be established beyond reasonable doubt that T2 particles can be visualized by the fluorescence technique, a simple additional tool is at our disposal for the observation of the release of this virus from infected cells. This may supplement the information gained in, for example, fluctuation tests of phage growth, or experiments in which the maturation of T2 is impeded by chemical agents. It is worth remembering in this context that phage maturation is blocked by proflavine, a compound closely related to acridine orange (DeMars, Luria, Fisher & Levinthal, 1953; DeMars, 1955). *E. coli* can be grown in concentrations of acridine orange higher than those used in maturation blocking experiments, and takes up sufficient stain to fluoresce satisfactorily. Work is planned to exploit this property in phage-infected cells.

Recent experiments have shown that minute particles exhibiting DNA fluorescence are liberated during lysis of u.v.-induced *Escherichia coli* K-12 (λ) and bodies of similar appearance are released from lysing cells of a non-lysogenic variant of K-12 externally infected with phage λ. It thus appears probable that individual particles of a number of phages can be rendered visible by fluorescence microscopy.

Experiments with lysogenic and non-lysogenic *Salmonella typhi* and with *Escherichia coli* suggest that the initial reactions of Entero-bacteriaceae to u.v. irradiation are similar, whether or not a prophage is present. However, the appearance of the axial filaments of DNA followed by the absorption of the centralized bacterial nuclear remnant, and the progressive filling of the organisms with what is presumably phage DNA in lysogenic cells, are in contrast to the formation of the tenuous DNA reticulum in non-lysogenic organisms. The differences observed in the later stages serve to emphasize still further the contrast between the response of inducible lysogenic and non-lysogenic bacteria to u.v. irradiation. Type A of *S. typhi* can be lysogenized with a temperate phage known as d_1 (Felix & Anderson, 1951; Anderson & Felix, 1953); the resulting culture is not inducible with u.v. The morphological changes through which this strain passes after irradiation are identical with those observed in non-lysogenic type A, so that the phenomena precipitated by irradiation of the inducible system are probably the result of destruction of the symbiotic state of the prophage and initiation of vegetative phage multiplication. It is not yet known, however, to what extent the changes observed are restricted to growth of temperate phages induced by irradiation as opposed to growth following external infection, and this must clearly be determined. Here again, information may be obtained from phage-infected cultures exposed to suitable concentrations of aminoacridines during growth, since L. E. Bertani (1957) has recently shown that proflavine influences the proportion of cells undergoing lysogenization in cultures of *E. coli* infected with phage P2. A fuller description of the systems mentioned here will be given elsewhere (Anderson & Wilson, to be published).

PLATE 1

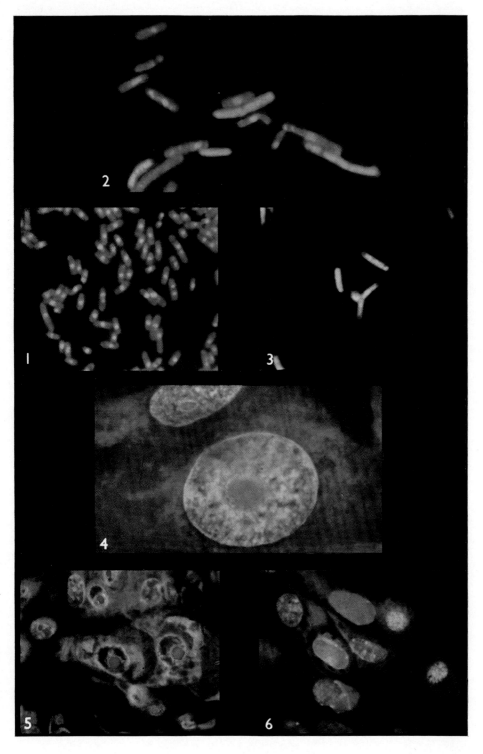

ANIMAL VIRUSES

Conventional methods of observation and microscopic examination of virus-infected tissues and organs have revealed in many instances a special affinity of particular viruses for certain types of host cell. The early recognition of striking cytotropism in two of the best known and most dreaded virus diseases, rabies and smallpox, as well as in vaccinia, encouraged a search for patterns of cell change which would characterize the etiological agent, just as the cellular arrangements in tumours and some bacterial diseases contribute to presumptive diagnosis in human and animal pathology. This quest for distinctive intracellular changes has resulted in the accumulation of a plethora of detailed information on nuclear and cytoplasmic abnormalities. Workers in virus cytopathology adopted the term 'inclusion' to designate abnormal structures found in the nucleus or cytoplasm. Although the cytologist might apply this term to any particulate material which can be rendered visible within a cell, it has in general come to have a predominantly virological connotation. When virus infection was suspected, unusual aggregates in the nucleus or cytoplasm, or both, were generally thought to be due to virus action, and have even been taken to indicate the site of virus multiplication. Cowdry (1934), discussing the significance of intranuclear inclusions in virus diseases, formulated a classification of this group of cellular abnormalities based on the degree and extent of nuclear reaction and staining properties. He emphasized, however, that since similar nuclear changes occur in non-infective conditions, inclusions may be a secondary result of virus action; and he questioned the contention of Goodpasture & Teague (1923) that the inclusions in herpes simplex consist of virus material. It gradually became obvious that not all virus infections produce sufficiently characteristic and striking intracellular stigmata by which the presence of a specific agent could reasonably be presumed in the absence of other evidence. This may be responsible in part for the unimpressive contribution so far made by light microscopy to our understanding of the intracellular changes and of the sequence of events leading to the formation and release of new infective virus particles.

The staining methods commonly used aim at emphasizing the contrast between normal and abnormal cells or between an inclusion body and its background of nucleus or cytoplasm. They usually employ either empirically balanced mixtures of dyes, as in the Romanowsky mixtures such as Giemsa's stain or in Mann's stain, or an acid followed by a basic dye as in the various eosin or phloxine and methylene blue methods; acid fuchsin is also a well-known inclusion body stain. The relative affinity for components of the stain shown by abnormal cell constituents, producing bluish or reddish colours or metachromatic effects, has given rise to a tinctorial classification not interpretable in chemical terms but frequently expressed as basophilia and eosinophilia (or acidophilia). Recently, however, Jacobson & Webb (1952) and Love (1957) have related the appearances of cells in mitosis, when stained with Giemsa's mixture or basic dyes alone, to their nucleoprotein structure; but so far these more rational methods have not been applied to detailed studies of virus-infected cells.

The examination of ultrathin sections with the electron microscope would appear to be an ideal way of discovering the site within a cell where new virus material is produced, and of visualizing the development of infective particles, but as Morgan, Rose & Moore (1958) have recently pointed out, the very high magnifications which must be used carry with them their own limitations. Thus hundreds of sections may be necessary for the complete examination of one cell and hundreds of cells may have to be examined to cover all the stages. Moreover, since there is no single characteristic morphological feature common to all viruses, difficulties of interpretation impose still further limitations on the technique (Morgan, Rose & Moore, 1957). Very valuable information has been obtained about the pox group and the adenoviruses, but a complete morphological picture, from the stage of virus penetration to the production and release of a fresh crop of infective particles, has still not become available for any animal virus.

Stimulating concepts applicable to the problems of virus replication and the interpretation of morphological changes in infected cells have emerged from recent investigations of the chemical structure of virus material. The analysis of purified preparations has revealed the constant presence of nucleic acid in all the viruses so far examined and it is now generally accepted that they all contain either DNA or RNA as an essential constituent. Utilizing the very high selective absorption of the nucleic acids in the ultraviolet at about 2600 Å, Caspersson and his school have studied extensively by means of u.v. microspectrophotometry the role of nucleic acids in normal protein synthesis, but application of this technique to a systematic investigation of virus-infected cells has been limited to the observations of Hydén & Caspersson (1945) and Hydén (1947a), who have described the points of attack in the cell of certain viruses and have related their findings to nucleoprotein synthesis. Although two well-known histochemical techniques, the Feulgen reaction for DNA and the methyl green-pyronin method for the simultaneous demonstration of both RNA and DNA, have been extensively employed in parallel with nuclease tests in the study of cell physiology (Brachet, 1942, 1947), recorded observations on virus-infected cells are still scanty. The reasons are not far to seek; the methyl green–pyronin method can be capricious and depends on a mixture of the proper components which are not always readily available; with the Feulgen method, a particle may be too small to be visible as a coloured object in the light field. Bland & Robinow (1939) failed to get a positive Feulgen reaction in individual elementary bodies of vaccinia dried on to a slide, although a centrifuged deposit gave the typical colour. Even in monolayer tissue cultures, which are optically ideal for cytopathological study, both of these techniques give weak or equivocal reactions on account of the extreme flattening of the cells on the supporting surface.

Since the technique of induced fluorescence using acridine orange cannot be satisfactorily employed after osmium tetroxide fixation, the morphological descriptions which follow necessarily use the terminology of standard fixation artifact. In the nucleus, terms such as chromatin, chromatin network and chromatin granules are used to indicate the nuclear DNA precipitated by fixation; associated chromatin refers to the DNA material surrounding the nucleolus. The technique of fluorescence microscopy exposes the large amount of RNA present in the cell cytoplasm with surprising clarity, especially in tissue culture cells where it has usually been difficult to demonstrate.

Adenovirus

Observations by conventional light microscopy have revealed profound and characteristic alterations of nuclear structure in HeLa cells infected with adenoviruses (Barski, 1956; Boyer, Leuchtenberger & Ginsberg, 1957); examination with the electron microscope has shown that such nuclei contain many recognizable virus particles which tend to occur in the form of a crystalline array (Kjellén, Lagermalm, Svedmyr & Thorsson, 1955; Morgan, Howe, Rose & Moore, 1956). The virus is thought to be of the DNA type in view of the Feulgen-positive nature of some of the intranuclear inclusions. A sequence of cytochemical changes in Carnoy-fixed monolayer cultures of the HEp-2 line of human cells after infection with type 6 adenovirus was traced recently with the acridine orange fluorescence technique (Armstrong & Hopper, 1959). In uninfected control cultures a greenish yellow fluorescence was emitted by the threads and granules of nuclear chromatin and by the nuclear membrane itself; a thin perinucleolar rim of yellow fluorescence (associated chromatin) was also a constant feature. The cytoplasm presented a partly reticulate and partly granular pattern of red-fluorescing RNA-containing material, and

similar fluorescence of moderate intensity was shown by the nucleolus.
Changes limited to the nuclei were detectable 24 hr. after infection (Pl. 1,
fig. 4). The nucleolus was enlarged and prominent, with a much in-
tensified red fluorescence; definite but less obvious rearrangement of
intranuclear DNA-containing material occurred. The DNA type of
fluorescence now seemed to originate from individually larger points
than in normal cells, giving the nucleus a peculiar granularity, and the
rim of associated chromatin around the nucleolus was frequently thicker
or more nodular than in normal nuclei. In cultures examined 2 and
3 days after infection the fluorescence of the cell nuclei had become
grossly abnormal, revealing structural changes closely comparable with
those already well known from ordinary microscopical observation.
Intranuclear material showing intense yellow fluorescence was present in
the form of one or more dense, irregularly shaped masses accompanied
by a system of vesicles or empty spaces situated beneath the nuclear
membrane. The dense material often formed a single centrally placed
body with which was associated a red-fluorescing hypertrophied
nucleolus. Material showing yellow fluorescence of the DNA type could
be seen in the cell cytoplasm only after 4 or 5 days, and then appeared
to be the result of nuclear disruption.

The development and distribution of abnormal intranuclear material
containing DNA seems to parallel the accumulation of virus particles as
observed by electron microscopy. The viral nature of at least part of this
material is further suggested by its reaction in standard nuclease digestion tests. Pretreatment of the infected cells with 0·01 % (w/v) DNase at
pH 7·4 did not interfere with the yellow fluorescence acquired by the
abnormal intranuclear material when subsequently stained with acridine
orange, although fluorescence of normal nuclear DNA was invariably
prevented by the same treatment. Resistance to the nuclease could be
abolished, however, by first incubating the specimen in 0·02 % (w/v)
pepsin at pH 2·0 for $1\frac{1}{2}$ hr. at 37°. Pepsin treatment alone did not inhibit
fluorescence, but did bring about a colour change from yellow to a
coppery shade, possibly due to acid hydrolysis of the DNA (see
Schümmelfeder et al. 1957). It is conceivable that the DNA content of
the abnormal intranuclear material of cells infected with adenovirus is in
some way protected from the action of DNase by a protein component.
If this interpretation proves to be correct, fluorescence microscopy will
have furnished additional evidence that adenoviruses contain DNA and
develop exclusively within the nucleus. Of interest also are the signs of
intranuclear activity involving RNA as well as DNA; enlargement and
enhanced RNA fluorescence of the nucleolus were the most obvious

features at an early stage of infection and we suggest that the nucleolus may play an important role in the establishment and multiplication of the virus. Nucleolar participation in normal protein synthesis is well known (Hydén, 1947b) and at least some degree of nucleolar hyper-trophy is common to all the host-virus systems we have studied.

Insect viruses

We are indebted to Dr Kenneth Smith, F.R.S., for a supply of infected larvae of *Tipula paludosa*, infected with either *Tipula*, iridescent virus or the virus of *Tipula* polyhedrosis. Both these viruses have been studied extensively with the electron microscope by Dr Smith and his collabora-tors (Smith & Williams, 1958). The iridescent virus produces its effects in the cells of the fat body and in ectodermal cells of the body wall; in *Tipula* polyhedrosis, the cells chiefly affected are the haemocytes of the blood. In the polyhedral disease electron microscopy revealed that virus rods appear within the nucleus; they accumulate in oval discrete masses adherent to the nuclear membrane, and are eventually discharged within crescentic polyhedra or 'crystals'. We have studied these stages in blood smears and tissue sections. In the least affected cells, the nuclei showed a dense network of greenish yellow material as well as one or more large homogeneous bodies giving a similar DNA fluorescence. At a later stage, part of the intranuclear fluorescent material became segre-gated in the form of oval, greenish yellow masses attached to the nuclear membrane, which was surrounded by a bright ring of cytoplasmic RNA material. Later, these greenish yellow masses came to lie within the red-fluorescing cytoplasm. At this stage, their fluorescence had become restricted to the inner border, that is, the surface last in contact with the nuclear membrane. Subsequently, as the cells disintegrated, they were discharged, and the extracellular polyhedra exhibited only a weak yellowish fluorescence. In the case of infection with *Tipula* iridescent virus the cell nuclei were enlarged, and there was a marked increase in the size of the nucleoli, but the most notable changes occurred in the cytoplasm. The affected cells were distended with granular material which emitted greenish yellow fluorescence of the DNA type, and replaced the normal cytoplasmic structures, including the lipoid vacuoles. This abnormal cytoplasmic material was resistant to direct digestion with DNase although the nuclear DNA of the infected cells was removed as readily as that of the normal cells. Pretreatment of the sections with pepsin did, however, render the cytoplasmic material entirely susceptible to DNase. In the case of *Tipula* polyhedrosis, however, pretreatment with pepsin had no such effect and the DNA of the infected cells remained resistant to the action of the specific nuclease. This result is in contrast with the finding that in cells infected with adenovirus, the abnormal intranuclear material did become susceptible to DNase following pepsin treatment.

Viruses of the pox group

Ectromelia (mouse pox) provided useful material for study since the virus produces diagnostic inclusions in squamous epithelium (Marchal, 1930). The disease is also characterized by necrosis in the liver, but, although virus can be recovered in high titre, no inclusions identical with those in the ectoderm are detected. It was rather surprising to find that these ectodermal inclusions gave a negative result with the acridine orange technique, a negative Feulgen reaction, and did not stain with either pyronin or methyl green. Since early work by Barnard & Elford (1931) had indicated that they contained virus elementary bodies it is obvious that this problem requires further study. The possibility exists, as now suggested for the Negri body of rabies (Croissant, Lépine & Wyckoff, 1955), that the inclusion is the result of virus activity, but is not composed of virus particles. In the liver, however, spherical bodies up to 3μ showing a typical greenish yellow DNA fluorescence were found in the cytoplasm of cells in which the nuclei, apart from nucleolar enlargement, were at first apparently normal. In cells containing such bodies, the normal cytoplasmic RNA fluorescence diminished and eventually disappeared. Meanwhile, the DNA-containing bodies increased in size and became more granular, and the intensity of their fluorescence diminished. As in the case of *Tipula* iridescent virus, the cytoplasmic DNA was resistant to the direct action of DNase but became susceptible to it after pretreatment with pepsin. In contrast with the ectodermal inclusion bodies in ectromelia, the Guarnieri bodies of vaccinia in corneal epithelium, which are known to be Feulgen-positive, gave a positive DNA fluorescence with the acridine orange technique.

Bearcroft & Jamieson (1958) have recently called attention to an infectious disease of rhesus monkeys, transmissible by filtered suspensions, which occurred at Yaba, Lagos, Nigeria: the disease is characterized by subcutaneous tumour-like lesions which persist for periods up to 10 weeks and then regress. It has provided interesting material for exploring the value of the acridine orange technique in a previously undescribed condition. The characteristic cells, apparently derived from fibroblasts, have large nuclei, with very prominent nucleoli, and the cytoplasm contains one or more dense paranuclear bodies of varying shape and size. Frequently these co-exist with areas of fine granularity in the same cell and a proportion of cells shows only diffuse granularity. The appearances thus suggest a series of developmental stages, the earliest being the dense inclusion which eventually becomes transformed into granular material. All these abnormal cytoplasmic constituents gave a striking DNA fluorescence with the acridine orange technique (Pl. 1, fig. 5), and, as in the case of other cytoplasmic virus DNA material already described, pretreatment with pepsin was necessary before it could be removed with DNase. Smears from the lesions showed the presence of numerous elementary bodies. Like vaccinia they exhibited fluorescence of the DNA type, and when examined with the electron microscope they resembled vaccinia in shape and size and in the possession of a pepsin-resistant central dense body.

Influenza virus

Our studies on the influenza virus are largely confined to calf kidney tissue cultures kindly provided by Dr D. A. J. Tyrrell. Virus titration of the tissue culture fluids showed that the progressive morphological changes which appeared during an observation period of 48 hr. broadly corresponded with an increasing yield of virus. The uninfected cells contained oval or circular nuclei with two or more nucleoli; the associated chromatin and a varying number of granules of precipitated chromatin, fluoresced a greenish yellow colour. The nuclear membrane showed up as a continuous line with an occasional small chromatin granule attached to it. In the cytoplasm, the RNA exhibited a diffuse fine granularity extending uniformly almost to the limit of the cell and closely surrounding the nucleus. Changes following infection appeared both in the nucleus and in the cytoplasm. Enlargement of the nucleoli was accompanied by the development of a diffuse red colour which filled the nucleus entirely . (Pl. 1, fig. 6). At first, the chromatin granules and the nucleoli could still be distinguished, but as the red fluorescence deepened all the other structures became invisible except the associated chromatin of the nucleoli which remained distinguishable as yellowish dots. The sharp outline of the nuclear membrane became indistinct and acquired a finely beaded appearance suggestive of breaks in continuity. The fluorescence of the fully developed intranuclear RNA was strikingly homogeneous and so contrasted with the fine granularity of the cytoplasmic RNA. Cytoplasmic changes were apparent at first only as an increased intensity of the RNA fluorescence, and various changes in the pattern of RNA fluorescence were not invariably associated with maximum development of intranuclear RNA. Sometimes very conspicuous tufts were seen extending from one or both poles of a nucleus which itself showed very little RNA; in other cells, the perinuclear cytoplasmic fluorescence was so intense that it was impossible to identify the nuclear membrane. Yet other cells showed very red nuclei and broad wavy streaks of intense, almost homogeneous, cytoplasmic fluorescence. After 48 hr., many of the cells disintegrated and we have not studied the changes beyond this point. The observations were carried out on both the W.S. and the MEL strains of influenza A. With the former, the intranuclear RNA fluorescence was very distinct, but only a proportion of the cells of the culture showed it at any given time. With the MEL strain, the intranuclear fluorescence was never so conspicuous, but the degree of cytological involvement was more uniform throughout the cultures. With both strains, the intranuclear RNA was completely susceptible to the action of RNase without the need of pretreatment with a proteolytic enzyme. As infection progressed, mitoses in the cultures became less numerous, but cells in division could still be found up to the end of the observation period. An interesting feature was noted in some dividing cells. In prophase and telophase, the chromosomes showed the intense yellow fluorescence characteristic of concentrated DNA. In metaphase and early anaphase, the chromosomes emitted a reddish fluorescence as though covered by a coating of RNA. Whether this represents the nucleolar RNA, which is alleged to be distributed on the chromosomal surfaces during certain stages of division, or is related to the virus infection has not yet been determined.

West Nile encephalitis virus

We wish to thank our colleague, Dr James Porterfield, for a supply of infected tissue cultures on which these preliminary observations have been made. Since the essential constituent of this virus is RNA (Colter, Bird, Moyer & Brown, 1957), this study has provided useful material for comparison with tissue cultures infected with influenza virus. The material consisted of monolayer cultures of chicken fibroblasts and the changes were observed for 6 days. The progression of events is thus considerably slower than in influenza or poliomyelitis (Tenenbaum, 1957; Anderson, Macrae & Wilson, 1957, unpublished). In contrast with influenza, the major site of activity in the early stage of infection was apparently in the cytoplasm. The fine RNA granularity became more coarse and its fluorescence brighter and this was accompanied by enlargement of the nucleus and of the nucleoli. The chromatin network appeared slightly more distinct, but at no time was this very conspicuous. On the third day after infection, however, the nucleoli of many of the cells assumed bizarre shapes, sometimes appearing as granular bands extending across the nucleus. About the fourth day, one or more prominent masses of bright-red-fluorescing material appeared in the cytoplasm and subsequently these could be seen close to the cell surfaces, attached to long tenuous cell processes or lying free. As the cytoplasmic aggregates accumulated, the nucleolar and nuclear fluorescence diminished. Apart from the nucleolar changes, the nuclear morphology remained singularly unaltered until degeneration was well advanced.

Extracellular virus

In addition to the virus-infected cells mentioned above we have examined a number of purified virus preparations in the form of fixed and dried smears. Epstein & Holt (1958) have also studied in this way pure preparations of the Rous sarcoma virus, and have obtained a positive reaction for RNA. Reference was made earlier to the DNA-type of fluorescence exhibited by the free elementary bodies of vaccinia virus the size of which is known to be about 200 mμ. The other materials tested were viruses of which the individual units are smaller than vaccinia; that is, ultramicroscopic. *Tipula* iridescent virus was examined in the form of Carnoy-fixed smears treated with acridine orange at pH 3·5. Diffuse greenish yellow fluorescence was given by the thicker parts of the smear, but elsewhere observation with the oil-immersion objective showed the fluorescence to be originating from many identical and minute point sources. The DNA content of this virus is already known and each particle measures 130 mμ (Williams & Smith, 1958). It is conceivable that in this instance, as with phage T2, each ultramicroscopic particle after combination with the fluorochrome is capable of forming a visible fluorescent image when activated with blue-violet light. The same result was not obtained with purified preparations of influenza (MEL, 1935; A/Persian Gulf/2/52) and poliomyelitis (Type 1: Mahoney) viruses, nor with samples of tobacco mosaic and turnip yellow mosaic viruses, all of which are known to contain RNA. Dried concentrates when fixed and treated with acridine orange in the usual manner gave diffuse red fluorescence, turnip yellow mosaic virus producing the strongest reaction. However, wider dispersal of these virus preparations resulted only in diminished intensity of the general red fluorescence, and in none was it possible to identify with conviction discrete point sources of emission which might be related to individual particles or filaments. Detection of such individual units by virtue of their RNA content is evidently beyond the limit of sensitivity of the technique, at least in its present form.

CONCLUSION

The acridine orange fluorescence technique has been developed as a cytochemical procedure for the study of intracellular nucleic acids, and its value in any investigation of the host–virus relationship and the formation of new virus is limited unless the observations are supported by biochemical and immunological data and electron microscope studies. Qualitative changes in the distribution of nucleic acids in normal sites may be the result of a reaction of the cell to the infection, but the appearance of RNA in the nuclei of cells infected with influenza and of DNA in the cytoplasm of cells infected with agents of the pox group and *Tipula* iridescent virus may, with some justification, be regarded as indications of certain critical stages in the formation of new virus. So far, no cytochemical method has been found of distinguishing host-cell RNA in cytoplasm from RNA which will become incorporated in virus; but in the case of DNA a relative insusceptibility to the action of DNase is a constant feature in the animal virus infections examined, and further study may reveal some distinguishing property of virus RNA. The experiments with bacteriophages and *Tipula* iridescent virus suggest that free virus particles beyond the range of the bright-field microscope can be visualized by fluorescence. This may provide us with a simple method of studying the release of some viruses from infected cells. A combination of the acridine orange technique with the fluorescent-antibody method of Coons & Kaplan (1950) for intracellular localization of virus antigens should also add substantially to our knowledge of the whole cycle of virus development.

Although the potentialities of fluorescence microscopy were first noted by Köhler as early as 1904, the value of induced fluorescence for the chemical exploration of normal and infected cells has only recently been recognized. We have attempted to indicate that in this field it possesses some unique advantages over other methods of microscopy and forms at least a valuable adjunct to them.

One of us (E.S.A.) is greatly indebted to Miss E. M. J. Wilson for her assistance with the work on bacterophage growth, and all the authors wish to acknowledge the advice and help with optical problems and fluorescence photomicrography given by Mr J. Smiles, O.B.E., and Mr M. R. Young of the Division of Biophysics and Optics, National Institute for Medical Research, Mill Hill, London, N.W. 7.

REFERENCES

ANDERSON, E. S. (1957). Visual observation of deoxyribonucleic acid changes in bacteria during growth of bacteriophage. *Nature, Lond.* **180**, 1336.

ANDERSON, E. S. & FELIX, A. (1953). The Vi-type-determining phages carried by *Salmonella typhi. J. gen. Microbiol.* **9**, 65.

ARMSTRONG, J. A. (1956). Histochemical differentiation of nucleic acids by means of induced fluorescence. *Exp. Cell Res.* **11**, 640.

ARMSTRONG, J. A. (1957). Further comments on tissue fluorescence induced by acridine orange R. *J. Anat., Lond.* **91**, 570.

ARMSTRONG, J. A. & HOPPER, P. K. (1959). Fluorescence and phase-contrast microscopy of human cell cultures infected with adenovirus (in the Press).

ARMSTRONG, J. A. & NIVEN, J. S. F. (1957). Histochemical observations on cellular and virus nucleic acids. *Nature, Lond.* **180**, 1335.

BARNARD, J. E. & ELFORD, W. J. (1931). The causative agent in infectious ectromelia. *Proc. roy. Soc.* B, **109**, 360.

BARSKI, G. (1956). Caractère spécifique de la lésion cellulaire causée *in vitro* par les virus du groupe A.P.C. et sa valeur diagnostique. *Ann. Inst. Pasteur*, **91**, 614.

BEARCROFT, W. G. C. & JAMIESON, M. F. (1958). An outbreak of subcutaneous tumours in rhesus monkeys. *Nature, Lond.* **182**, 195.

BEERS, JUN., R. F., HENDLEY, D. D. & STEINER, R. F. (1958). Inhibition and activation of polynucleotide phosphorylase through the formation of complexes between acridine orange and polynucleotides. *Nature, Lond.* **182**, 242.

BERTALANFFY, L. VON & BICKIS, I. (1956). Identification of cytoplasmic basophilia (ribonucleic acid) by fluorescence microscopy. *J. Histochem. Cytochem.* **4**, 481.

BERTALANFFY, L. VON, MASIN, F. & MASIN, M. (1956). Use of acridine orange fluorescence technique in exfoliative cytology. *Science*, **124**, 1024.

BERTANI, G. (1951). Studies on lysogenesis. I. The mode of phage liberation by lysogenic *Escherichia coli. J. Bact.* **62**, 293.

BERTANI, G. (1953a). Infections bactériophagiques secondaires des bactéries lysogènes. *Ann. Inst. Pasteur*, **84**, 273.

BERTANI, G. (1953b). Lysogenic versus lytic cycle of phage multiplication. *Cold Spr. Harb. Symp. quant. Biol.* **18**, 65.

BERTANI, G. & NICE, S. J. (1954). Studies on lysogenesis. II. The effect of temperature on the lysogenization of *Shigella dysenteriae* with phage P1. *J. Bact.* **67**, 202.

BERTANI, L. E. (1957). The effect of the inhibition of protein synthesis on the establishment of lysogeny. *Virology*, **4**, 53.

BEUTNER, E. H., HARTMAN, P. E., MUDD, S. & HILLIER, J. (1953). Light and electron microscopic studies of *Escherichia coli*–coliphage interactions. I. Preparative method. Comparative light and electron microscopic cytology of the *E. coli* B-T2 system. *Biochem. biophys. Acta*, **10**, 143.

BLAND, J. & ROBINOW, C. F. (1939). The inclusion bodies of vaccinia and their relationship to the elementary bodies studied in cultures of the rabbit's cornea. *J. Path. Bact.* **48**, 381.

BOGEN, H. G. (1953). Anfärbung, Schädigung und Abtötung von Hefezellen durch Acridinorange. *Arch. Mikrobiol.* **18**, 170.

BOYER, G. S., LEUCHTENBERGER, C. & GINSBERG, H. (1957). Cytological and cytochemical studies of HeLa cells infected with adenoviruses. *J. exp. Med.* **105**, 195.

BRACHET, J. (1942). La localisation des acides pentose nucléiques dans les tissus animaux et les œufs d'amphibiens en voie de développement. *Arch. Biol., Paris*, **53**, 207.

BRACHET, J. (1947). Nucleic acids in the cells and the embryo. *Symp. Soc. exp. Biol.* **1**, 207.

BUKATSCH, F. & HAITINGER, M. (1940). Beiträge zur Fluoreszenzmikroskopischen Darstellung des Zellinhaltes, insbesondere des Cytoplasmas und des Zellkerns. *Protoplasma*, **34**, 515.

CLARK, A. M. (1953). The mutagenic activity of dyes in *Drosophila melanogaster*. *Amer. Nat.* **87**, 295.

COLTER, J. S., BIRD, H. H., MOYER, A. W. & BROWN, R. A. (1957). Infectivity of ribonucleic acid isolated from virus infected tissues. *Virology*, **4**, 522.

COONS, A. H. & KAPLAN, M. H. (1950). Localization of antigen in tissue cells. II. Improvements in a method for the detection of antigen by means of fluorescent antibody. *J. exp. Med.* **91**, 1.

COWDRY, E. V. (1934). The problem of intranuclear inclusions in virus diseases. *Arch. Path.* **18**, 527.

CRAIGIE, J. & YEN, C. (1938). The demonstration of types of *B. typhosus* by means of preparations of Type II Vi-phage. *Canad. publ. Hlth J.* **29**, 448, 484.

CROISSANT, O., LÉPINE, P. & WYCKOFF, R. W. (1955). Recherches sur l'ultrastructure des corps de Negri examinés au microscope électronique. *Ann. Inst. Pasteur*, **89**, 183.

DE BRUYN, P. P. H., FARR, R. S., BANKS, H. & MORTHLAND, F. W. (1953). *In vivo* and *in vitro* affinity of diaminoacridines for nucleoproteins. *Exp. Cell Res.* **4**, 174.

DE BRUYN, P. P. H., ROBERTSON, R. C. & FARR, R. S. (1950). *In vivo* affinity of diaminoacridines for nuclei. *Anat. Rec.* **108**, 279.

DEMARS, R. I. (1953). Chemical mutagenesis in bacteriophage T2. *Nature, Lond.* **172**, 964.

DEMARS, R. I. (1955). The production of phage-related materials when bacteriophage development is interrupted by proflavine. *Virology*, **1**, 83.

DEMARS, R. I., LURIA, S. E., FISHER, H. & LEVINTHAL, C. (1953). The production of incomplete bacteriophage particles by the action of proflavine and the properties of the incomplete particles. *Ann. Inst. Pasteur*, **84**, 113.

EPHRUSSI, B. & HOTTINGUER, H. (1950). Direct demonstration of the mutagenic action of euflavine on baker's yeast. *Nature, Lond.* **166**, 956.

EPSTEIN, M. A. & HOLT, S. J. (1958). Observations on the Rous Virus; integrated electron microscopical and cytochemical studies of fluorocarbon-purified preparations. *Brit. J. Cancer*, **12**, 363.

FELIX, A. & ANDERSON, E. S. (1951). Bacteriophages carried by the Vi-phage types of *Salmonella typhi*. *Nature, Lond.* **167**, 603.

GÄRTNER, K. (1943). Ein Beitrag zur Färbbarkeit der lebenden und toten Bakterienzelle. Gleichzeitig eine Mitteilung über die Bakterienstruktur und deren chemotherapeutische Beeinflussbarkeit. *Z. Hyg. InfektKr.* **125**, 86.

GOODPASTURE, E. W. & TEAGUE, O. (1923). Experimental production of herpetic lesions in organs and tissues of the rabbit. *J. med. Res.* **44**, 121.

GÖSSNER, W. (1949). Zur Histochemie des Strugger-Effektes. *Verh. dtsch. path. Ges.* **33**, 102.

HAGEMANN, P. K. H. (1937). Virus-Fluoreszenzmikroskopie. Eine neue Sichtbarmachung filtrierbarer Viruskörperchen. *Münch. med. Wschr.* **84**, 761.

HAITINGER, M. (1938). Die Fluoreszenzmikroskopie. In *Handbuch der Virusforschung*, vol. 1. Edited by R. Doerr and C. Hallauer. Vienna: Julius Springer.

HARTMAN, P. E., MUDD, S., HILLIER, J. & BEUTNER, E. H. (1953). Light and electron microscopic studies of *Escherichia coli*–coliphage interactions. III. Persistence of mitochondria reductase activity during infections of *Escherichia coli* B with T2 phage. *J. Bact.* **65**, 706.

HERSHEY, A. D. (1953). Nucleic acid economy in bacteria infected with bacteriophage T2. II. Phage precursor nucleic acid. *J. gen. Physiol.* **37**, 1.

HERSHEY, A. D. & CHASE, M. (1952). Independent functions of viral protein and nucleic acid in growth of bacteriophage. *J. gen. Physiol.* **36**, 39.

HERSHEY, A. D., KAMEN, M. D., KENNEDY, J. W. & GEST, H. (1951). The mortality of bacteriophage containing assimilated radioactive phosphorus. *J. gen. Physiol.* **34**, 305.

HYDÉN, H. (1947a). The nucleoproteins in virus reproduction. *Cold Spr. Harb. Symp. quant. Biol.* **12**, 104.

HYDÉN, H. (1947b). Protein and nucleotide metabolism in the nerve cell under different functional conditions. *Symp. Soc. exp. Biol.* **1**, 152.

HYDÉN, H. & CASPERSSON, T. (1945). Högre virusarters förökning. *Nord. med. Ark.* **28**, 2631.

IRVIN, J. L. & IRVIN, E. M. (1954). The interaction of a 9-aminoacridine derivative with nucleic acids and nucleoproteins. *J. biol. Chem.* **206**, 39.

IRVIN, J. L., IRVIN, E. M. & PARKER, F. S. (1949). The interaction of antimalarials with nucleic acids. I. Acridines. II. Quinolines. *Science*, **110**, 426.

JACOBSON, W. & WEBB, M. (1952). The two types of nucleoproteins during mitosis. *Exp. Cell Res.* **3**, 163.

KELLENBERGER, E. (1953). Les formes caractéristiques des nucléoïdes de *E. coli* et leurs transformations dues à l'action d'agents mutagènes-inducteurs et de bactériophages. *Symp. on Bacterial Cytology. VIth Int. Congr. Microbiol.* Inst. Sup. Sanità, Rome, 1953, p. 45.

KELLENBERGER, G. & KELLENBERGER, E. (1957). Electron microscopical studies of phage multiplication. III. Observation of single cell bursts. *Virology*, **3**, 275.

KELLENBERGER, E. & SÉCHAUD, J. (1957). Electron microscopical studies of phage multiplication. II. Production of phage-related structures during multiplication of phages T2 and T4. *Virology*, **3**, 256.

KJELLÉN, L., LAGERMALM, G., SVEDMYR, A. & THORSSON, K. G. (1955). Crystalline-like patterns in the nuclei of cells infected with an animal virus. *Nature, Lond.* **175**, 505.

KÖHLER, A. (1904). Eine mikrophotographische Einrichtung für das ultraviolette Licht und damit angestellte Untersuchungen organischer Gewebe. *Wien. med. Wschr.* **54**, 2067.

KREBS, A. T. & GIERLACH, Z. S. (1951). Vital staining with the fluorochrome acridine orange and its application to radiobiology. 1. Alpha-ray effects. *Amer. J. Roentgenol.* **65**, 93.

KRIEG, A. (1953a). Fluoreszcenzanalyse und Fluorochromie in Biologie und Medizin. *Klin. Wschr.* **31**, 350.

KRIEG, A. (1953b). Fluoreszenzmikroskopischer Nachweis von Kernäquivalenten in Bakterien. *Naturwissenschaften.* **40**, 414.

KRIEG, A. (1954). Mikroskopische Studien *in vivo* zur Zytologie der Hefezelle. *Experientia*, **10**, 172.

LASNITZKI, I. & WILKINSON, J. H. (1948). The effect of acridine derivatives on growth and mitosis of cells *in vivo*. *Brit. J. Cancer*, **2**, 369.

LAWLEY, P. D. (1956). Interaction studies with DNA. IV. The binding of 5-aminoacridine studied fluorimetrically, and its comparison with the binding of rosaniline. *Biochim. biophys. Acta*, **22**, 451.

LEVADITI, J. C. (1944). Étude comparée de la fluorescence provoquée chez les bactéries par la thioflavine ou par l'orange d'acridine. *C.R. Soc. Biol., Paris*, **138**, 136.

LEVADITI, J. C., LÉPINE, P. & AUGIER, J. (1948). Étude au moyen de la microscopie en fluorescence, des inclusions intracellulaires acidophiles provoquées par les virus de la rage, de la vaccine, de la maladie de Borna. *C.R. Acad. Sci., Paris,* **227**, 1061.

LEVADITI, J. C. & PANTHIER, R. (1945). La microscopie en fluorescence de *Rickettsia prowazeki. C.R. Soc. Biol., Paris,* **139**, 890.

LEVADITI, J. C., REINIÉ, L., STAMATIN, MME., LE-VAN-SEN & BÉQUIGNON, R. (1940). Ultravirus et fluorescence. Le virus vaccinal. Pt. 1. *Ann. Inst. Pasteur,* **64**, 359.

LOVE, R. (1957). Distribution of ribonucleic acid in tumour cells during mitosis. *Nature, Lond.* **180**, 1338.

LURIA, S. E. & HUMAN, M. L. (1950). Chromatin staining of bacteria during bacteriophage infection. *J. Bact.* **59**, 551.

LURIA, S. E. & PALMER, J. L. (1946). Cytological studies of bacteria and bacteriophage growth. *Carnegie Inst. Wash. Yearbook,* **45**, 153.

MARCHAL, J. (1930). Infectious ectromelia. *J. Path. Bact.* **33**, 713.

MCILWAIN, H. (1941). A nutritional investigation of the antibacterial action of acriflavine. *Biochem. J.* **35**, 1311.

MORGAN, C., HOWE, C., ROSE, H. M. & MOORE, D. H. (1956). Structure and development of viruses observed in the electron microscope. IV. Viruses of the RI-APC group. *J. biophys. biochem. Cytol.* **2**, 351.

MORGAN, C., ROSE, H. M. & MOORE, D. H. (1957). An evaluation of host cell changes accompanying viral multiplication as observed in the electron microscope. *Ann. N.Y. Acad. Sci.* **68**, 302.

MORGAN, C., ROSE, H. M. & MOORE, D. H. (1958). Use of the electron microscope in the study of intracellular virus. *Bull. N.Y. Acad. Med.* **34**, 85.

MORTHLAND, F. W., DE BRUYN, P. P. H. & SMITH, N. H. (1954). Spectrophotometric studies on the interaction of nucleic acids with aminoacridines and other basic dyes. *Exp. Cell Res.* **7**, 201.

MUDD, S., HILLIER, J., BEUTNER, E. & HARTMAN, P. E. (1953). Light and electron microscopic studies of *Escherichia coli*–coliphage interactions. II. The electron microscopic cytology of the *E. coli* B-T2 system. *Biochem. biophys. Acta,* **10**, 153.

MURRAY, R. G. E., GILLEN, D. H. & HEAGY, F. C. (1950). Cytological changes in *Escherichia coli* produced by infection with phage T2. *J. Bact.* **59**, 603.

MURRAY, R. G. E. & WHITFIELD, J. F. (1953). Cytological effects of infection with T5 and some related phages. *J. Bact.* **65**, 715.

PEACOCKE, A. R. & SKERRETT, J. N. H. (1956). The interaction of aminoacridines with nucleic acids. *Trans. Faraday Soc.* **52**, 261.

ROBINOW, C. F. (1942). A study of the nuclear apparatus of bacteria. *Proc. roy. Soc.* B, **130**, 299.

ROBINOW, C. F. (1944). Cytological observations on *Bact. coli, Proteus vulgaris* and various aerobic spore-bearing bacteria with special reference to the nuclear structures. *J. Hyg., Camb.* **43**, 413.

ROBINOW, C. F. (1945). Nuclear apparatus and cell structure of rod-shaped bacteria. Addendum to R. J. Dubos, *The Bacterial Cell.* Harvard University Press, Cambridge, Mass.

SCHULER, R. (1952). Die vitale Darstellung der Chromatinstrukturen von *Bacterium-coli* mit Hilfe des Fluoreszenzmikroskopes. *Naturwissenschaften,* **39**, 90.

SCHULER, R. (1954). Die vitale Darstellung der Chromatinstrukturen von *Bacterium-coli* mit Hilfe des Fluoreszenzmikroskopes. *Arch. Protistenk.* **99**, 227.

SCHÜMMELFEDER, N., EBSCHNER, K. J. & KROGH, E. (1957). Die Grundlage der differenten Fluorochromierung von Ribo- und Desoxyribonucleinsäure mit Acridinorange. *Naturwissenschaften,* **44**, 467.

SMITH, K. M. & WILLIAMS, R. C. (1958). Insect viruses and their structure. *Endeavour*, **17**, 12.

STEINER, R. F. & BEERS, JUN., R. F. (1958) Spectral changes accompanying binding of acridine orange by polyadenylic acid. *Science*, **127**, 335.

STOCKINGER, L. (1958). Fluoreszenzuntersuchungen an Gewebekulturen. I. Die metachromatische Vitalfluoreszenz mit Acridinorange. *Z. Naturf.* **13**b, 407.

STRUGGER, S. (1940). Fluoreszenzmikroskopische Untersuchungen über die Aufnahme und Speicherung des Acridinorange durch lebende und tote Pflanzenzellen. *Jena. Z. Naturw.* **73**, 97.

STRUGGER, S. (1949). *Fluoreszenzmikroskopie und Mikrobiologie.* Hanover: M. and H. Schaper.

TENENBAUM, E. (1957). Changes in cellular nucleic acids during infection with poliomyelitis virus as studied by fluorescence microscopy. *Nature, Lond.* **180**, 1044.

VISCONTI, N. & DELBRÜCK, M. (1953). The mechanism of genetic recombination in phage. *Genetics*, **38**, 5.

WHITFIELD, J. F. & MURRAY, R. G. E. (1954). A cytological study of the lysogenization of *Shigella dysenteriae* with P1 and P2 bacteriophages. *Canad. J. Microbiol.* **1**, 216.

WHITFIELD, J. F. & MURRAY, R. G. E. (1956). The effects of the ionic environment on the chromatin structures of bacteria. *Canad. J. Microbiol.* **2**, 245.

WHITFIELD, J. F. & MURRAY, R. G. E. (1957). Observations on the initial cytological effects of bacteriophage infection. *Canad. J. Microbiol.* **3**, 493.

WILLIAMS, R. C. & SMITH, K. (1958). The polyhedral form of the *Tipula* iridescent virus. *Biochim. biophys. Acta*, **28**, 464.

ZEIGER, K., HARDERS, H. & MÜLLER, W. (1951). Der Strugger-Effekt an der Nervenzelle. *Protoplasma*, **40**, 76.

ELECTRON-MICROSCOPIC OBSERVATIONS ON ADENOVIRUSES AND VIRUSES OF THE INFLUENZA GROUP

COUNCILMAN MORGAN AND HARRY M. ROSE

Department of Microbiology, College of Physicians and Surgeons, Columbia University, New York

INTRODUCTION

The two viruses chosen for discussion are presented in somewhat different ways. Due to the fact that adenoviruses were discovered relatively recently and possess several peculiar properties which impede investigation by immunological and chemical means, the bulk of our information derives from morphological study. Accordingly, viral structure and the types of host-cell response which accompany viral multiplication are described in considerable detail. Our knowledge concerning the influenza viruses, on the other hand, has accumulated during two decades through intensive investigation with a variety of techniques. Consequently, in presenting this second group of viruses an attempt has been made to correlate morphology observed in the electron microscope with data acquired by other methods.

In each instance it will become evident that the studies to be reported are preliminary in nature. The factors responsible for this state of affairs apply to any investigation by electron microscopy of intracellular events, and are therefore worthy of mention. Only 1/500 the volume of any cell is contained within a section.* Moreover, examination of high resolution micrographs is the sole method whereby details of viral structure are rendered visible. Considering the number of cells growing in a tissue culture tube or composing the surface of a chorio-allantoic membrane, it becomes evident that a certain degree of caution must be exercised in interpreting electron-microscopic data. Statistically significant information is even harder to acquire when the changes accompanying viral proliferation are confined to a small locus, or do not occur regularly in every infected cell. Difficulty also arises when one attempts to correlate structure with function. Most immunological and chemical data represent composite results obtained from the interaction of large

---

* Average section thickness approximates $0\cdot03\mu$ (Morgan, Ellison, Rose & Moore, 1955).

viral and cell populations over a period of time, whereas a micrograph depicts part of a cell containing relatively few viral particles fixed at one moment in time. These are some of the problems.

ADENOVIRUSES

Following the initial isolation of adenoviruses from tissue cultures of human adenoidal cells (Rowe, Huebner, Gilmore, Parrott & Ward, 1953) and from HeLa cells inoculated with throat washings of a patient with acute respiratory disease (Hilleman & Werner, 1954), at least six-teen serotypes have been identified (Rowe, Huebner & Bell, 1957). Of these the first eight are under study in our laboratory.

Kjellén, Lagermalm, Svedmyr & Thorsson (1955) first recognized that adenoviruses crystallize *in vivo*, a fact confirmed by Harford, Hamlin & Parker (1955). Several papers subsequently appeared (Morgan, Howe, Rose & Moore, 1956; Harford, Hamlin, Parker & van Ravenswaay, 1956; Lagermalm, Kjellén, Thorsson & Svedmyr, 1957) which illustrate the structure of the virus and the appearances of infected nuclei. Diffi-culty was encountered, however, in determining the temporal sequence of nuclear changes. Since a relatively small proportion of cells can be infected with the initial inoculum, it has proved impossible to assemble sufficient data by electron microscopy before the first release of virus. Infection of the remaining cells occurs at random intervals thereafter, so that a variety of stages coexist. Study of stained coverslip preparations in the light microscope, however, permits recognition of the temporal progression of morphological changes (Boyer, Leuchtenberger & Gins-berg, 1957) by virtue of the fact that whole cells can be visualized and large cell-populations surveyed. The advantages of the light microscope may be added to those of the electron microscope (high resolution and minimal superimposition of structure) simply by examining the same cells with both techniques in contiguous thick and thin sections (Bloch, Morgan, Godman, Howe & Rose, 1957). In collaboration with Dr Gab-riel C. Godman, infected cultures of HeLa and HEp-2 cells were fixed and stained at intervals from 12 to 36 hr. after inoculation and the sequence of nuclear changes established by light microscopy. Cultures exhibiting more extensive cytopathology were then viewed in contiguous thick and thin sections, and, by correlation with the light-microscope studies, the stages of viral development revealed in the electron micro-graphs could be arranged consecutively with some degree of certainty.*

* Unless specific mention is made of another fixative, all the material to be illustrated and described was fixed in 1 % buffered, isotonic osmium tetroxide.

The results of these investigations have confirmed the sequence tentatively proposed on the basis of electron microscopy alone (Morgan, Howe, Rose & Moore, 1956).

Development

The first recognizable manifestation of infection is the aggregation of dense reticulum at multiple foci within the nucleus, as shown in Pl. 1, fig. 1. A few viral particles are present in the lower right corner of the field. Pl. 1, fig. 2 illustrates part of a nucleus at a later stage. Adjacent to the aggregates of reticulum the virus has now formed clusters, most of which exhibit crystalline order. In the light microscope the reticulum is eosinophilic and Feulgen-negative, whereas the viral clusters are basophilic and Feulgen-positive. At higher magnification (Pl. 2, fig. 3) the reticular material is more clearly defined and its close association with the virus becomes evident. This spatial relationship, together with the observation that the reticulum diminishes as the virus increases, suggests that the reticular material contributes in some manner to propagation of the virus. Ill-defined particles are often visible within the reticulum, but forms which could be considered to represent consecutive stages in differentiation have been difficult to identify. Probably individual particles evolve rapidly with the result that fixation in 'mid-passage' rarely occurs. Nucleoli appear to remain intact and exhibit no consistent orientation with respect to the developing virus.

Crystallization

Comparison of Pl. 1, fig. 2 and Pl. 2, fig. 3, illustrating adenoviral types 3 and 1, respectively, draws attention to a striking difference in the propensity of the virus to crystallize. The strains of types 3, 4, 7 and 8, which have been studied, commonly form numerous crystals, whereas types 1, 2, 5 and 6 exhibit less tendency to crystallize. The question naturally arises as to why viruses which appear to be so similar in structure and manner of development should differ in the extent to which they crystallize. The theory could be advanced that the sparse nuclear matrix shown in Pl. 2, fig. 3 facilitates diffusion of the particles. In many instances, however, the matrix adjacent to randomly oriented virus is indistinguishable from that enclosing crystals. It appears more likely that crystallization depends on the rapidity of viral differentiation at any given template site. If large amounts of virus formed within a short interval of time, the nuclear matrix might be displaced, thus allowing the electrostatic forces carried by the particles to operate before dispersal occurred. In other words, a high degree of purity occurring even briefly at one or more foci would predispose toward crystallization. Supporting this concept is the fact that at sites where orientation of the virus into crystalline arrays is apparently beginning, no matrix of the type seen in Pl. 2, fig. 3 separates particles within the clusters. The observation that type 3 propagates at a slower rate than types 1 and 2 (Ginsberg, 1958) does not conflict with the foregoing hypothesis, since the infectivity of a culture at any given stage depends upon the total number of template sites, as well as the duration and the rapidity of viral development at each site.

Pl. 2, fig. 4 illustrates a rhomboidal-shaped crystal of type 3 adeno-virus. The differing particle density is characteristic of all the adeno-viruses which have been examined. In the left third of the figure are six tubules (five cross-sectioned and one cut obliquely) composed of lami-nated membranes. Nuclear membranes, either forming tubules or arranged as parallel lamellae (Morgan, Rose & Moore, 1957), have been repeatedly encountered in association with type 3. Interestingly enough, incubation of infected cells in media devoid of serum increases the ten-dency of the nucleus to behave in this peculiar manner. Although such structures exhibit no consistent spatial relationship to the adenovirus, nuclear membranes do appear to play an important role in the develop-ment and release of herpes simplex virus (C. Morgan, to be published). This suggests the possibility that two viruses differing markedly in morphology can incite a common host cell response which proves of benefit to one but is quite useless to the other.

The crystals may attain considerable size, as shown in Pl. 3, fig. 5. This section is relatively thick, resulting in some superimposition of particles. The irregular crystalline faces and dispersed virus in the nuclear matrix are commonly found at late stages of infection and are believed to reflect early dissolution of the crystal.

Study of crystals sectioned at differing angles indicates that the lattice is cubic body-centred (Low & Pinnock, 1956). Since the crystals appear to be pure with no visible material separating adjacent viral particles and since they are strongly and consistently stained with the Feulgen reaction (Bloch et al. 1957), one is led to conclude that the virus itself probably contains deoxyribonucleic acid. Boyer, Leuchtenberger & Ginsberg (1957), employing microspectrophotometry, observed an increase in nuclear DNA, but they did not make quantitative determinations nor estimate the proportion of viral, as opposed to host cell, nucleic acid.

Structure

Turning to the morphology of the virus, it is evident that, although there are intermediate forms, two types predominate. One is dense with little visible internal structure; the other, which constitutes the majority of particles, is less dense and contains an internal body. Pl. 4, fig. 6 illustrates an unusually thin section wherein these differences are evident.* The internal body is approximately 250 Å in diameter. Taking into account compression caused by sectioning, the particles themselves average 600 Å. The closest centre-to-centre spacing of the virus in this field approaches 700 Å, whereas in most of the crystals it measures 650 Å. Such discrepancies suggest that minor variations in the degree of packing can occur during preparation of the specimen. Fixation with formalin instead of osmium tetroxide alters the appearance of the virus, as shown in the crystal illustrated by Pl. 4, fig. 7.† Several particles exhibit an internal body which approximates the size of the virus (600 Å) observed in osmium-fixed preparations. In addition, there is a sharply defined, frequently incomplete, peripheral membrane, c. 650 Å in diameter. A crystalline array is hardly recognizable due to the fact that many particles are ill-defined or missing entirely. Presumably the dense particles have been preserved, whereas those of lesser density were distorted or obliterated. Pl. 4, fig. 8 illustrates randomly dispersed, formalin-fixed virus. This section was exposed to fumes of osmium tetroxide before examination in the electron microscope. The particles of lesser density are now quite clearly defined, suggesting that their destruction in the preceding preparation resulted from impact of the electron beam. Similar disintegration after formalin fixation and stabilization by osmium tetroxide have been noted for other viruses (Morgan, Moore & Rose, 1956).

Thus adenoviral particles appear to differ not only morphologically, but also in their resistance, after formalin fixation at least, to bombardment by electrons. It is unlikely that the structural differences reflect stages in development, since the proportion of the two major forms remains relatively constant regardless of the duration of infection. If one form represents aberrant, non-infectious virus, the discrepancy between the high particle counts and low infectivity titres observed by Hilleman, Tousimis & Werner (1955) could be explained.

Size

The actual size of the virus is not known. In osmium-fixed crystals, a zone 50 Å wide and containing no discernible structure separates the viral particles, which are generally spaced at 650 Å. In formalin-fixed crystals a limiting membrane 650 Å in diameter encloses the virus. It is possible, therefore, that the particles are contiguous, but that fixation in

---

* Poorly demarcated particles are probably eccentric to the plane of section.
† Pl. 4, figs. 6, 7 and 8 are reproduced at the same magnification.

osmium tetroxide, while preserving the crystalline lattice, fails to render visible the peripheral viral membrane. If there is indeed contiguity, then X-ray crystallographic determination of unit-cell dimensions in the hydrated state should provide an accurate measurement of viral size.

Shape

In preparations of virus fixed with osmium and dried from suspension the particles have a polyhedral shape (Valentine & Hopper, 1957; Tousimis & Hilleman, 1957). The surface forces accompanying the process of drying, however, make these observations difficult to evaluate. It appears unlikely that the procedure of embedding or sectioning would obliterate a pre-existing polyhedral shape, since sections of *T. paludosa* virus clearly reveal a six-sided contour (Williams & Smith, 1957). We are inclined, therefore, toward the belief that the spherical shape of the adenoviruses in thin sections does not represent an artifact.

Stability

The virus appears to be remarkably stable and intact particles abound in necrotic cells, showing dissolution of most cytological components. Occasionally, however, viral disintegration is encountered. Pl. 4, fig. 9 illustrates an intranuclear crystal composed of particles, many of which are indistinct and devoid of recognizable structure. It would be of interest to know what proportion of the virus is destroyed before release.

Release

Correlation of the pathological changes observed by light microscopy with titres of intra- and extracellular virus led Ginsberg (1958) to conclude that 'a unique feature of the adenoviruses studied is the inability of the virus to dissociate from host cells to any great extent, even when cells have undergone marked cytopathic alterations'. This view is supported by electron micrographs, which reveal that the majority of nuclei remain intact as long as the cells adhere to the glass wall of the tissue culture tube. Many swollen nuclei resemble sacks stuffed with virus. A puzzling observation in this regard is the striking dissociation between the extent of nuclear change and the amount of virus produced. Two nuclei may appear similar morphologically—both markedly swollen and possessing few remnants of the matrix; and, yet, one is filled with virus, whereas the other is nearly devoid of recognizable particles.

When the nuclear membrane does disrupt, virus is released into the cytoplasm, an event which can occur at any stage of infection. The crystals undergo dissolution and the virus disperses. Pl. 5, fig. 10 illustrates cytoplasm near the cell surface, which traverses the left third of the field vertically. Four intracellular viral particles are evident in the lower half. Close inspection of the cell membrane shows that it is discontinuous and that fragments of the cytoplasm are extruding into the extracellular space, which occupies the right portion of the field. Several cytoplasmic extensions from a neighbouring cell are visible near the right border, and four viral particles lie free in the extracellular space. The frequent presence of virus adjacent to ruptured host cells, together with the fact that virus has not been encountered in transit either through nuclear membranes or cell walls, leads one to agree with Ginsberg (1958) that 'it is problematical whether spontaneous dissociation of virus from intact infected cells ensues at all', at least under these experimental conditions.

Cytoplasmic reaction

Unless concentrated inocula are used, the cytoplasm may show little alteration until relatively late in the course of infection, when the nuclear reaction is far advanced.* This prolonged interval during which cellular integrity is preserved probably accounts for the continued uptake of vital dyes (Ginsberg, 1957), utilization of glucose (Levy, Rowe, Snellbaker & Hartley, 1957) and production of lactic acid (Fisher & Ginsberg, 1957), as well as for the difficulty encountered in obtaining satisfactory plaques in tissue culture. When degeneration of the cytoplasm does occur, it is indistinguishable in appearance from the necrosis observed under a variety of conditions (Morgan, Rose & Moore, 1957) and can therefore be called non-specific.

Crystallization of non-viral protein

Although type 5 adenovirus resembles types 1, 2 and 6 by virtue of its low propensity to crystallize and the morphology of the nuclear response, it has the remarkable property of inciting the formation of Feulgen-negative crystals (Leuchtenberger & Boyer, 1957), which are protein in nature and devoid of viral particles (Morgan, Godman, Rose, Howe & Huang, 1957). Pl. 5, fig. 11 shows such a crystal appearing as an ill-defined structure containing parallel lines. Each line is believed to result from superimposition of elongated molecules packed in crystalline array.† The surrounding nuclear matrix has been found by light micro-

* Degenerative changes are not infrequently observed in the cytoplasm at early stages of infection, but the percentage of cells with similar changes is appreciable in control cultures as well.

† A similar phenomenon was observed in sections of insect viral, polyhedral crystals (Morgan, Bergold, Moore & Rose, 1955), although the spacing was considerably closer. The possibility, of course, cannot be excluded that the dense regions represent the intermolecular spaces which have been infiltrated by osmium.

scopy to stain in a manner similar to, but less intensely than, the crystals. In view of this observation, the diffuse crystalline faces which are repeatedly seen at early stages of infection and are evident in Pl. 5, fig. 11 suggest that crystallization from the matrix was in progress. Although viral particles are generally present in the vicinity, they are rarely enclosed within the crystalline lattice.

At later stages of infection the crystals, which may exceed 20μ in length, possess sharply defined faces. Pl. 5, fig. 12 illustrates part of two crystals lying at right angles. The upper crystal has been cross-sectioned and exhibits an array of dense points, undoubtedly reflecting the molecular lattice. The lower crystal, which appears to have grown in such a manner as partially to enclose the upper crystal, was cut longitudinally and reveals a linear pattern. At sufficient magnification the molecular spacing can be seen to be about 400 Å. Numerous viral particles are present in the adjacent nuclear matrix.

Different strains of type 5 adenovirus vary in the extent to which they incite crystallization of non-viral protein. Crystals may be so rare that only a few can be identified by careful search of whole cell mounts with the light microscope, a fact which could account for the failure to recognize non-viral crystals in the study of type 5 adenovirus by Lagermalm, Kjellén, Thorsson & Svedmyr (1957). Preliminary histochemical examination suggests that Feulgen-negative protein is present in the nuclei of cells infected with other types of adenovirus. Characteristic crystals, however, have not been found. Presumably the protein in these instances does not achieve sufficient concentration at any site within the nucleus to crystallize.

Contemplation of the foregoing remarks brings to mind certain insect viruses. *Porthetria dispar* (gipsy moth) and *Bombyx mori* (silkworm) viruses (Smith, 1955; Bergold, 1958), for example, resemble type 5 adenovirus, in that they develop within nuclei, contain DNA, and incite the formation of crystals (polyhedra), the protein of which appears to be Feulgen-negative. Release of crystals into the cytoplasm is accompanied by disruption of the nuclear membrane, and into the extracellular space by disintegration of the cell wall. On the other hand, these insect viruses do not of themselves crystallize. An even more puzzling difference is that the polyhedral protein crystals enclose large amounts of virus and yet the crystals associated with type 5 adenovirus contain only occasional particles. Moreover, the molecular spacing of the former is about 65 Å in sections (Morgan, Bergold, Moore & Rose, 1955), as opposed to the 400 Å spacing of the latter. Finally, the latter appear to dissolve upon entering the cytoplasm, whereas the polyhedra are remarkably resistant and thus afford protection to the virus for long periods of time. These differences, as well as the similarities, warrant study, for it is probable that further investigation of the intranuclear polyhedral insect viruses with the techniques currently available will, by analogy, throw light on several puzzling aspects of adenoviral development.

INFLUENZA VIRUSES

By way of contrast with the adenoviruses, members of the influenza group characteristically develop in an entirely different manner. Infected entodermal cells of chicken chorio-allantoic membranes fail to show recognizable viral particles either in the nucleus or in the depths of the cytoplasm, the virus being visible only at the cellular surface (Morgan, Rose & Moore, 1956). Moreover, two morphologic forms—spherical and filamentous—may be readily distinguished among the viral population, their relative numerical proportions apparently depending in large part on the strain, adaptation to the cell system and conditions of passage. In general, spherical particles tend to predominate in certain well-established egg-passage lines, for example, PR8 and Lee, whereas large numbers of filaments are usually found in newly isolated strains, as originally noted by Chu, Dawson & Elford (1949).

Cellular changes

Propagation of virus may occur in cells whose nuclear and cytoplasmic components show no evident abnormal changes. Pl. 6, fig. 13 illustrates a section of a cell infected by the PR8 strain. Numerous viral particles, mostly short rod-like forms, can be seen extending from the undulant, free surface. The nucleus and adjacent cytoplasm, including several mitochondria, are entirely normal in appearance. However, in other instances, as shown in Pl. 6, fig. 14, it has recently been observed that infection by the same strain of virus (PR8) under similar conditions may result in cellular damage. The nucleus of the cell depicted therein exhibits irregular condensations of chromatin, interspersed with peculiar clear areas which apparently represent transformation of the nucleoplasm into finely reticular and granular material. Details of the endoplasmic reticulum have been lost and the mitochondria have undergone degenerative changes. Many spherical viral particles, arranged in mosaic patterns in some places, are seen at the cell surface. Similar nuclear and cytoplasmic changes may occur in cells infected by other viral strains, as illustrated by Pl. 7, fig. 15 which shows the effects of influenza B virus

(Lee). Margination and clumping of nuclear chromatin, together with the presence of large 'clear' areas are evident, as are the cytoplasmic alterations. A few rod-shaped viral particles may be seen at the cell margin. In Pl. 7, fig. 16 are shown two cells of a membrane infected by the A/Columbia/3/57 strain of Asian-type virus. The nucleus of the cell toward the left of the figure appears relatively normal, but the nuclear changes evident in the cell toward the right are indistinguishable from those just referred to in connexion with the PR8 and Lee strains of virus. This curious juxtaposition, in infected chorio-allantoic membranes, of cells which appear normal, save for the occurrence of viral particles on the surface, and others which display cytopathic changes, has been repeatedly observed. It is not clear whether this is the result of differences in the temporal sequence and stages of infection, or whether it reflects variations in the susceptibility of individual cellular elements. In any event, morphological evidence of damage from infection by viral strains which are well adapted to chicken embryos, for example, PR8 and Lee, occurs in only a small proportion of cells when dilute inocula are used, even though the virus multiplies to full infectivity and haemagglutinin titres. More extensive damage is usually observed when either of these viruses is passed serially in the form of undiluted infective chorio-allantoic fluid; concurrently the relative number of filamentous viral particles tends to increase. The most striking and extensive cellular changes, particularly in nuclei, have been observed in association with Asian-type strains of virus, as illustrated in Pl. 8, fig. 17. Many cells of infected membranes characteristically exhibit intranuclear aggregations of dense, coarse, strand-like material, similar to that shown in this figure, in association with the 'clear' areas mentioned earlier. The appearance of the nuclei is so striking and consistent as to suggest that it reflects an unusual or even unique property of Asian influenza virus; this hypothesis remains to be tested by examining membranes which have been infected with strains from former years, using virus either in early egg passage or newly re-isolated from stored throat washings. The factors responsible for the nuclear changes are currently unknown, but in all likelihood they are related in some way to elaboration of a viral component: presumably 'S' antigen, since this has been shown by immunohistological methods, using fluorescent antibody, to occur in cells infected with both influenza and fowl plague viruses (Watson & Coons, 1954; Liu, 1955; Breitenfeld & Schäfer, 1957). However, the production of such a component of itself is probably not the determining factor, since, as has already been pointed out, cells infected with certain strains of influenza virus under appropriate conditions will exhibit many newly formed viral particles at their surface without any evidence of damage to either nucleus or cytoplasm.

Viral structure

It is now generally recognized that influenza virus presents two distinct morphological forms—spherical and filamentous. Spherical particles usually predominate in well-established egg-passage strains, for example, PR 8 and Lee, whereas large numbers of filaments are generally found in newly isolated lines of virus. Pl. 9, fig. 18 shows a relatively thick section through the surface of an entodermal cell of chicken chorio-allantoic membrane infected by the PR 8 strain. Numerous spherical particles are visible and toward the right-hand margin of the micrograph they exhibit an orderly array which suggests close packing or even crystalline arrangement. Several cytoplasmic extensions can also be discerned; one of them, running obliquely on the left of the field, shows three particles protruding from its surface. Many of the particles reveal evidence of internal structure, which is better shown at higher magnification in Pl. 9, fig. 19, as has been described in an earlier report (Morgan, Rose & Moore, 1956). The basic structural elements are an internal body, an external limiting membrane and a diffuse outer coat, which may be observed not only in spherical particles but also in those having a somewhat elongated or ellipsoidal appearance. The internal body is of great interest since it is absent in the truly filamentous form; moreover, in certain particles it appears not to be homogeneous but to consist of seven or eight small dense bodies. These bodies may correspond to the complement-fixing or 'soluble' components of the virus which, according to Hoyle and co-workers, are released by ether treatment (Hoyle, 1952; Hoyle, Reed & Astbury, 1953) and to the 'gebundenes g-antigen' of fowl plague virus, described by Schäfer (1957). Pl. 9, fig. 20 shows numerous rod-shaped particles of PR 8 virus, both in longitudinal and in cross-section, in an intercellular cleft. Most show no evidence of internal structure, but a few contain a small dot-like or linear density, centrally placed at the distal extremity and several of the longitudinally sectioned particles indicate clearly their continuity with the cytoplasm. In filamentous forms of the virus, illustrated in Pl. 10, fig. 21, no inner structure can be made out, the central area of the filaments having an electron density approaching that of the embedding plastic. Occasional constriction of the filaments can be seen, but regular and consistent segmentation has never been observed, thus indicating that spherical particles probably do not arise primarily by this mechanism. The large bulbous tips of viral filaments, described by Hoyle (1950) in dark-field microscopic studies of infected cells, and by Lindenmann (1957) in stained preparations of chorio-allantoic fluid, have not been encountered during electron-microscopic examination of thin-sectioned tissue infected by any of the virus strains used thus far, namely PR8, FM1, A/Persian Gulf/2/52, Lee, A/Jap/305/57, A/Columbia/2/57 and A/Columbia/3/57. The observation regarding lack of internal structure in filamentous forms of virus, which was made initially (Morgan, Rose & Moore, 1956) in examining sections of chorio-allantoic membrane infected with the PR8, Lee and A/Persian Gulf/2/52 strains, has been confirmed in monkey kidney cell cultures, as shown in Pl. 11, fig. 22. This figure illustrates filaments of FM1 in both longitudinal and cross section; the lack of inner structure and the resemblance to filaments of virus arising from a cell of the chorio-allantoic membrane (Pl. 9, fig. 20) is obvious. The above-mentioned differences in structure between the filamentous and the spherical or ellipsoidal forms of influenza virus led the authors to postulate that the former may be relatively or completely non-infective, whereas the latter represents the elemental infectious units (Morgan, Rose & Moore, 1956). They also suggested that nucleic acid constitutes part of the inner bodies of the spherical units and that a comparison of the nucleic acid content of the two forms be undertaken. Such studies have since been carried out and it has been ascertained that the relative amount of RNA is actually reduced considerably in preparations consisting mainly of filaments (Burke, Isaacs & Walker, 1957). Moreover, in a combined population of filaments and spheres, destruction of the former by osmotic factors causes little change in infectivity (Burnet, 1956; Burnet & Lind, 1957). These findings reinforce the concept that the filamentous form either is non-infective or contains only a single infective locus. Further work bearing on this point is needed.

Haemadsorption

Vogel & Shelokov (1957) reported that the development of influenza virus in cultures of monkey kidney cells could be detected by adding erythrocytes to the culture tubes, washing the cell sheets after an interval of time and observing microscopically whether there was binding of the erythrocytes to the cell surfaces, presumably by a mechanism similar to that of viral haemagglutination. This phenomenon was entitled haemadsorption. For the sake of interest an example is shown in Pl. 11, fig. 23. This illustrates binding of a chicken erythrocyte to the surface of a cell of the chorio-allantoic membrane infected with PR8 virus. That the viral particles at the cellular surface are responsible is shown by the clearly delineated 'bridging' effect. The micrograph also illustrates again, as noted in the discussion of Pl. 9, fig. 18, the differentiation of viral particles at the surface of the cell, including cytoplasmic extensions.

CONCLUSIONS

The electron microscope has contributed information concerning viral structure and the morphology of the host cell response. Nevertheless, we lack detailed correlation of the chemical events accompanying viral multiplication with the morphological changes. This deficiency stems in part, at least, from the fact that events at the molecular level are invisible, becoming manifest only when alteration of normal cellular components results, or when complex aggregation of the molecules produces discernible structure. As was pointed out in the discussion of influenza virus, for example, the striking alteration of nuclear architecture may quite possibly reflect synthesis of viral antigens at a site removed from the cell surface, where differentiation of infective units occurs. In the case of type 5 adenovirus, a protein component either of the host or of the virus is rendered visible by orientation of the molecules within a crystalline lattice. It will be remembered, however, that influenza virus can develop without morphological alteration of the nucleus and that adenoviruses can multiply in the absence of protein crystals.

Two methods of approach seem at present to hold some promise of extending our vision: (1) adaptation of suitable histochemical techniques; (2) labelling of viral components so that they may be identified in the electron microscope by methods analogous to those currently employing fluorescent or radioactive compounds. Whether these can be accomplished remains for the future to answer. One thing is obvious today, namely that electron microscopy by itself, disassociated from allied or complementary techniques, can raise new questions, but it cannot provide the answers.

REFERENCES

BERGOLD, G. H. (1958). Viruses of Insects. In *Handb. Virusforsch.* 4, (Suppl. 3) 60.

BLOCH, D. P., MORGAN, C., GODMAN, G. C., HOWE, C. & ROSE, H. M. (1957). A correlated histochemical and electron microscopic study of the intranuclear crystalline aggregates of adenovirus (RI-APC virus) in HeLa cells. *J. biophys. biochem. Cytol.* 3, 1.

BOYER, G. S., LEUCHTENBERGER, C. & GINSBERG, H. S. (1957). Cytological and cytochemical studies of HeLa cells infected with adenoviruses. *J. exp. Med.* 105, 195.

BREITENFELD, P. M. & SCHÄFER, W. (1957). The formation of fowl plague virus antigens in infected cells, as studied with fluorescent antibodies. *Virology*, 4, 328.

BURKE, D. C., ISAACS, A. & WALKER, J. (1957). The nucleic acid content of influenza virus. *Biochim. biophys. Acta*, 26, 576.

BURNET, F. M. (1956). Filamentous forms of influenza virus. *Nature, Lond.* **177**, 103.

BURNET, F. M. & LIND, P. E. (1957). Studies on filamentary forms of influenza virus with special reference to the use of dark-ground microscopy. *Arch. ges. Virusforsch.* **7**, 413.

CHU, C. M., DAWSON, I. M. & ELFORD, W. J. (1949). Filamentous forms associated with newly isolated influenza virus. *Lancet*, i, 602.

FISHER, T. N. & GINSBERG, H. S. (1957). Accumulation of organic acids by HeLa cells infected with type 4 adenovirus. *Proc. Soc. exp. Biol., N.Y.* **95**, 47.

GINSBERG, H. S. (1957). Biological and physical properties of the adenoviruses. *Ann. N.Y. Acad. Sci.* **67**, 383.

GINSBERG, H. S. (1958). Characteristics of the adenoviruses. III. Reproductive cycle of types 1 to 4. *J. exp. Med.* **107**, 133.

HARFORD, C. G., HAMLIN, A. & PARKER, E. (1955). Electron microscopy of HeLa cells infected with ARD virus. *Trans. Ass. Amer. Phycns*, **68**, 82.

HARFORD, C. G., HAMLIN, A., PARKER, E. & VAN RAVENSWAAY, T. (1956). Electron microscopy of HeLa cells infected with adenoviruses. *J. exp. Med.* **104**, 443.

HILLEMAN, M. R., TOUSIMIS, A. J. & WERNER, J. H. (1955). Biophysical characterization of the RI(RI-67) viruses. *Proc. Soc. exp. Biol., N.Y.* **89**, 587.

HILLEMAN, M. R. & WERNER, J. H. (1954). Recovery of new agent from patients with acute respiratory illness. *Proc. Soc. exp. Biol., N.Y.* **85**, 183.

HOYLE, L. (1950). The multiplication of influenza viruses in the fertile egg. *J. Hyg., Camb.* **48**, 277.

HOYLE, L. (1952). Structure of the influenza virus. The relation between biological activity and chemical structure of virus fractions. *J. Hyg., Camb.* **50**, 229.

HOYLE, L., REED, R. & ASTBURY, W. T. (1953). Electron microscope studies of the structure of the influenza virus. *Nature, Lond.* **171**, 256.

KJELLÉN, L., LAGERMALM, G., SVEDMYR, A. & THORSSON, K.-G. (1955). Crystalline-like patterns in the nuclei of cells infected with an animal virus. *Nature, Lond.* **175**, 505.

LAGERMALM, G., KJELLÉN, L., THORSSON, K.-G. & SVEDMYR, A. (1957). Electron microscopy of HeLa cells infected with agents of the adenovirus (APC-RI-ARD) group. *Arch. ges. Virusforsch.* **7**, 221.

LEUCHTENBERGER, C. & BOYER, G. S. (1957). The occurrence of intranuclear crystals in living HeLa cells infected with adenoviruses. *J. biophys. biochem. Cytol.* **3**, 323.

LEVY, H. B., ROWE, W. P., SNELLBAKER, L. F. & HARTLEY, J. W. (1957). Biochemical changes in HeLa cells associated with infection by type 2 adenovirus. *Proc. Soc. exp. Biol., N.Y.* **96**, 732.

LINDENMANN, J. (1957). The staining of influenza virus filaments. *J. gen. Microbiol.* **16**, 759.

LIU, C. (1955). Studies on influenza infection in ferrets by means of fluorescein-labelled antibody. II. The role of 'soluble antigen' in nuclear fluorescence and cross-reactions. *J. exp. Med.* **101**, 677.

LOW, B. W. & PINNOCK, P. R. (1956). The packing structure of crystalline RI-APC virus. *J. biophys. biochem. Cytol.* **2**, 483.

MORGAN, C., BERGOLD, G. H., MOORE, D. H. & ROSE, H. M. (1955). The macromolecular paracrystalline lattice of insect viral polyhedral bodies demonstrated in ultrathin sections examined in the electron microscope. *J. biophys. biochem. Cytol.* **1**, 187.

MORGAN, C., ELLISON, S. A., ROSE, H. M. & MOORE, D. H. (1955). Serial sections of vaccinia virus examined at one stage of development in the electron microscope. *Exp. Cell Res.* **9**, 572.

MORGAN, C., GODMAN, G. C., ROSE, H. M., HOWE, C. & HUANG, J. S. (1957). Electron microscopic and histochemical studies of an unusual crystalline protein occurring in cells infected by type 5 adenovirus. Preliminary observations. *J. biophys. biochem. Cytol.* **3**, 505.

MORGAN, C., HOWE, C., ROSE, H. M. & MOORE, D. H. (1956). Structure and development of viruses observed in the electron microscope. IV. Viruses of the RI-APC group. *J. biophys. biochem. Cytol.* **2**, 351.

MORGAN, C., MOORE, D. H. & ROSE, H. M. (1956). Some effects of the microtome knife and electron beam on methacrylate-embedded thin sections. *J. biophys. biochem. Cytol.* Supplement, **2**, 21.

MORGAN, C., ROSE, H. M. & MOORE, D. H. (1956). Structure and development of viruses observed in the electron microscope. III. Influenza virus. *J. exp. Med.* **104**, 171.

MORGAN, C., ROSE, H. M. & MOORE, D. H. (1957). An evaluation of host cell changes accompanying viral multiplication as observed in the electron microscope. *Ann. N.Y. Acad. Sci.* **68**, 302.

ROWE, W. P., HUEBNER, R. J. & BELL, J. A. (1957). Definition and outline of contemporary information on the adenovirus group. *Ann. N.Y. Acad. Sci.* **67**, 255.

ROWE, W. P., HUEBNER, R. J., GILMORE, L. K., PARROTT, R. H. & WARD, T. G. (1953). Isolation of a cytopathogenic agent from human adenoids undergoing spontaneous degeneration in tissue culture. *Proc. Soc. exp. Biol., N.Y.* **84**, 570.

SCHÄFER, W. (1957). Units isolated after splitting fowl plague virus. In *Ciba Foundation Symposium on The Nature of Viruses*. Edited by G. E. W. Wolstenholme and E. C. P. Millar. London: Churchill.

SMITH, K. M. (1955). Morphology and development of insect viruses. *Advanc. Virus Res.* **3**, 199.

TOUSIMIS, A. J. & HILLEMAN, M. R. (1957). Electron microscopy of type 4 adenovirus strain RI-67. *Virology*, **4**, 499.

VALENTINE, R. C. & HOPPER, P. K. (1957). Polyhedral shape of adenovirus particles as shown by electron microscopy. *Nature, Lond.* **180**, 928.

VOGEL, J. & SHELOKOV, A. (1957). Adsorption-haemagglutination test for influenza virus in monkey kidney tissue culture. *Science*, **126**, 358.

WATSON, B. K. & COONS, A. H. (1954). Studies of influenza virus infection in the chick embryo using fluorescent antibody. *J. exp. Med.* **99**, 419.

WILLIAMS, R. C. & SMITH, K. M. (1957). A crystallizable insect virus. *Nature, Lond.* **179**, 119.

EXPLANATION OF PLATES

PLATE 1

Fig. 1. Part of the nucleus of a HeLa cell from a tissue culture inoculated 17 hr. previously with type 3 adenovirus. Aggregations of dense reticulum are apparent and a few viral particles are visible near the lower right corner. × 13,000.

Fig. 2. A nucleus from the same culture showing clumps of reticulum and viral clusters, many of which exhibit crystalline arrays. × 12,000.

PLATE 2

Fig. 3. Type 1 adenovirus dispersed at random in the vicinity of dense reticulum. × 54,000.

Fig. 4. A crystal composed of type 3 adenovirus. The electron opacity of the particles differs. On the left are laminated membranes in the form of tubules, one of which has been obliquely sectioned and contains viral particles. × 39,000.

PLATE 3

Fig. 5. Part of a large viral crystal. The nuclear membrane traverses the right and lower margins. × 33,000.

PLATE 1

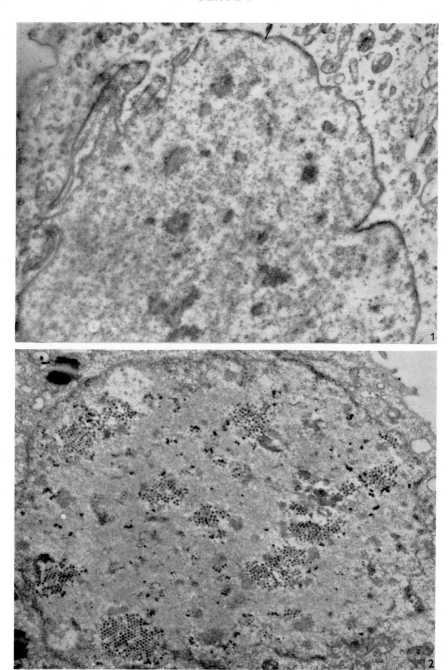

PLATE 2

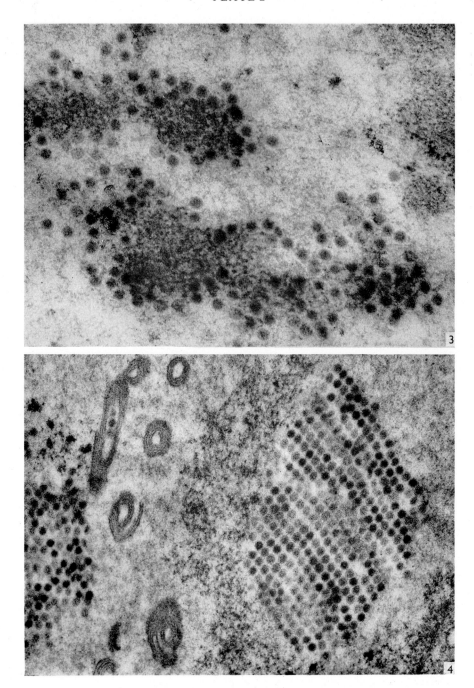

PLATE 3

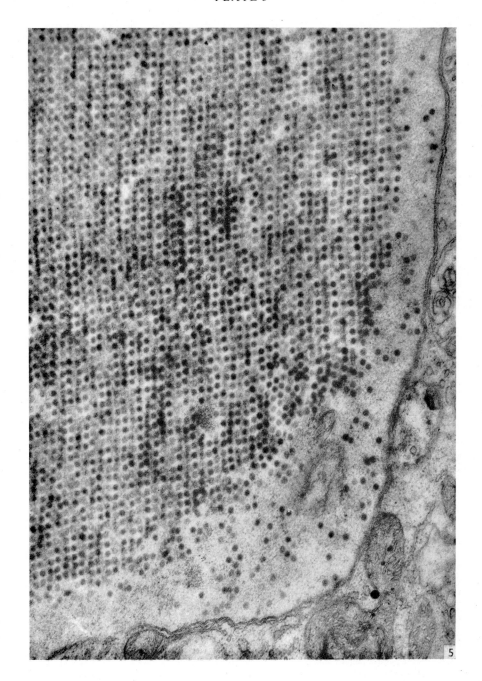

5

PLATE 4

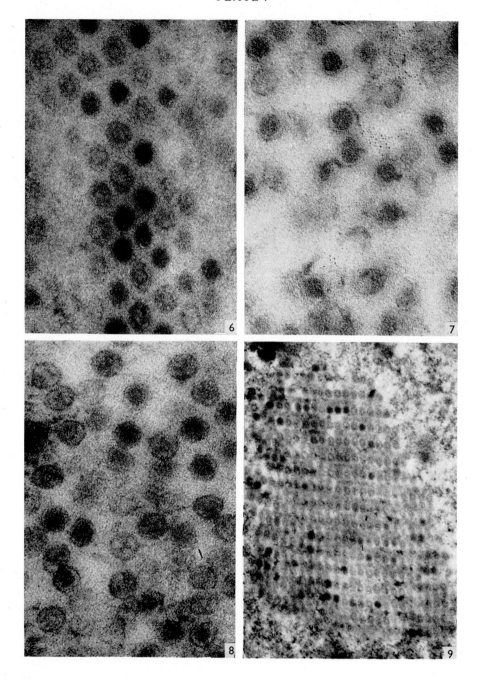

PLATE 5

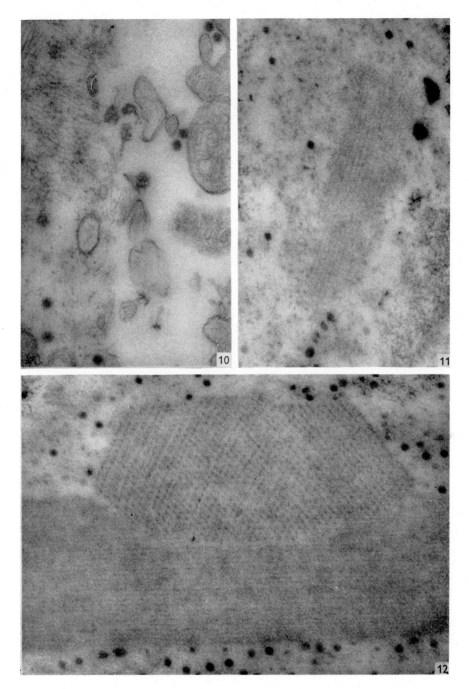

PLATE 6

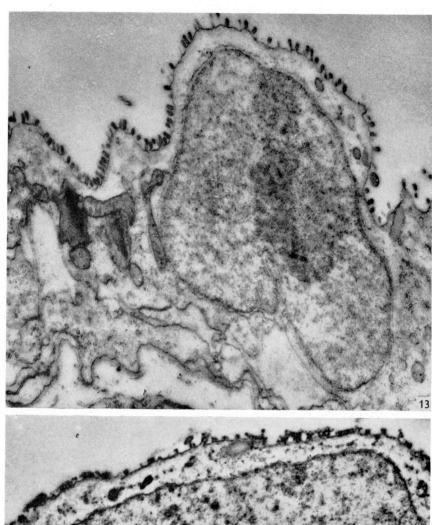

13

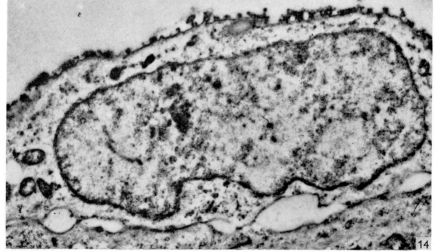

14

PLATE 7

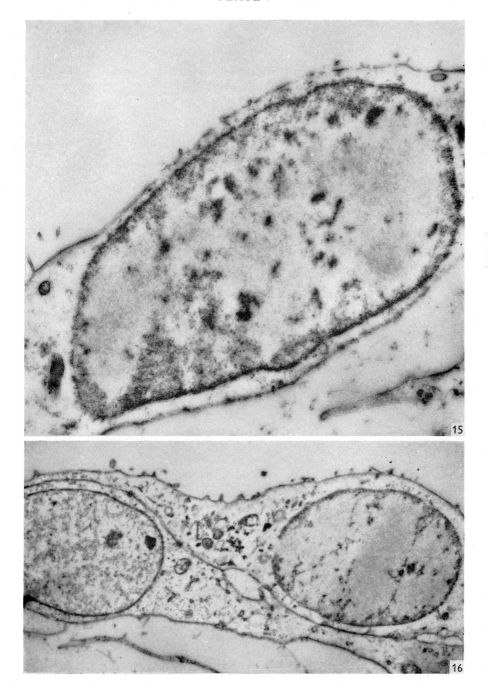

PLATE 8

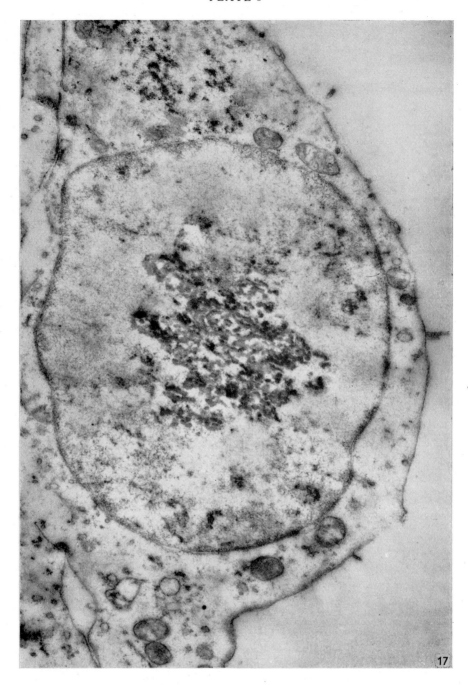

17

PLATE 9

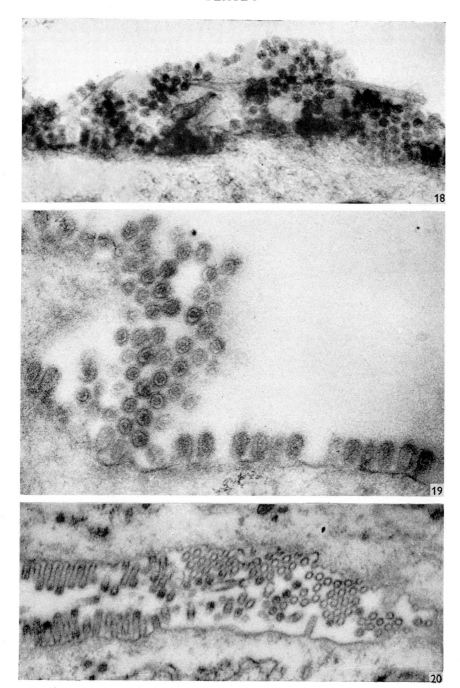

PLATE 10

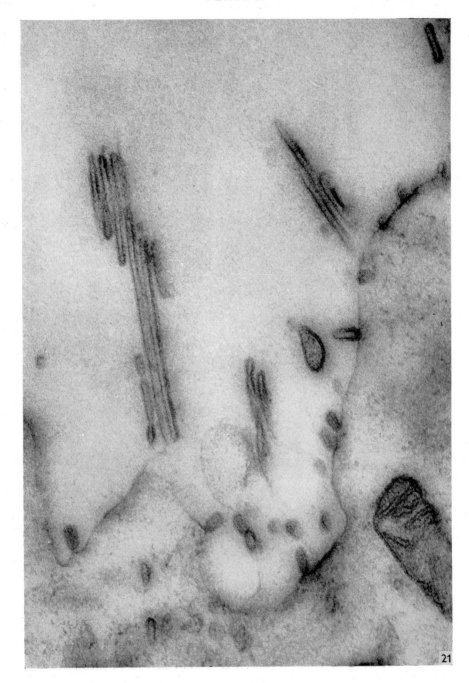

21

PLATE 11

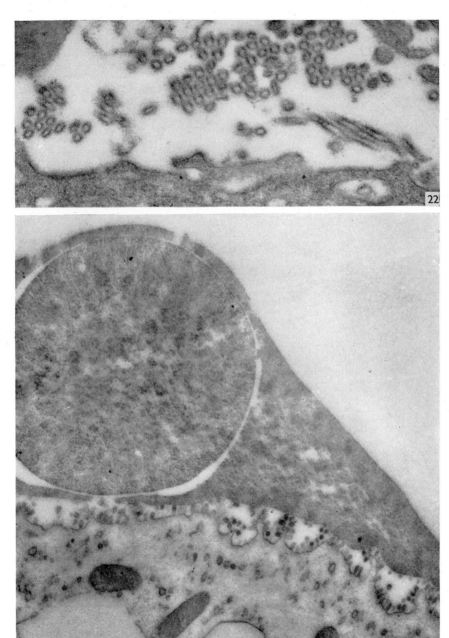

PLATE 4

Fig. 6. Type 3 adenovirus fixed in osmium tetroxide. × 116,000.

Fig. 7. Type 7 adenovirus fixed in formalin. × 116,000.

Fig. 8. Type 5 adenovirus fixed in formalin. This section was placed in osmium fumes before examination. × 116,000.

Fig. 9. An intranuclear crystal composed of viral particles, many of which are indistinct. × 37,000.

PLATE 5

Fig. 10. Viral particles in the cytoplasm (on the left) and in the extracellular space (on the right). The cell has begun to disrupt. × 52,000.

Fig. 11. An intranuclear protein crystal associated with type 5 adenovirus. The diffuse margins are believed to occur during crystallization. No viral particles are present within the linear array which reflects the molecular lattice. × 43,000.

Fig. 12. Two non-viral crystals lying at right angles to each other. The upper has been cross-sectioned, the lower cut longitudinally. The molecular arrays are visible. × 37,000.

PLATE 6

Fig. 13. A cell in the chorio-allantoic membrane infected with the PR 8 strain of influenza virus. Viral particles line the free surface at the top. The nucleus is indistinguishable from those encountered in control preparations. × 20,000.

Fig. 14. A nucleus showing small aggregates of reticular material (chromatin) as well as irregular 'clear' areas. Spherical viral particles are evident at the cell surface near the upper border of the field. × 12,000.

PLATE 7

Fig. 15. A cell infected with the Lee strain of influenza virus. Margination of chromatin, clumps of dense material and large 'clear' areas are apparent within the nucleus. A few viral filaments are visible at the cell surface. × 13,000.

Fig. 16. Two cells of a membrane infected by the A/Columbia/3/57 (Asian) strain of virus. The nucleus of the cell lining the allantoic cavity at the top has undergone changes resembling those illustrated in the preceding picture. The nucleus at the left is normal in appearance. × 8,000.

PLATE 8

Fig. 17. Characteristic changes encountered in the nuclei of cells infected with Asian strains of virus. At the centre dense amorphous material has aggregated. There is irregular margination of chromatin, and a network of fine reticulum traverses the areas of diminished density. The cytoplasm shows early signs of degeneration. Several viral filaments project from the free surface at the right. × 19,000.

PLATE 9

Fig. 18. A moderately thick section containing viral spheres with dense internal bodies. Groups of particles exhibit surprisingly regular arrays. The cytoplasm of the host cell occupies the lower portion of the field. × 41,000.

Fig. 19. Viral particles cut sufficiently thin to reveal structure clearly. The internal bodies of several spheres near the middle of the cluster appear to be composed of subunits arranged in a rosette pattern. Particles central to the plane of section exhibit a sharply defined, peripheral membrane and a diffuse outer coat. A few of the ellipsoidal particles lining the surface of the cell near the lower border of the micrograph possess an elongated internal body. × 69,000.

Fig. 20. An intercellular cleft containing numerous rod-shaped forms of virus. Those which have been cross-sectioned reveal no central structure, whereas a few seen in longitudinal section (toward the left of the field) seem to contain a linear density at the distal tip. These cells were inoculated with undiluted chorio-allantoic fluid containing the PR 8 strain of virus. × 42,000.

PLATE 10

Fig. 21. Filaments viewed in longitudinal section. A few irregular constrictions are apparent. When studied in serial sections, filaments which have become detached from the host cell can be demonstrated to possess a continuous membrane, as shown by the short rod in the upper right corner. × 60,000.

PLATE 11

Fig. 22. Filaments of the FM1 strain grown in monkey kidney cell cultures. The diffuse outer coat, sharply defined membrane and interior devoid of structure are indistinguishable from the components of filaments encountered on the chorio-allantoic membranes. × 43,000.

Fig. 23. Part of a nucleated chicken erythrocyte attached to the surface of an entodermal cell. Viral particles are clearly visible bridging the space between both cells. × 22,000.